Solid-State
Communications

TEXAS INSTRUMENTS ELECTRONICS SERIES

The Engineering Staff of
Texas Instruments Incorporated ▪ SOLID-STATE COMMUNICATIONS

The Engineering Staff of
Texas Instruments Incorporated ▪ TRANSISTOR CIRCUIT DESIGN

Runyan ▪ SILICON SEMICONDUCTOR TECHNOLOGY

Sevin ▪ FIELD-EFFECT TRANSISTORS

Solid-State Communications

Design of Communications Equipment Using Semiconductors

Prepared by the Engineering Staff of
Texas Instruments Incorporated

Edited by
John R. Miller
Technical Publications Editor

Contributors

Harry F. Cooke
Bob Crawford
Ralph Dean
Stan Holcomb
George Johnson
Peter Norris
Frank Opp
L. J. Sevin
Ted Small
Bill Tulloch
Roger Webster

McGRAW-HILL BOOK COMPANY

New York   San Francisco   Toronto   London   Sydney

SOLID-STATE COMMUNICATIONS

Preface

This book was originally published by the Texas Instruments Microlibrary as a two-part paperback, under the title "Communications Handbook." The objective of the work is to give the communications circuit designer as much useful and current information as can be presented in a work of less than 400 pages.

We have not attempted to present comprehensive coverage of the vast field of communications. Rather, we have chosen material that has proved to be of current interest, as evidenced by response to papers delivered at Texas Instruments technical seminars, and by requests from customers for special information.

We intend to publish new editions of this book periodically, to reflect improvements in design techniques and devices. Queries regarding material presented in this book may be addressed to the individual author, in care of Texas Instruments Incorporated, Post Office Box 5012, Dallas, Texas 75222.

Texas Instruments Incorporated
Semiconductor-Components Division

Contents

DALCOM COMMUNICATIONS TRANSISTORS APPLICATIONS CHART

Small Signal

FREQUENCY RANGE	RF AMPLIFIERS	IF AMPLIFIERS	MIXERS & CONVERTERS
0-20 KC			
20 KC TO 2 MC	USA2N929/USA2N930 (Si Planar) 2N2586 (Si Planar) TI363 (Alloy) 2N2188 Series (Alloy) 2N332-338 (Grown) 2N780 (Si Mesa) USA2N760A (Si Mesa) 2N1566A/2N736A (Si Mesa)	USA2N929/USA2N930 (Si Planar) 2N2586 (Si Planar) TI363/364 (Alloy) 2N1302-2N1309 (Alloy) 2N2188 Series (Alloy) 2N332-2N338 (Grown) 2N780 (Si Mesa) USA2N760A (Si Mesa) 2N1566A/2N736A (Si Mesa)	USA2N929/USA2N930 (Si Planar) 2N2586 (Si Planar) TI363/64 (Alloy) 2N2188 Series (Alloy) 2N332-2N338 (Grown) 2N780 (Si Mesa) USA2N760A (Si Mesa) 2N1566A/2N736A (Si Mesa)
2-10 MC	2N1141/42/43 (Ge Mesa) USA2N929/USA2N930 (Si Planar) 2N2586 (Si Planar) 2N2188 Series (Alloy) 3N34/35 (Grown) 2N780 (Si Mesa) USA2N760A (Si Mesa) 2N1566A/2N736A (Si Mesa)	2N1141/42/43 (Ge Mesa) USA2N929/USA2N930 (Si Planar) 2N2586 (Si Planar) 2N2188 Series (Alloy) 3N34/35 (Grown) 2N780 (Si Mesa) USA2N760A (Si Mesa) 2N1566A/2N736A (Si Mesa)	2N1141/42/43 (Ge Mesa) USA2N929/USA2N930 (Si Planar) 2N2188 Series (Alloy) 3N34/35 (Grown) 2N780 (Si Mesa) USA2N760A (Si Mesa) 2N1566A/2N736A (Si Mesa)
10-30 MC	2N1141/42/43 (Ge Mesa) 2N2996/97/98 (Ge Mesa) USA2N929/USA2N930 (Si Planar) 2N743/44 (Si Planar) 2N706A (Si Planar) USA2N760A. (Si Mesa) 2N780 (Si Mesa) 2N2411/2N2412 (Si Planar) 2N2188 Series (Alloy) 3N34/35 (Grown) TIX3032 (Ge Planar) 2N2865 (Si Planar) 2N2586 (Si Planar)	2N1141/42/43 (Ge Mesa) 2N2996/97/98 (Ge Mesa) 2N2861/62 (Si Planar PNP) USA2N929/USA2N930 (Si Planar) 2N744/44 (Si Planar) 2N706A (Si Planar) 2N2188 Series (Alloy) 3N34/35 (Grown) TIX3032 (Ge Planar) USA2N760(A) (Si Mesa) 2N2865 (Si Planar)	2N1141/42/43 (Ge Mesa) 2N2996/97/98 (Ge Mesa) USA2N929/USA2N930 (Si Planar) 2N2188 Series (Alloy) 3N34/35 (Grown) 2N780 (Si Mesa) USA2N760A (Si Mesa) TIX3032 (Ge Planar) 2N2586 (Si Planar) 2N2865 (Si Planar)
30-70 MC	2N1141/42/43 (Ge Mesa) 2N2996/97/98 (Ge Mesa) 2N2415/16 (Ge Mesa) 2N743/44 (Si Planar) 2N918 (Si Planar) 2N2191 (Alloy) 3N35 (Grown) TIX3032 (Ge Planar) USA2N760A (Si Mesa) 2N2865 (Si Planar) 2N3570/71/72 (Si Planar)	2N2996/97/98 (Ge Mesa) 2N1141/42/43 (Ge Mesa) 2N2415/16 (Ge Mesa) 2N3570/71/72 (Si Planar) TIX3032 (Ge Planar) 2N2861/62 (Si Planar PNP) 2N918 (Si Planar) 2N2189 (Alloy) 2N2191 (Alloy) 3N35 (Grown) 2N2865 (Si Planar)	2N2996/97/98 (Ge Mesa) 2N1141/42/43 (Ge Mesa) 2N918 (Si Planar) TIX3032 (Ge Planar) 2N2189 (Alloy) 2N2191 (Alloy) 3N35 (Grown) 2N780 (Si Mesa) USA2N760A (Si Mesa) 2N3570/71/72 (Si Planar) 2N2865 (Si Planar)
70-400 MC	2N1141/42/43 (Ge Mesa) 2N2996/97/98 (Ge Mesa) 2N2415/16 (Ge Mesa) 2N918 (Si Planar) 2N2865 (Si Planar) 2N3570/71/72 (Si Planar) TIX3024 (Ge Planar)	2N1141/42/43 (Ge Mesa) 2N2996/97/98 (Ge Mesa) 2N2415/16 (Ge Mesa) 2N918 (Si Planar) 2N2865 (Si Planar) 2N3570/71/72 (Si Planar) TIX3024 (Ge Planar)	2N2996/97/98 (Ge Mesa) 2N1141/42/43 (Ge Mesa) 2N2415/16 (Ge Mesa) 2N918 (Si Planar) 2N818 (Si Planar) 2N3570/71/72 (Si Planar) TIX3024 (Ge Planar)
400 MC TO 3 GC	2N2998/99 (Ge Mesa) 2N2415/16 (Ge Mesa) 2N2865 (Si Planar) TIX3024 (Ge Planar) 2N918 (Si Planar) 2N3570 (Si Planar)	2N2998/99 (Ge Mesa) 2N2415/16 (Ge Mesa) 2N2865 (Si Planar) TIX3024 (Ge Planar) 2N918 (Si Planar) 2N3570 (Si Planar)	2N2998/99 (Ge Mesa) 2N2415/16 (Ge Mesa) 2N2865 (Si Planar) TIX3024 (Ge Planar) 2N918 (Si Planar) 2N3570 (Si Planar)

DALCOM COMMUNICATIONS TRANSISTORS APPLICATIONS CHART

Small Signal (Continued)

FREQUENCY RANGE	LOW-LEVEL OSCILLATORS	HIGH-LEVEL OSCILLATORS	LOW-POWER AUDIO/VIDEO AMPLIFIERS
0-20 KC			2N780 (Si Mesa) 2N2861/62 (Si Planar PNP) USA2N929/USA2N930 (Si Planar) 2N2586 (Si Planar) USA2N760A (Si Mesa) 2N650A-2N652A (Alloy) 2N524-2N527 (Alloy) 2N1273/74 (Alloy) 2N1370-2N1383 (Alloy) 2N2500 (Si FET) 2N1149-2N1153 (Grown) 2N332-2N338 (Grown) 2N1566A/2N736A (Si Mesa)
20 KC TO 2 MC	TI363/64 (Alloy) 2N1302-2N1305 (Alloy) 2N2188 Series (Alloy) 2N332-2N338 (Grown) 2N780 (Si Mesa) USA2N929/USA2N930 (Si Planar) 2N2586 (Si Planar) USA2N760A (Si Mesa) 2N1566A/2N736A (Si Mesa)	2N696 (Si Planar) 2N697 (Si Planar) 2N698/99 (Si Planar)	2N697 (Si Mesa) 2N780 (Si Mesa) USA2N929/USA2N930 (Si Planar) 2N2861/62 (Si Planar PNP) 2N696 (Si Mesa) 2N698/99 (Si Mesa) 2N524-2N527 (Alloy) 2N650A-2N652A (Alloy) 2N332-2N338 (Grown) 2N1149-2N1153 (Grown) USA2N760A (Si Mesa) 2N1566A/2N736A (Si Mesa)
2-10 MC	2N1141/42/43 (Ge Mesa) 2N1302-2N1309 (Alloy) 2N2188 Series (Alloy) 3N34/35 (Grown) 2N780 (Si Mesa) USA2N929/USA2N930 (Si Planar) 2N2586 (Si Planar) 2N1566A/2N736A (Si Mesa)	2N1141/42/43 (Ge Mesa) 2N696 (Si Planar) 2N697 (Si Planar) 2N698/99 (Si Planar) 2N2863 (Si Planar) 2N2864 (Si Planar)	2N1141/42/43 (Ge Mesa) 2N697 (Si Planar) 2N696 (Si Planar) 2N780 (Si Mesa) 2N2861/62 (Si Planar PNP) USA2N929/USA2N930 (Si Planar) 2N698/99 (Si Mesa) USA2N760A (Si Mesa) 2N1566A/2N736A (Si Mesa)
10-30 MC	2N1141/42/43 (Ge Mesa) 2N2996/97/98 (Ge Mesa) 2N743/44 (Si Planar) 2N2188 Series (Alloy) 3N34/35 (Grown) USA2N929/USA2N930 (Si Planar) 2N780 (Si Mesa) USA2N760A (Si Mesa) 2N2586 (Si Planar) TIX3032 (Ge Planar) 2N2865 (Si Planar)	2N1142/43 (Ge Mesa) 2N698/99 (Si Planar) 2N706A (Si Planar) 2N696/97 (Si Planar) 2N743/44 (Si Planar) 2N2863 (Si Planar) 2N2864 (Si Planar)	2N1141/42/43 (Ge Mesa) 2N698/99 (Si Planar) 2N2861/62 (Si Planar PNP) 2N696/97 (Si Planar) USA2N760A (Si Mesa) 2N1566A/2N736A (Si Mesa) 2N2217-2N2222 (Si Planar) 2N3570/71/72 (Si Planar)
30-70 MC	2N1141/42/43 (Ge Mesa) 2N2996/97/98 (Ge Mesa) 2N743/44 (Si Planar) 2N2188 Series (Alloy) 3N35 (Grown) 2N780 (Si Mesa) USA2N760A (Si Mesa) 2N1566A/2N736A (Si Mesa) 2N2865 (Si Planar) 2N918 (Si Planar) 2N3570/71/72 (Si Planar)	2N1141/42/43 (Ge Mesa) 2N706A (Si Planar) 2N743/44 (Si Planar) 2N2863 (Si Planar) 2N2864 (Si Planar) 2N3570/71/72 (Si Planar)	2N2861/62 (Si Planar PNP) 2N743/44 (Si Planar) 2N2217-2N2222 (Si Planar) 2N3570/71/72 (Si Planar)
70-400 MC	2N1141/42/43 (Ge Mesa) 2N2415/16 [Ge Mesa) 2N2996/97/98 (Ge Mesa) 2N918 (Si Planar) TIXS09 (Si Planar) TIXS10 (Si Planar) 2N2865 (Si Planar) 2N3570/71/72 (Si Planar)	2N1141/42/43 (Ge Mesa) 2N743/44 (Si Planar) 2N2863 (Si Planar) 2N2864 (Si Planar) 2N3570 (Si Planar) TIXS09 (Si Planar) TIXS10 (Si Planar) 2N2883/84 (Si Planar)	2N1141/42/43 (Ge Mesa) 2N743/44 (Si Planar) 2N2861/62 (Si Planar PNP) 2N2217-2N2222 (Si Planar) 2N3570/71/72 (Si Planar) TIXS09 (Si Planar) TIXS10 (Si Planar)
400 MC TO 3 GC	2N2998/99 (Ge Mesa) 2N3570 (Si Planar) TIX3016A (Si Planar) TIXS09 (Si Planar) TIXS10 (Si Planar)	2N3570 (Si Planar) TIX3016A (Si Planar) TIXS09 (Si Planar) TIXS10 (Si Planar) TIXS12 (Si Planar) TIXS13 (Si Planar)	2N3570 (Si Planar) TIX3016A (Si Planar) TIXS09 (Si Planar) TIXS10 (Si Planar) TIXS12 (Si Planar) TIXS13 (Si Planar)

DALCOM COMMUNICATIONS TRANSISTORS
APPLICATIONS CHART

Large Signal

FREQUENCY RANGE	POWER AMPLIFIERS ONE WATT OR LESS	POWER AMPLIFIERS LESS THAN FIVE WATTS	POWER AMPLIFIERS GREATER THAN FIVE WATTS
0-20 KC	2N243/44 (Grown Diff Si) 2N342B (Grown Diff Si) 2N343B (Grown Diff Si)	2N497/98 (Diff Si) 2N656/57 (Diff Si) 2N1038-2N1041 (Alloy) 2N2564-2N2567 (Alloy)	2N1046 (Alloy) 2N250/51 (Alloy) 2N456A-2N458A (Alloy) 2N1021/22 (Alloy) 2N511-2N514B (Alloy) 2N2552/2N1045 (Alloy) 2N389 (Diff Si) 2N424 (Diff Si) 2N1047-2N1050 (Diff Si)
20 KC TO 2 MC	2N1141/42/43 (Ge Mesa) 2N2863 (Si Planar) 2N2864 (Si Planar)	2N1131/32 (Si Planar) 2N696/97/98/99 (Si Planar) 2N1613-2N1711 (Si Planar) 2N1890 (Si Planar) 2N1893 (Si Planar) 2N1899 (Si Planar) 2N497/98 (Diff Si) 2N656/57 (Diff Si) 2N2863 (Si Planar) 2N2864 (Si Planar)	2N1046/2N1908 (Alloy Diff) 2N389 (Diff Si) 2N424 (Diff Si) 2N1047-2N1050 (Diff Si)
2-10 MC	2N1141/42/43 (Ge Mesa) 2N1714-2N1717 (Si Mesa) 2N2863 (Si Planar) 2N2864 (Si Planar) 2N2987-2N2994 (Si Planar)	2N1131/32 (Si Planar) 2N1714-2N1721 (Si Planar) 2N1722-2N1724 (Si Mesa) 2N1890/93/99 (Si Planar) 2N1936/37 (Si Mesa) 2N2150/51 (Si Mesa) 2N2863/64 (Si Planar) 2N2983-2N2986 (Si Mesa) 2N2987-2N2994 (Si Planar) TI-816 (Si Planar)	2N1046/2N1908 (Alloy Diff) 2N1047B-2N1050B (Si Mesa) 2N1722-2N1724 (Si Mesa) 2N1723-2N1725 (Si Mesa) 2N1936/37 (Si Mesa) 2N2150/51 (Si Mesa) 2N2983-2N2986 (Si Mesa)
10-30 MC	2N1141/42/43 (Ge Mesa) 2N743/44 (Si Planar) 2N706A (Si Planar) 2N2863 (Si Planar) 2N2864 (Si Planar)	2N1131/32 (Si Planar) 2N2863 (Si Planar) 2N2864 (Si Planar) TI 816 (Si Planar)	2N2876 (Si Planar)
30-70 MC	2N1141/42/43 (Ge Mesa) 2N743/44 (Si Planar) 2N706A (Si Planar) 2N2863 (Si Planar) 2N2864 (Si Planar) 2N2217-2N2219 (Si Planar) 2N2883/84 (Si Planar)	2N2863 (Si Planar) 2N2864 (Si Planar) 2N2884 (Si Planar)	2N2876 (Si Planar)
70-400 MC	2N1141/42/43 (Ge Mesa) 2N743/44 (Si Planar) 2N2863 (Si Planar) 2N2864 (Si Planar) 2N2217-2N2219 (Si Planar) TIXS09 (Si Planar) TIXS10 (Si Planar) 2N2883/84 (Si Planar)	2N2863 (Si Planar) 2N2864 (Si Planar) 2N2884 (Si Planar) 2N2876 (Si Planar) TIX3016A (Si Planar)	
400 MC TO 3 GC	TIX3016A (Si Planar) TIXS12 (Si Planar) TIXS13 (Si Planar)	TIX3016A (Si-Planar) TIXS12 (Si Planar)	

Solid-State Communications

1

New Communications Devices

by Ted Small

This chapter is designed to familiarize the communications equipment designer with linear communications devices that are new at this writing. We have included information that will supplement the basic data sheet information, and in some cases, we have summarized important device characteristics in tabular form.

SUMMARY OF HIGH-FREQUENCY SMALL-SIGNAL AMPLIFIER CHARACTERISTICS

Tables 1 and 2 and Fig. 1 provide a graphic summary of solid-state high-frequency small-signal amplifier characteristics.

SILICON SMALL-SIGNAL TRANSISTORS

2N3570 and TIX3016A are silicon planar epitaxial transistors with seven-finger interdigitated geometry. Frequency capability is extremely high, and power capability will enable designers to use them as low-power klystron replacements. It is entirely possible that these devices will make feasible airborne microwave equipment.

Table 1. High-frequency Germanium Transistors

Type & package	f_{max} Guaranteed minimum	F_T Typical	F_T Guaranteed minimum	Noise figure Typical	Noise figure Guaranteed maximum	Fundamental oscillator PO	Area of operation
TIX3024 TI-line	4.5 Gc	1.7 Gc	1.5 Gc	1.6 db at 200 Mc 4.0 db at 1 Gc	5.0 db at 1 Gc		L & S band amplifier
2N2999 TO-18	3.3 Gc	1.6 Gc	1.4 Gc	5.0 db at 1.0 Gc	7.0 db at 1.0 Gc		L band amplifier S band oscillator
2N2998 TO-18	2.2 Gc	1.0 Gc	600 Mc	6.5 db at 1.0 Gc	8.0 db at 1.0 Gc		UHF amplifier L band oscillator
2N2415 TO-18	1.6 Gc	800 Mc	500 Mc	2.5 db at 200 Mc	3.0 db at 200 Mc		UHF amplifier
TIX3032 TO-18	1.8 Gc	700 Mc	500 Mc	3.5 db at 200 Mc	4.0 db at 200 Mc	20 mw at 1 Gc; 12 v, 12 ma; 14% eff. 10 mw at 1 Gc; 12 v, 6 ma	VHF amplifier UHF oscillator
2N2997 TO-18	1.4 Gc	700 Mc	400 Mc	3.0 db at 200 Mc	4.5 db at 200 Mc		UHF amplifier
2N2996 TO-18	1.1 Gc	600 Mc	400 Mc	3.5 db at 200 Mc	5.0 db at 200 Mc		VHF amplifier UHF oscillator

NOTE: Any of the above devices can be supplied in TO-18, μmesa, or TI-line packages.   For other specifications, refer to individual data sheets.

Table 2. High-frequency Silicon Transistors

Type & package	f_{max} Guaranteed minimum	F_T Typical	F_T Guaranteed minimum	Noise figure Typical	Noise figure Guaranteed maximum	Fundamental oscillator PO Typical	Fundamental oscillator PO Guaranteed minimum	Area of operation
TI3016A		1.7 Gc		6 db at 1 Gc		50 mw at 2.0 Gc	30 mw at 2 Gc 20 v, 15 ma	L & S band oscillator
TIXS09		1.4 Gc		3.5 db at 450 Mc		60 mw at 1.5 Gc	30 mw at 1.5 Gc 20 v, 15 ma	UHF oscillator
TIXS10		1.2 Gc		4.5 db at 450 Mc		70 mw at 1.0 Gc	30 mw at 1.0 Gc 20 v, 15 ma	VHF oscillator
2N3570	2.75 Gc	1.7 Gc	1.5 Gc	6 db at 1 Gc	7 db at 1 Gc $R_g = 50$ ohms	60 mw at 1.0 Gc		UHF & L band amplifier
2N3571	2.20 Gc	1.4 Gc	1.2 Gc	3.5 db at 450 Mc	4 db at 450 Mc $R_g = 100$ ohms			Low-noise VHF-UHF amp.
2N3572	1.80 Gc	1.2 Gc	1.0 Gc	4.5 db at 450 Mc	6 db at 450 Mc $R_g = 100$ ohms			VHF-UHF amplifier
2N2865	1.25 Gc	900 Mc	600 Mc	3.5 db at 200 Mc	4.5 db at 200 Mc $R_g = 75$ ohms	55 mw at 500 Mc	40 mw at 500 Mc 10 v, 12 ma	Low-noise VHF-UHF amp.
2N918		900 Mc	600 Mc	3.0 db at 60 Mc	6 db at 60 Mc $R_g = 400$ ohms	50 mw at 500 Mc	30 mw at 500 Mc 15 v, 8 ma	Gen. Purpose VHF amplifier
2N917	510 Mc	800 Mc	500 Mc	3.0 db at 60 Mc	6 db at 60 Mc $R_g = 400$ ohms	20 mw at 500 Mc	10 mw at 500 Mc 15 v, 8 ma	Gen. Purpose RF amplifier

NOTE: Any of the above devices can be supplied in TO-18, μmesa, or TI-line packages. For other specifications, refer to individual data sheets.

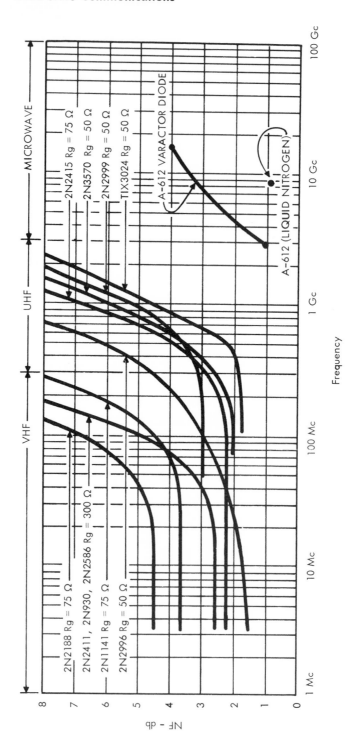

Figure 1

Gc, a harmonic oscillator, or a power driver for varactor multiplier chains; multiple chips can be paralleled in one package.

Figure 2, showing power output vs. frequency, demonstrates what we feel are the present capabilities of these oscillator configurations. The units are available in a TO-18, μmesa*, TI-axial*, or TI-line* package.

2N2865 has an NF specification better than that of the 2N918, which has no maximum 200-mc NF specification.

GERMANIUM SMALL-SIGNAL TRANSISTORS

TIX3032 is a germanium planar transistor. Development of the germanium planar technology permits the use of expanded lead contacts similar to those used in silicon planar transistors. This reduces bonding problems, will permit the use of smaller geometries eventually (giving higher frequency capability), and permits oxide passivation of the surface. This transistor could become the work horse in the VHF-UHF amplifier area. Note that its frequency capabilities

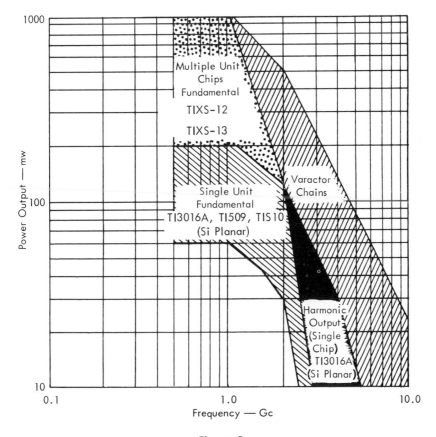

Figure 2

*Trademark of Texas Instruments

place it between the 2N2997 and the 2N2415. As an oscillator, it is specified at two current levels, demonstrates 14% efficiency, and is usable over a 2:1 range of collector current.

TIX3024 is a planar germanium epitaxial transistor designed as an amplifier. As an amplifier, its capability exceeds the 2N2999 in both gain and noise figure. The primary package is the TI-line package.

Amplifier applications are in the 1- to 3-Gc range, but the unit is also ideal in a broadband amplifier from 500 mc upwards, or as the first-stage amplifier following a balanced mixer.

DIODES

Characteristics of TI varactor diodes and voltage variable capacitors are summarized in Table 3.

The following covers the major characteristics of each of these families:

XA706 Series. The XA706 is an epitaxial silicon varactor diode intended primarily for use in frequency multiplier chains, but it may also be used effectively as a tuning element, microwave switch, or parametric amplifier diode. The proven microwave cartridge package houses the device. This package gives the advantage of low series inductance (0.4 nanohenry typical) plus matched temperature coefficients of expansion for added reliability.

When used in frequency multiplier chains (doubler, tripler, etc.) the XA706 can provide up to 10 watts depending on available power input and circuit efficiency. The capacitance-voltage relationship approximates the $\frac{1}{2}$ power law obtained with a theoretical abrupt junction.

XA900 Series. The XA900 is an epitaxial gallium arsenide varactor diode intended primarily for microwave frequency multiplication, but it, too, may be used effectively as a tuning element, microwave switch, or parametric amplifier diode. This unit has the highest available breakdown voltage for the highest available cutoff frequency, typically 50-V_R breakdown and 300-Gc f_{co} at -6 volts.

The microwave double-pill-prong package offers low series inductance (0.4 nanohenry) plus matched temperature coefficients of expansion for added reliability; the package is adaptable to coaxial circuit configurations. This unit will provide highly reproducible results when used in multiplier circuits with inputs at 1 to 10 Kmc.

XA580 Series. This series of voltage variable capacitance diodes comprises epitaxial silicon units with a voltage-capacitance relationship that approximates the $\frac{1}{2}$ power law associated with the theoretical abrupt junction. The units were designed primarily for tuning applications, but they may also be used effectively as frequency multipliers and AFC diodes.

The units are glass-passivated for high reliability and are packaged in the Moly/G® hard glass case. They offer a close capacitance tolerance and very good tracking qualities. When used in tuning applications, they give very uniform performance from unit to unit.

XD500 Series. The XD500, A610, and A600 Series diodes were the first gallium arsenide varactor diodes, and continue to be highly reliable performers.

Table 3. High-frequency Diodes

Unit type (series)	Package	f_{co}	CT (range)	BV_R (range)	Operating range	Primary application	Technology
XA706	Cartridge	140 Gc	0.4-30 pf	24-120 v	1-5 Gc	Harmonic generator	Si epitaxial
XA900	Dbl. pill prong	300 Gc	0.4-1.4 pf	30-50 v	1-10 Gc	Harmonic generator	GaAs epitaxial
XA580	Moly/G®	5 Gc	22-47 pf	35-65 v	DC-500 Mc	Electronic tuning (Voltage variable capacitor)	Si epitaxial
XD500	Cartridge	150 Gc	0.4-1.0 pf	8 v	1-5 Gc	Parametric amplifier	Diffused GaAs
TIVO1	Pill	300 Gc	0.35-1.0 pf	6 v	1-15 Gc	Parametric amplifier	Diffused GaAs

NOTE: Where range is given, it means that the *family* of devices covers the range — not necessarily each device.

Applications: • **Harmonic Generators**
• **Electronic Tuning**
• **Parametric Amplifiers**

TIV01 Series. This series comprises state-of-the-art parametric amplifier diode types that offer extremely high cutoff frequencies. Device structures are fabricated using a gallium arsenide diffused epitaxial process. TIV01 Series devices are ideally designed for low-noise parametric amplifier operation.

HIGH-FREQUENCY TRANSISTOR PACKAGES

TI developed co-axial and TI-line packages to permit full utilization of the maximum frequency capability of the transistor chip. The package must have a low series equivalent resistance and inductance at the desired frequency or the full performance of the transistor chip can not be realized.

Figure 3 is a plot of the equivalent series resistance vs. frequency of our present microwave packages. Note that the TO-18 is usable only to 1 Gc. Preferred packages above 1 Gc are definitely the TI-line and co-axial.

Co-axial Package. This case is designed for co-axial circuit configurations. The base connection is the center flange, whose area provides an excellent means of grounding the base. The emitter contact (short stud) is a heavy low-inductance

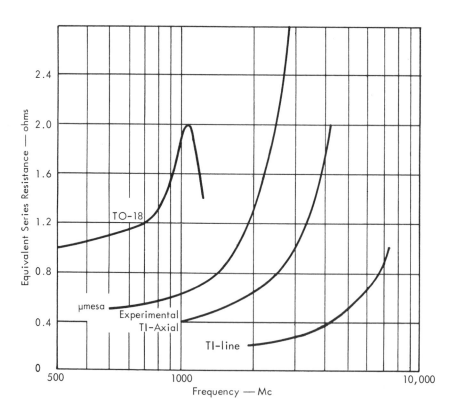

Figure 3

copper contact to the emitter strip. The chip is mounted directly on the longer copper stud, providing maximum heat conductivity.

The flange, being of larger diameter than the ceramic, allows the unit to be placed in a hole cut in a ground plane and to be clamped around its periphery to attain maximum RF ground. The co-axial package is still being improved, and ultimately should have as low an equivalent series resistance as the TI-line package.

TI-line Package. This package is similar to the μmesa package only in appearance and dimensions. An exploded view is shown in Fig. 4; the basing is as shown

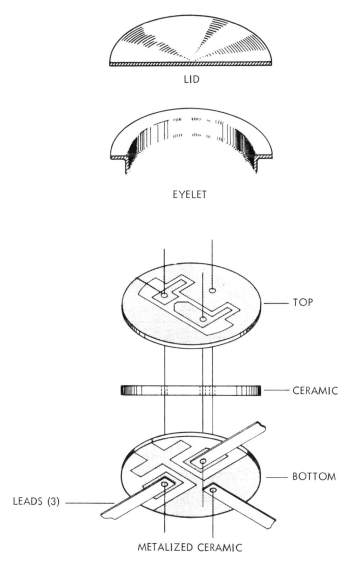

LID

EYELET

TOP

CERAMIC

BOTTOM

LEADS (3)

METALIZED CERAMIC

Figure 4

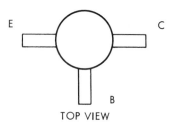

E   C

B

Figure 5   TOP VIEW

in Fig. 5. This revised basing gives better separation of the input and output circuits (E&C leads are adjacent in the μmesa package). The emitter and collector lines of this package can be controlled to have a 50-ohm impedance to the wafer. (A TI patent disclosure has been filed on this package.)

Chief advantages of the TI-line package are its low equivalent series resistance, its controlled 50-ohm impedances, and its suitability to strip-line configurations. The leads are gold-plated silver, giving maximum electrical and heat conductivity. In the future, this will allow us to increase the dissipation rating of devices in this package.

SOLID CIRCUIT® SEMICONDUCTOR NETWORKS

Two New Series 52 Operational/Differential Amplifiers. *SN525A:* Even though this amplifier (Fig. 6) features an open-loop gain of 88 db, it is unconditionally stable when used with two external capacitors in a frequency-response-shaping circuit. Typical differential input-voltage offset is only one millivolt. Two common-mode feedback loops provide a common-mode rejection ratio of 100 db.

SN526A: This general-purpose operational amplifier incorporates a class-B output stage formed by a complementary pair of NPN and PNP transistors. The circuit is capable of a 10-volt signal swing with a 600-ohm load. Output-current peak is 10

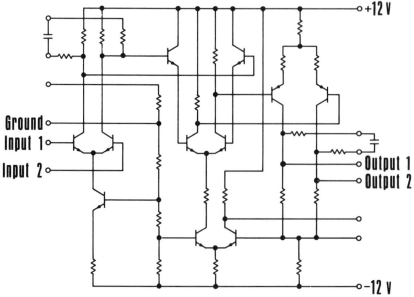

Fig. 6. Circuit diagram

Table 4. Amplifier Performance/Cost Comparison

Characteristic	Typical Discrete-component Amplifier	1962 SN521A	1965	
			SN525A	SN526A
Gain, Open-loop, db	94	62	88	60
Input-voltage Offset, mv	1	2	1	3
Temp. Coefficient, Input-voltage Offset, $\mu v/°C$	5	8	5	10
Input-current Offset, μa	0.2	0.5	0.3	0.03
Common-mode Rejection, db	92	60	100	80
Output-voltage Swing, v	± 11	± 45	± 8	± 10
Output-current Peak, ma	2	1	1	10
Input-Impedance, megohms	0.3	0.01	0.07	2
Price Index	100%	50%	60%	60%

milliamps. Differential input offset is six millivolts maximum over the full −55 to +125°C temperature range. A pair of Darlington transistors gives an input impedance of two megohms. Common-mode feedback provides more than 75 db rejection to common-mode signals.

Improved Network Bar: The improved Series 52 bar features twice as many transistors as earlier versions — 10 NPN and four PNP. There are 68 resistors totaling 300,000 ohms — making 82 components in all.

Table 4 shows performance/cost advantages of the new devices as compared with the SN521A (which was announced late in 1962), and a typical amplifier assembled from discrete components.

New Series 55 High-frequency Amplifiers. This new series offers excellent high-frequency performance and low power dissipation. The first two networks in the series are the SN5500, a sense amplifier for magnetic-core memory applications, and the SN5510, a video differential amplifier.

Diffused transistors in this series have f_T as high as 1.2 Gc under low current and low V_{ce} conditions. Frequency response from dc to 100 Mc is possible.

The large numbers of elements on the two Master Slice bars make possible the fabrication of very complex circuits. The SN5510 Master Slice bar incorporates 36 NPN transistors and 210,000 ohms of resistance. Four thin-film capacitors — totaling up to 400 pf of capacitance — may be deposited on each bar. Customized variations can be built quickly and economically simply by changing the metallic interconnection patterns.

SN5510: This video differential input and output amplifier (Fig. 7) gives a flat frequency response and low phase shift from dc to 40 Mc. Typical single-ended gain at mid-band is 40 db. Common-mode feedback is employed to give common-

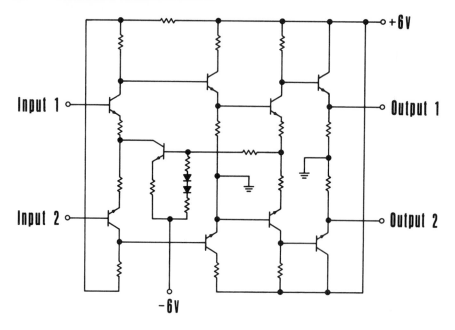

Fig. 7. Circuit diagram

mode rejection ratios of 60 db or greater. Typical input impedance is 2000 ohms, and typical output impedance is less than 300 ohms.

POWER COMMUNICATIONS PRODUCTS

2N2876 and 2N2631: These planar epitaxial transistors are capable of 3 watts output at 150 Mc. Wafer construction employs interdigitated geometry to achieve a high ratio of emitter periphery to emitter area. The emitter region consists of 10 emitter fingers which are about 18 mils long and 2 mils wide.

The 2N2876 is supplied in a VHF low-profile isolated-stud package for minimum lead length and maximum dissipation. The 2N2631 uses the same wafer in a TO-5 package for less critical applications.

Three 2N2876 devices have been used in parallel to build a 30-watt 50-Mc class-C amplifier with power gain higher than 6 db, and 65 percent efficiency.

2

Dependence of Transistor y Parameters on Bias, Frequency, and Temperature

by George Johnson

INTRODUCTION

The application of two-port theory to linear active networks is not new.[1-3]* The vacuum tube has been treated in this way and tabulations of its two-terminal properties are recorded in the literature.[4,6] Many authors have used these techniques in the analysis of electric networks that have linear active networks buried within the structure.[6-8] Lately these methods have been applied to transistors.[9-11] Notable among these references is the work done by Cote and Oakes[7] and Pettit and McWhorter.[11] Both of these references use modern network theory as a foundation for a unified treatment of linear active circuits with equal emphasis on tubes and transistors.

Since the theoretical analysis has been well developed, one logical extension is to apply it to modern high-frequency transistor circuit design. As a first step, we briefly define the two-port parameters and discuss measuring instruments used to develop the parameters. The effects of bias, frequency, and temperature on the y parameters of a germanium mesa transistor are then presented.

TWO-PORT PARAMETERS

Since emphasis will be placed on the two-terminal y parameters and h parameters, only these will be mentioned. It should be stated however that, in general, any set of two-port parameters (z, y, h, or g) may be used.

A complete description of the small-signal a-c behavior of any two-terminal structure can be accomplished by specifying its y parameters, defined as follows:

y_{11} = input admittance for a-c short-circuited output
y_{12} = reverse transfer admittance for a-c short-circuited input
y_{21} = forward transfer admittance for a-c short-circuited output
y_{22} = output admittance for a-c short-circuited input

---

*Superscript numbers refer to bibliography entries at end of chapter.

These parameters, which may or may not be complex, may be grouped into an array called the y matrix:

$$[y] = \begin{bmatrix} y_{11} & y_{12} \\ y_{21} & y_{22} \end{bmatrix}$$

In a similar manner a set of small-signal hybrid parameters may be defined as follows:

h_{11} = input impedance for a-c short-circuited output
h_{12} = reverse voltage transfer ratio for a-c open-circuited input
h_{21} = forward current transfer ratio for a-c short-circuited output
h_{22} = output admittance for a-c open-circuited input

These parameters may also be grouped into a square array called the h matrix:

$$[h] = \begin{bmatrix} h_{11} & h_{12} \\ h_{21} & h_{22} \end{bmatrix}$$

Numerical subscripts are customarily used in passive network analysis, and refer to Fig. 1. When *active* networks are used, the subscripts are changed to indicate more clearly the meaning of the parameter. For instance, if the common-emitter configuration is considered, then the admittance matrix is

$$[y_e] = \begin{bmatrix} y_{ie} & y_{re} \\ y_{fe} & y_{oe} \end{bmatrix}$$

Table 1 is provided to facilitate conversion between y and h parameters. The two-port equivalent circuits corresponding to the parameters defined are shown in Fig. 2. The polarities are defined in Fig. 1.

Table 1. Conversion between h and y parameters for a like common terminal

y_i	y_r	$\dfrac{1}{h_i}$	$\dfrac{-h_r}{h_i}$
y_f	y_o	$\dfrac{h_f}{h_i}$	$\dfrac{\Delta h}{h_i}$
h_i	h_r	$\dfrac{1}{y_i}$	$\dfrac{-y_r}{y_i}$
h_f	h_o	$\dfrac{y_f}{y_i}$	$\dfrac{\Delta y}{y_i}$

$$\Delta y = y_i y_o - y_f y_r = \frac{h_o}{h_i}$$

$$\Delta h = h_i h_o - h_f h_r = \frac{y_o}{y_i}$$

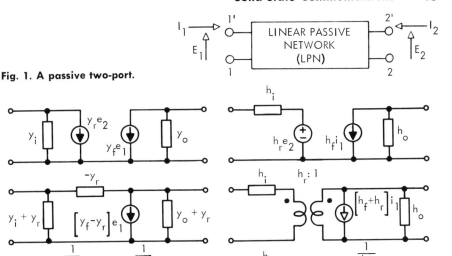

Fig. 1. A passive two-port.

Fig. 2. One- and two-generator equivalent circuits in terms of:
(a) y parameters; (b) h parameters.

MEASUREMENT OF THE y PARAMETERS

The measurement of high-frequency transistor two-port (or for that matter, internal) parameters is a technology in itself. Basically, two problems are encountered when any high-frequency two-port measurements are contemplated:

1. Which two-port parameters are best to measure?
2. Which instrument will most accurately measure these parameters?

In order to answer the first question, consider the elements of the admittance matrix for a transistor as shown in Fig. 3. A set of equations describing this network is given in Eqs. (1), (2), and (3).

$$I_b = y_{bb}V_b + y_{be}V_e + y_{bc}V_c \tag{1}$$

$$I_e = y_{eb}V_b + y_{ee}V_e + y_{ec}V_c \tag{2}$$

$$I_c = y_{cb}V_b + y_{ce}V_e + y_{cc}V_c \tag{3}$$

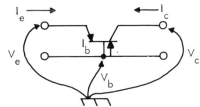

Fig. 3. A three-terminal network.

REFERENCE POINT

The matrix of the elements y_{ij} is called the indefinite admittance matrix because the reference node is unspecified. The elements y_{ij} of the indefinite matrix may be identified as the current flowiing into node i when one volt is applied between node j and ground, with all nodes but node j short-circuited to ground. Therefore, y_{eb} is the current flowing into terminal e from ground when one volt is impressed between the base and ground and all other terminals are grounded. Figure 4 defines the various currents for each orientation.

Consider Eqs. (1), (2), and (3). Strike out all b's. The remaining set [Eqs. (4) and (5)] defines the common-base matrix:

$$I_e = y_{ee}V_e + y_{ec}V_c \tag{4}$$

$$I_c = y_{ce}V_e + y_{cc}V_c \tag{5}$$

When we repeat the same process for the e's and c's, the following sets result. [Eqs. (6) through (9).]

$$I_b = y_{bb}V_b + y_{bc}V_c \tag{6}$$

$$I_c = y_{cb}V_b + y_{cc}V_c \tag{7}$$

$$I_b = y_{bb}V_b + y_{be}V_e \tag{8}$$

$$I_e = y_{eb}V_b + y_{ee}V_e \tag{9}$$

Now when we compare Eqs. (6) and (8), it is evident that y_{11} for the common-emitter set is equal to y_{11} for the common-collector set. Further comparisons result in Table 2. Now consider Fig. 3 again. Using Kirchoff's current rule, the sum of the currents I_b, I_e, and I_c must be zero for a specified voltage. Since V_e and V_c are zero for the common-base condition, Eq. (10) may be written:

$$I_b + I_e + I_c = 0 = V_b(y_{bb} + y_{cb} + y_{eb}) \tag{10}$$

Since

$$V_b \neq 0$$

then

$$y_{bb} + y_{cb} + y_{eb} = 0$$

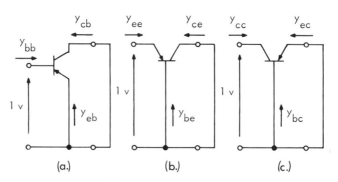

Fig. 4. Orientations: (a) common emitter; (b) common base; (c) common collector.

Table 2. Relationship among the parameters of the indefinite matrix

$y_{bb} = y_{ie} = y_{ic}$	$y_{be} = y_{rc}$	$y_{bc} = y_{re}$
$y_{eb} = y_{fc}$	$y_{ee} = y_{ib} = y_{oc}$	$y_{ec} = y_{rb}$
$y_{cb} = y_{fe}$	$y_{ce} = y_{fb}$	$y_{cc} = y_{ob} = y_{oe}$

In other words, the sum of the admittances in any row or column of the matrix of the coefficients of Eqs. (1) through (3) must add to zero. It is therefore evident that, in general, four parameters of the indefinite matrix set will be sufficient to allow calculation of all the parameters. From a practical standpoint, certain parameters are more desirable to measure than others, and considering such things as bridge loading and resolution we can eliminate some of the parameters. Probably the best set to choose is: y_{ie}, y_{ib}, y_{oe}, and y_{re}; this answers our first question.

Before the second question is discussed it should be mentioned that the y data presented in this chapter are for a consistent set of parameters. This yields a usable set of data as measured, without conversion.

The problem of determining the most accurate and practical measuring instrument is not answerable directly. The value of the two-port parameters and the frequency range are only two of the considerations that influence this choice. Two of the more popular bridges in use are the General Radio transfer function and immittance bridge and the Wayne Kerr bridge. Figures 5, 6, 7, and 8 show schematically each of these bridges.

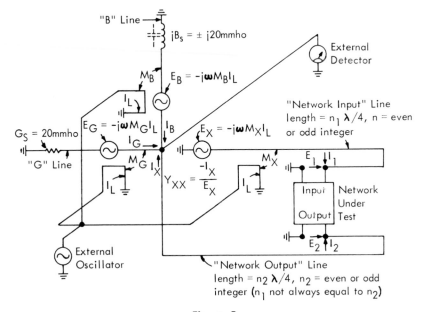

Figure 5

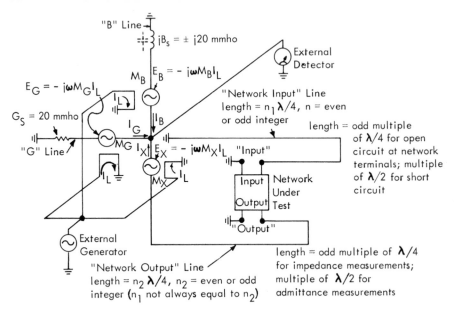

Figure 6

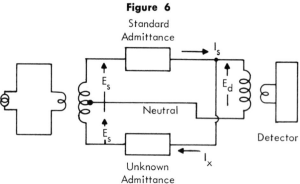

Fig. 7. Simplified diagram of Wayne Kerr bridge used for two-terminal measurements.

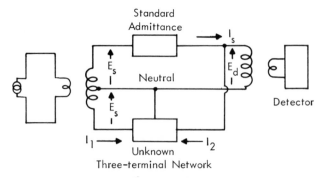

Fig. 8. Simplified diagram of Wayne Kerr bridge as used to measure the transfer admittance of a three-terminal network.

The bridge chosen for the measurement of the y parameters presented here is the General Radio bridge, because it covers a broader frequency range, and it does not require a separate jig as does the Wayne Kerr bridge.

SENSITIVITY OF y PARAMETERS

This section displays graphically the change in the y parameters of a high-performance germanium transistor with changes in bias, frequency, and temperature. The transistor selected is the 2N2415. No effort is made to relate these changes to any particular internal parameter change. The primary objective is to present accurately measured two-port data for use in practical designs. The curves of Figs. 9 through 26 contain these data.

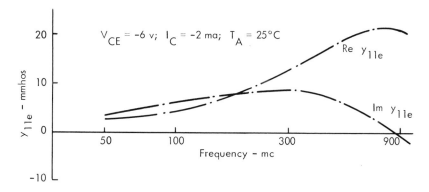

Figure 9

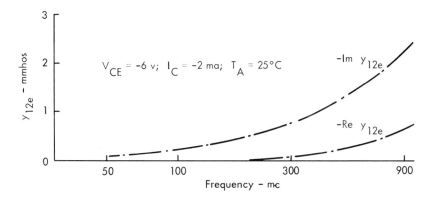

Figure 10

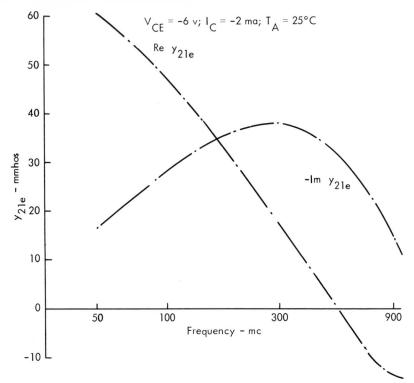

Figure 11

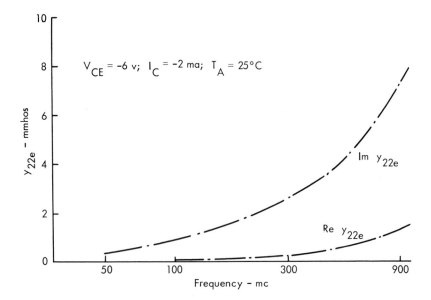

Figure 12

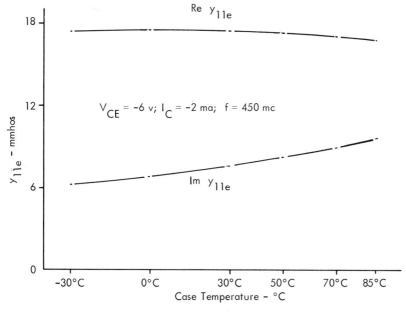

Figure 13

Figure 14

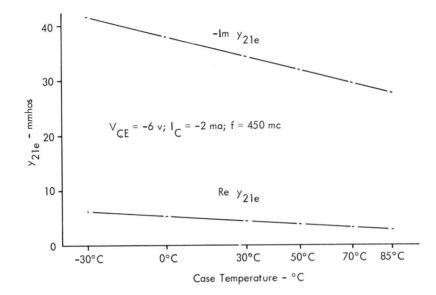

Figure 15

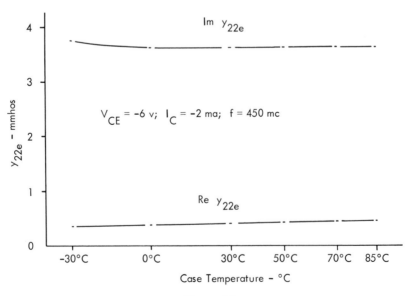

Figure 16

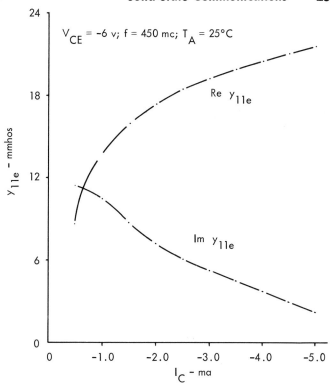

Figure 17

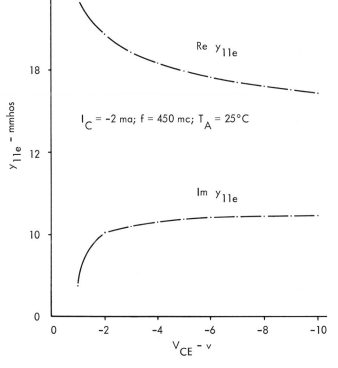

Figure 18

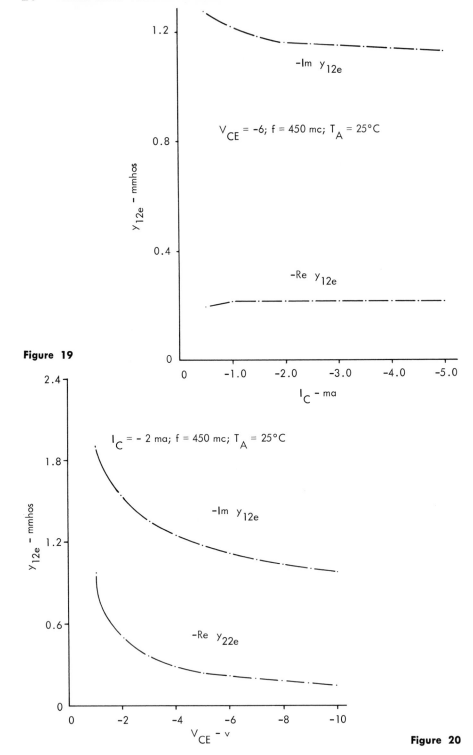

Figure 19

$V_{CE} = -6$; $f = 450$ mc; $T_A = 25°C$

$-Im\ y_{12e}$

$-Re\ y_{12e}$

y_{12e} - mmhos

I_C - ma

$I_C = -2$ ma; $f = 450$ mc; $T_A = 25°C$

$-Im\ y_{12e}$

$-Re\ y_{22e}$

y_{12e} - mmhos

V_{CE} - v

Figure 20

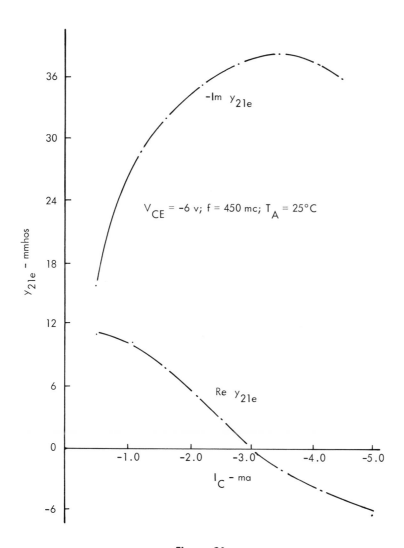

Figure 21

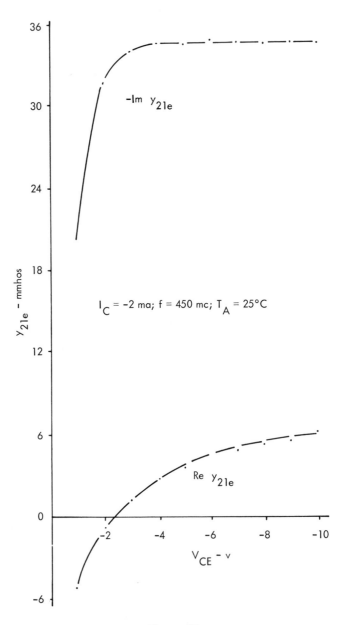

Figure 22

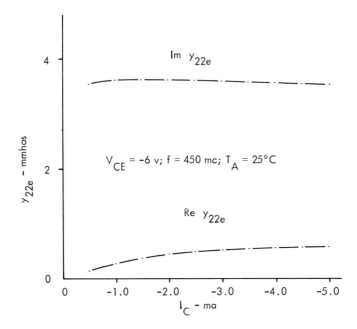

Figure 23

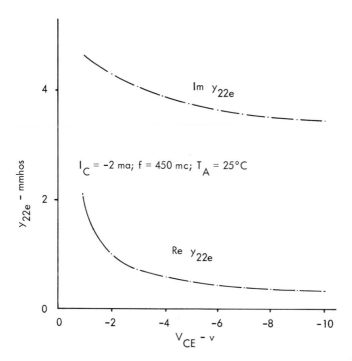

Figure 24

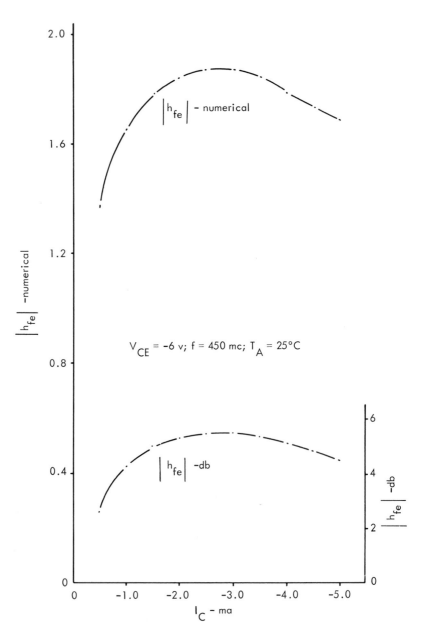

Figure 25

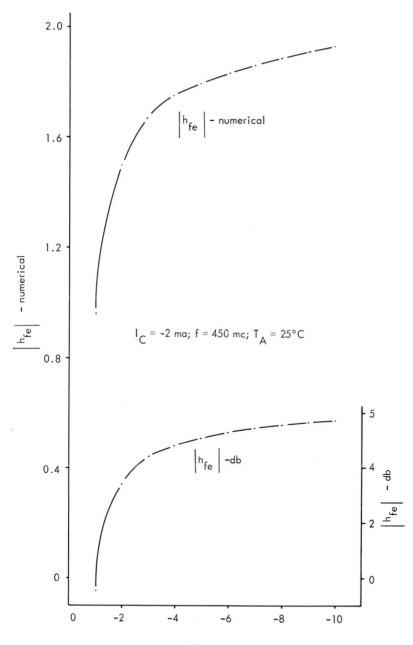

Figure 26

BIBLIOGRAPHY

1. Peterson, L. C.: Equivalent Circuits of Linear Active Four-terminal Networks, *Bell System Tech. J.,* 27, (4) pp. 593–622, October, 1948.
2. Giacoletto, L. J.: Terminology and Equations for Linear Active Four-terminal Networks, Including Transistors, *RCA Rev.,* 14, (1) pp. 28–46, March, 1953.
3. Standards on Electron Tubes: Methods of Testing, 1950, *Proc. IRE,* 38, (8) pp. 917–948, August, 1950.
4. Brown, J. S., and F. D. Bennett: The Application of Matrices to Vacuum-tube Circuits, *Proc. IRE,* 36, (7) pp. 848–849, July, 1948.
5. Deards, S. R.: Matrix Theory Applied to Thermionic Valve Circuits, *Electronic Eng.,* 24, pp. 264–267, June, 1952.
6. Bode, H. W.: "Network Analysis and Feedback Amplifier Design," D. Van Nostrand Company, September, 1945.
7. Cote, A. J., and J. B. Oakes: "Linear Vacuum-tube and Transistor Circuits," McGraw-Hill Book Company, Inc., New York, 1961.
8. Nodelman, H. M., and F. W. Smith: "Mathematics for Electronics," chaps. 5–8, McGraw-Hill Book Company, Inc., New York, 1956.
9. Gärtner, W. W.: "Transistors: Principles, Design, and Applications," D. Van Nostrand Company, 1960.
10. Linvill, J. G., and J. F. Gibbons: "Transistors and Active Circuits," McGraw-Hill Book Company, Inc., New York, 1961.
11. Pettit, J. M., and M. M. McWhorter: "Electronic Amplifier Circuits," McGraw-Hill Book Company, Inc., New York, 1961.

3

Typical y Parameter Data

prepared by George Johnson

INTRODUCTION

The following two-port parameters and data are provided as an aid to the design of high-frequency circuits.

The y-parameters were obtained, in general, from a typical sample selected from a larger lot. Therefore, they represent the typical terminal properties of the

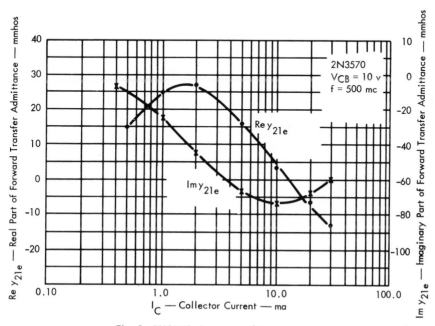

Fig. 1. 2N3570: Re y_{21e} and Im y_{21e} vs. I_C.

transistor in question at that time. All the parameters were measured on a General Radio transfer function and immittance bridge.

The list of transistors includes both silicon and germanium. The range of f_t represented by this selection of transistors is from 200 mc to 1.6 Gc. For further information on both a-c and d-c parameters, see the pertinent TI data sheets.

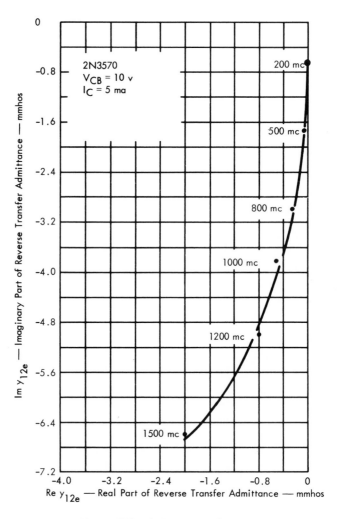

Fig. 2. 2N3570: Im y_{12e} vs. Re y_{12e}.

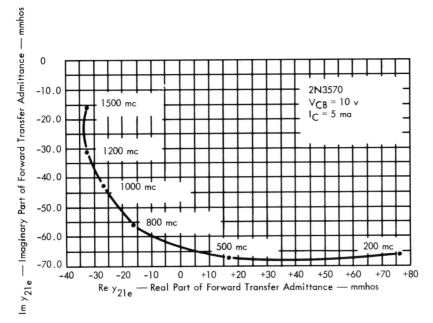

Fig. 3. 2N3570: Im y_{21e} vs. Re y_{21e}.

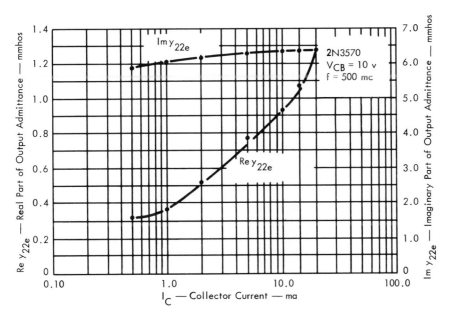

Fig. 4. 2N3570: Re y_{22e} and Im y_{22e} vs. I_C.

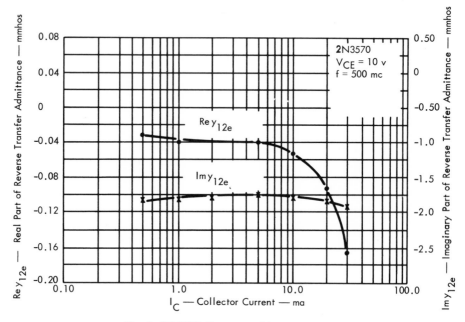

Fig. 5. 2N3570: Re y$_{12e}$ and Im y$_{12e}$ vs. I$_C$.

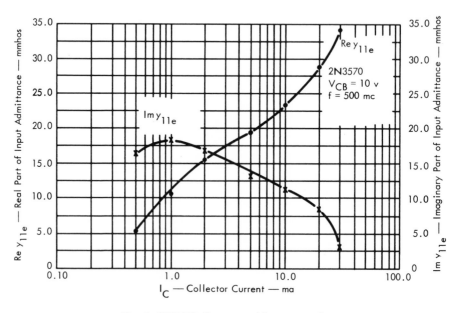

Fig. 6. 2N3570: Re y$_{11e}$ and Im y$_{11e}$ vs. I$_C$.

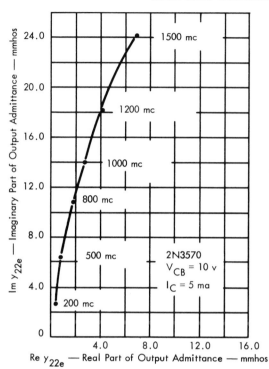

Fig. 7. 2N3570: Im y$_{22e}$ vs. Re y$_{22e}$.

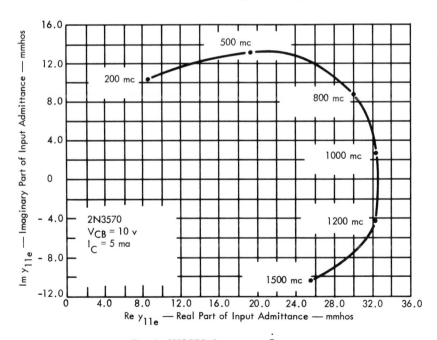

Fig. 8. 2N3570: Im y$_{11e}$ vs. Re y$_{11e}$.

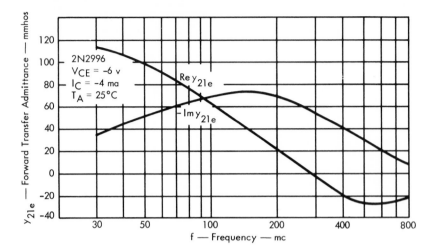

Fig. 9. 2N2996: y_{21e} vs. f.

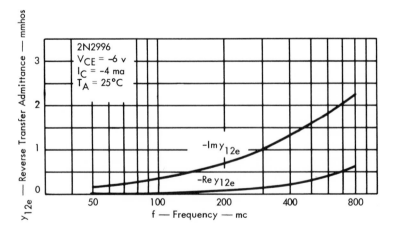

Fig. 10. 2N2996: y_{12e} vs. f.

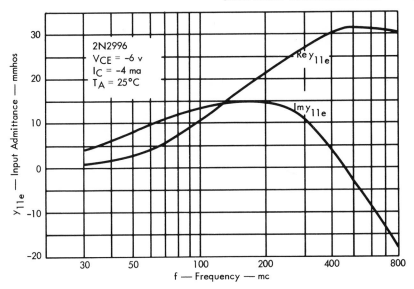

Fig. 11. 2N2996: y$_{11e}$ vs. f.

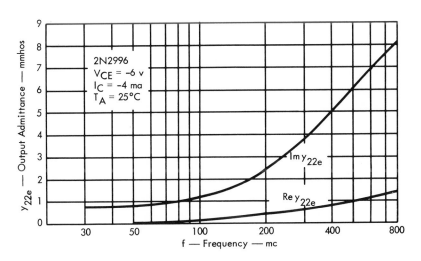

Fig. 12. 2N2996: y$_{22e}$ vs. f.

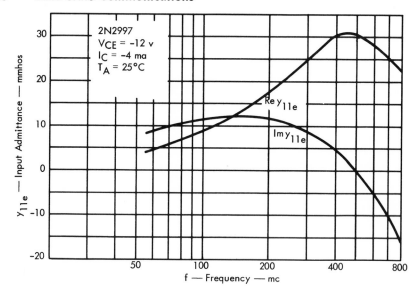

Fig. 13. 2N2997: y_{11e} vs. f.

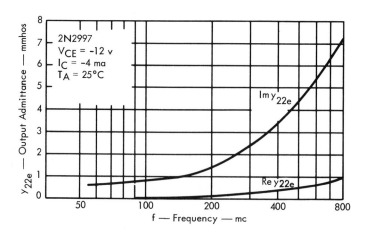

Fig. 14. 2N2997: y_{22e} vs. f.

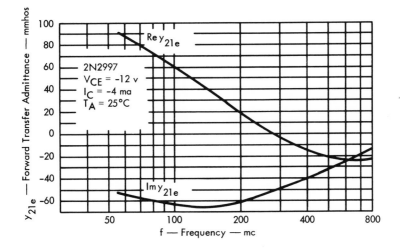

Fig. 15. 2N2997: y_{21e} vs. f.

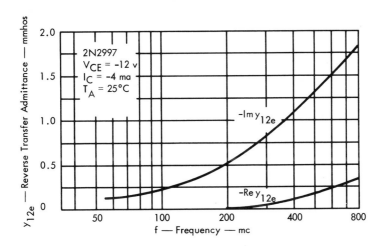

Fig. 16. 2N2997: y_{12e} vs. f.

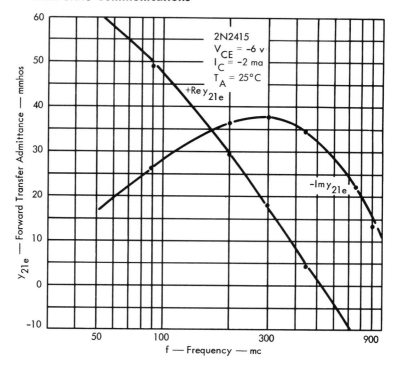

Fig. 17. 2N2415: y$_{21e}$ vs. f.

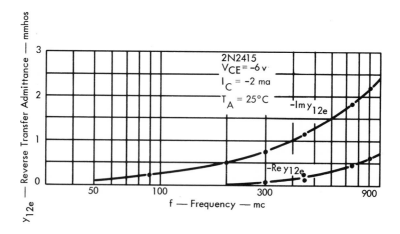

Fig. 18. 2N2415: y$_{12e}$ vs. f.

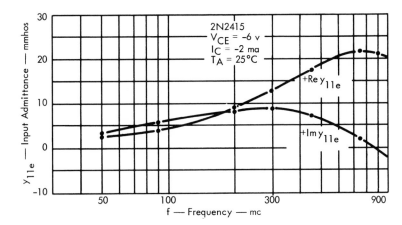

Fig. 19. 2N2415: y_{11e} vs. f.

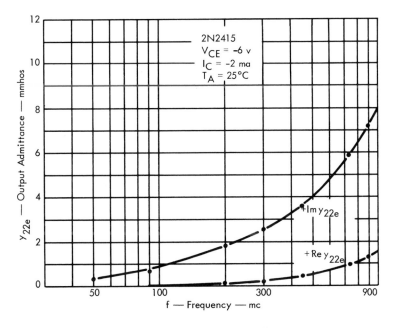

Fig. 20. 2N2415: y_{22e} vs. f.

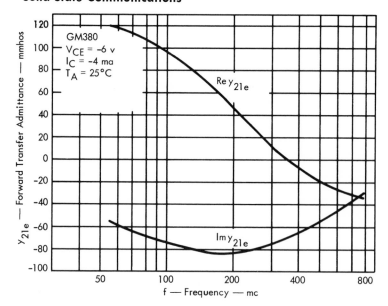

Fig. 21. GM380: y_{21e} **vs. f.**

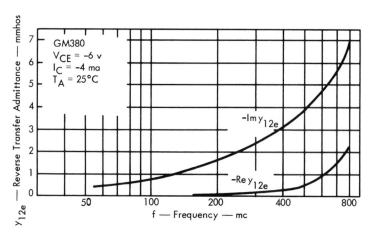

Fig. 22. GM380: y_{12e} **vs. f.**

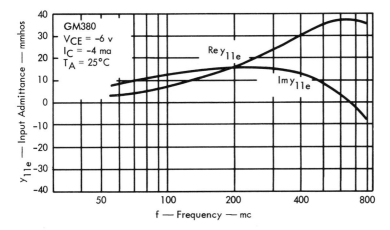

Fig. 23. GM380: y_{11e} **vs. f.**

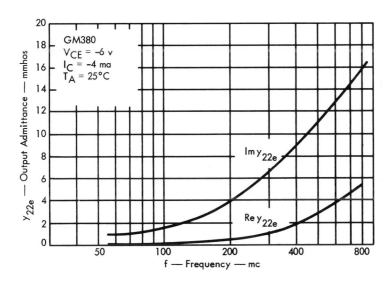

Fig. 24. GM380: y_{22e} **vs. f.**

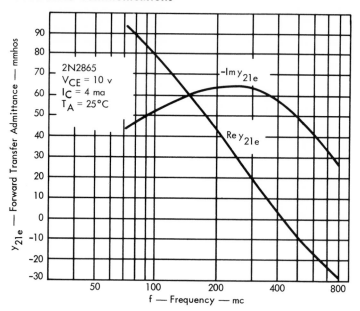

Fig. 25. 2N2865: y$_{21e}$ vs. f.

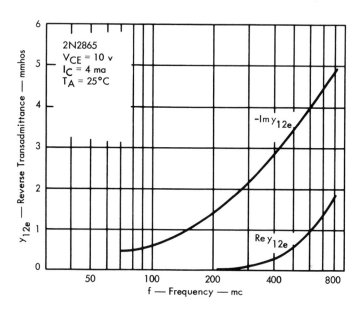

Fig. 26. 2N2865: y$_{12e}$ vs. f.

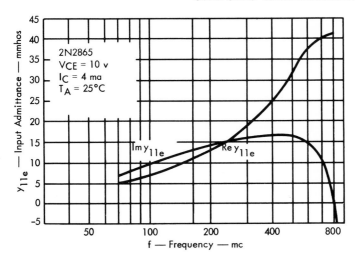

Fig. 27. 2N2865: y_{11e} vs. f.

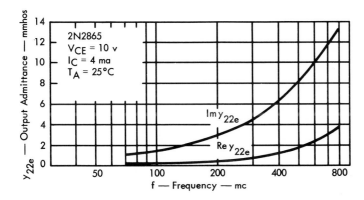

Fig. 28. 2N2865: y_{22e} vs. f.

4

Power Gain and Stability in Linear Active Two-ports

by George Johnson

INTRODUCTION

Characterization of high-frequency transistors may be accomplished by either of two methods. The first is based on a set of transistor internal parameters; they are derived from a suitable model, and can be related directly to the physical properties of the transistor. High-frequency circuit design based on this internal parameter method of transistor characterization has been well documented in the literature. The advantages of this method are ease of measurement of the internal parameters, speed and simplicity of analysis, and strong relationship to the physical device. One of the major disadvantages is that the equivalent circuit chosen may not be an accurate representation of the physical device over a particular high-frequency range because of simplifying approximations.

The second method is the two-port method. Because it emphasizes the measured terminal parameters rather than internal parameters in a specific structure, it exactly characterizes the linear active network. Principal advantages of this method are its applicability to any two-port active device, its freedom from any approximations that may have been made in arriving at a simple equivalent circuit model for the device, and all of the advantages of matrix analysis. The principal disadvantage is that information about the physical structure of the transistor is lost.

EQUIVALENT CIRCUITS

To establish a relationship between terminal parameters and internal parameters, consider the Giacoletta hybrid-π equivalent circuit shown in Fig. 1. This equivalent circuit is not necessarily a true representation of any given transistor at any given frequency, but it may be used to establish relationships between terminal parameters and internal parameters. The h and y parameters for this equivalent circuit are presented in Tables 1 and 2.

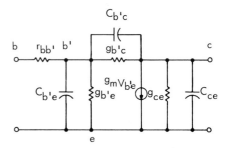

Fig. 1. Hybrid-π equivalent circuit.

These equations present the two-port parameters in terms of internal parameters of an equivalent circuit which has good correlation to the physical model. The base spreading resistance is accounted for by $r_{b'b}$, and the remaining structure represents the behavior of the intrinsic transistor. It is possible to establish still closer identity to the physical model by deriving the hybrid-π components in terms of the basic physical quantities such as diffusion lengths, base widths, doping densities, etc.

However, for most purposes, the identities presented here will be quite satisfactory.

Pritchard has made certain simplifications to the equivalent circuit of Fig. 1. Figure 2 shows the approximate high-frequency equivalent circuit for junction transistors in the common-emitter configurations. The h parameters may be written by inspection when the condition $c_c \ll 1/\omega_t r_e'$ is used.

$$h_{ie} = \left(r_b' + \frac{\omega_t r_e'}{j\omega} \right) \text{ ohms} \tag{1}$$

$$h_{re} = \omega_t r_e' c_c \tag{2}$$

$$h_{fe} = -j \frac{\omega_t}{\omega} \tag{3}$$

$$h_{oe} = (\omega_t c_c + j\omega c_c) \text{ mhos} \tag{4}$$

The resulting y parameters are

$$y_{ie} = \frac{1}{r_b' - j(\omega_t/\omega) r_e'} \tag{5}$$

$$y_{re} = \frac{-\omega_t r_e' c_c}{r_b' - j(\omega_t/\omega) r_e'} \tag{6}$$

$$y_{fe} = -\frac{j(\omega_t/\omega)}{r_b' - j(\omega_t/\omega) r_e'} \tag{7}$$

$$y_{oe} = \frac{\omega_t c_c (r_b' + r_e') + j\omega c_c (r_b')}{r_b' - j(\omega_t/\omega) r_e'} \tag{8}$$

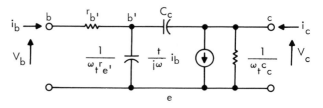

Fig. 2. Approximate high-frequency equivalent circuit of a junction transistor.

Table 1. h Parameters for the Hybrid-π Equivalent Circuit

$$h_{ie} = h'_{ie}\frac{1+\tau_1 S}{1+\tau_2 S}$$

where:

$$h'_{ie} = \frac{g_{bb'} + g_{b'e} + g_{b'c}}{g_{bb'}(g_{b'e}+g_{b'c})}$$

$$\tau_1 = \frac{C_{b'e}+C_{b'c}}{g_{bb'}+g_{b'e}+g_{b'c}} = \tau_1$$

$$\tau_2 = \frac{C_{b'e}+C_{b'c}}{g_{b'e}+g_{b'c}} = \tau_2$$

$$h_{re} = h'_{re}\frac{1+\tau_3 S}{1+\tau_4 S}$$

where:

$$h'_{re} = \frac{g_{b'c}}{g_{b'e}+g_{b'c}}$$

$$\tau_3 = \frac{C_{b'c}}{g_{b'c}}$$

$$\tau_4 = \frac{C_{b'e}+C_{b'c}}{g_{b'e}+g_{b'c}} = \tau_2$$

$$h_{fe} = h'_{fe}\frac{1-\tau_5 S}{1+\tau_6 S}$$

where:

$$h'_{fe} = \frac{g_m-g_{b'c}}{g_{b'e}+g_{b'c}}$$

$$\tau_5 = \frac{C_{b'c}}{g_m-g_{b'c}}$$

$$\tau_6 = \frac{C_{b'e}+C_{b'c}}{g_{b'c}+g_{b'e}} = \tau_4 = \tau_2$$

$$h_{oe} = h'_{oe1}\left(\frac{1+\tau_7 S}{1+\tau_8 S}\right) + h'_{oe2}(1+\tau_9 S)$$

where:

$$h'_{oe1} = \frac{(g_{b'e}+g_m)\,g_{b'c} + S^2\,(C_{b'c}C_{b'e})}{g_{b'e}+g_{b'c}}$$

$$h'_{oe2} = g_{ce}$$

$$\tau_7 = \frac{C_{b'c}\,(g_{b'e}+g_m) + C_{b'e}\,g_{b'c}}{(g_{b'e}+g_m)\,(g_{b'e}) + S^2\,(C_{b'c}C_{b'e})}$$

$$\tau_8 = \frac{C_{b'e}+C_{b'c}}{g_{b'e}+g_{b'c}}$$

$$\tau_9 = \frac{C_{ce}}{g_{ce}}$$

Table 2. y Parameters for the Hybrid-π Equivalent Circuit

$$y_{ie} = y'_{ie}\frac{1+\tau_2 S}{1+\tau_{10} S}$$

where:

$$y'_{ie} = \frac{g_{bb'}(g_{b'e}+g_{b'c})}{g_{bb'}+g_{b'e}+g_{b'c}}$$

$$\tau_2 = \frac{C_{b'e}+C_{b'c}}{g_{b'e}+g_{b'c}}$$

$$\tau_{10} = \frac{C_{b'e}+C_{b'c}}{g_{bb'}+g_{b'e}+g_{b'c}} = \tau_1$$

$$y_{re} = -y'_{re}\frac{1+\tau_3 S}{1+\tau_{10} S}$$

where:

$$y'_{re} = \frac{g_{bb'}\,g_{b'c}}{g_{bb'}+g_{b'e}+g_{b'c}}$$

$$\tau_3 = \frac{C_{b'c}}{g_{b'c}}$$

$$\tau_{10} = \frac{C_{b'e}+C_{b'c}}{g_{bb'}+g_{b'e}+g_{b'c}} = \tau_1$$

$$y_{fe} = \frac{y'_{fe1}}{(1+\tau_{10}S)} - y'_{fe2}\frac{(1+\tau_3 S)}{(1+\tau_{10}S)}$$

where:

$$y'_{fe1} = \frac{g_{bb'}\,g_m}{g_{bb'}+g_{b'e}+g_{b'c}}$$

$$y'_{fe2} = \frac{g_{bb'}\,g_{b'c}}{g_{bb'}+g_{b'e}+g_{b'c}}$$

$$\tau_3 = \frac{C_{b'c}}{g_{b'c}}$$

$$\tau_{10} = \frac{C_{b'e}+C_{b'c}}{g_{bb'}+g_{b'e}+g_{b'c}} = \tau_1$$

$$y_{oe} = y'_{oe1}(1+\tau_9 S) + y'_{oe2}\frac{(1+\tau_3 S)(1+\tau_{11}S)}{(1+\tau_{10}S)}$$

where:

$$y'_{oe1} = g_{ce}$$

$$y'_{oe2} = \frac{(g_{bb'}+g_m+g_{b'e})\,g_{b'c}}{g_{bb'}+g_{b'e}+g_{b'c}}$$

$$\tau_9 = \frac{C_{ce}}{g_{ce}}$$

$$\tau_{10} = \frac{C_{b'e}+C_{b'c}}{g_{bb'}+g_{b'e}+g_{b'c}}$$

$$\tau_{11} = \frac{C_{b'e}}{g_{bb'}+g_m+g_{b'e}}$$

These equations establish the approximate correlation between internal parameters and terminal parameters. Since most of these expressions are rather involved, it is simpler to express circuit design equations in terms of the terminal parameters. The discussion of stability and power gain that follows is therefore based on these terminal parameters.

POWER GAIN EQUATIONS

The power gain of a Linear Active Network (LAN) may be specified in many ways. This section defines some of the more important power gain expressions and shows their derivations.

Power Gain. The term G_p is defined as:

$$G_p = \text{Power gain} = \frac{\text{Power delivered to load}}{\text{Power delivered to input of LAN}}$$

$$G_p = \frac{|I_2|^2 \operatorname{Re}(Z_L)}{|I_1|^2 \operatorname{Re}(Z_{in})} \tag{9}$$

This power gain is independent of the generator impedance and allows the gain of a LAN to be evaluated as a function of load. It is derived as follows: from two-port theory,

$$\frac{I_2}{I_1} = \frac{Y_L h_{21}}{Y_L + h_{22}} \tag{10}$$

$$\operatorname{Re}(Z_L) = R_L \tag{11}$$

$$\operatorname{Re}(Z_{in}) = \operatorname{Re}\left(h_{11} - \frac{h_{12} h_{21}}{h_{22} + Y_L}\right) \tag{12}$$

Combining these gives

$$G_p = \frac{|(Y_L)|^2 |h_{21}|^2 \operatorname{Re}(Z_L)}{|Y_L + h_{22}|^2 \operatorname{Re}\left(h_{11} - \dfrac{h_{12} h_{21}}{h_{22} + Y_L}\right)} = \frac{|h_{21}|^2 \operatorname{Re}(Y_L)}{|Y_L + h_{22}|^2 \operatorname{Re}\left(h_{11} - \dfrac{h_{12} h_{21}}{h_{22} + Y_L}\right)} \tag{13}$$

As with all the power gain terms to be derived later, this expression is general in form. Therefore, Eq. (14) may be written

$$G_p = \frac{|y_{21}|^2 \operatorname{Re}(Y_L)}{|Y_L + y_{22}|^2 \operatorname{Re}\left(y_{11} - \dfrac{y_{12} y_{21}}{y_{22} + Y_L}\right)} \tag{14}$$

The general expression is given by Eq. (15)

$$G_p = \frac{|K_{21}|^2 M_{Lr}}{|K_{22} + M_L|^2 \operatorname{Re}\left(K_{11} - \dfrac{K_{12} K_{21}}{K_{22} + M_L}\right)} \tag{15}$$

A special form of this power gain is obtained by conjugately matching the load Y_L to y_{22}. Using

$$Y_L{}^* = y_{22} \tag{16}$$

in the G_p expression gives:

$$G_p' = \frac{|y_{21}|^2 M_{Lr}}{|Y_{Lr} - Im\,(Y_L) + y_{22r} + Im\,(y_{22})|^2} \quad Re\left(y_{11} - \frac{y_{12}\,y_{21}}{Re\,(y_{22}) + Im\,(y_{22}) + Re\,(Y_L) - Im\,(Y_L)}\right) \quad (17)$$

$$G_p' = G_{oo} = \frac{|y_{21}|^2}{4g_{11}\,g_{22} - 2Re\,(y_{12}y_{21})} \quad (18)$$

The term G_{oo} is the basic gain expression in the Linvill method. It serves as a useful figure of merit.

Transducer Gain. The transducer gain is the ratio of the power the LAN delivers to a load, divided by the power the generator would deliver to that load, if the load were conjugately matched to the generator. The maximum available power from the generator is

$$P_{AVS} = \frac{|E_g|^2}{4Re\,(Z_g)} \quad (19)$$

The output power is

$$P_{out} = |V_2|^2\,Re\,(Y_L) \quad (20)$$

Therefore, the transducer gain is

$$G_T = \frac{4Re\,(Z_g)\,Re\,(Y_L)\,|V_2|^2}{|E_g|^2} \quad (21)$$

Consider the LAN shown in Fig. 3. From two-port theory,

$$E_g = (h_{11} + Z_g)\,I_1 + h_{12}\,V_2 \quad (22)$$

$$I_2 = h_{21}\,I_1 + h_{22}\,V_2 \quad (23)$$

$$V_2 = \frac{\begin{vmatrix} h_{11} + Z_g & E_g \\ h_{21} & I_2 \end{vmatrix}}{\begin{vmatrix} h_{11} + Z_g & h_{12} \\ h_{21} & h_{22} \end{vmatrix}} = \frac{h_{11} + Z_g}{\Delta h}\,I_2 - \frac{h_{21}}{\Delta h}\,E_g \quad (24)$$

But $-I_2 = V_2\,Y_L$, so that

$$V_2 = -\left(\frac{h_{11} + Z_g}{\Delta h}\right)(V_2\,Y_L) - \left(\frac{h_{21}}{\Delta h}\right)E_g \quad (25)$$

$$V_2\left[1 + \frac{(h_{11} + Z_g)}{\Delta h}\,Y_L\right] = -\left(\frac{h_{21}}{\Delta h}\right)E_g \quad (26)$$

$$V_2\left[\frac{\Delta h + (h_{11} + Z_g)\,Y_L}{\Delta h}\right] = -\left(\frac{h_{21}}{\Delta h}\right)E_g \quad (27)$$

$$\frac{V_2}{E_g} = \frac{-h_{21}}{(h_{11} + Z_g)\,Y_L + \Delta h} = \frac{-h_{21}}{(h_{11} + Z_g)(h_{22} + Y_L) - h_{12}\,h_{21}} \quad (28)$$

$$\left|\frac{V_2}{E_g}\right|^2 = \frac{|h_{21}|^2}{|(h_{11} + Z_g)(h_{22} + Y_L) - h_{12}\,h_{21}|^2} \quad (29)$$

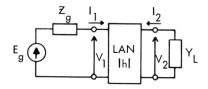

Fig. 3. General two-port.

Therefore

$$G_T = \frac{4\mathrm{Re}(Z_g)\,\mathrm{Re}(Y_L)\,|\,h_{21}\,|^2}{|\,(h_{11} + Z_g)\,(h_{22} + Y_L) - h_{12}\,h_{21}\,|^2}$$
(30)

The general form is given by Eq. (31)

$$G_T = \frac{4\,|\,K_{21}\,|^2\,\mathrm{Re}(M_L)\,\mathrm{Re}(M_g)}{|\,(K_{11} + M_g)\,(K_{22} + M_L) - K_{12}\,K_{21}\,|^2}$$
(31)

Maximum Available Power Gain. The term "maximum available power gain" cannot be discussed without discussing stability. Certain terminations may cause a linear active two-port that is not unilateral to oscillate. Such a two-port is therefore termed potentially unstable. If no such terminations are possible, then it is unconditionally stable. If it is unconditionally stable the maximum available gain G_{max} may be achieved by conjugately matching the generator to the input immittance of the terminated LAN and conjugately matching the load to the output immittance with the input network in place. If the LAN is potentially unstable, the value of G_{max} is unbounded, and the term becomes meaningless. The variation of G_{max} vs frequency is shown in Fig. 4.

To derive the expression for G_{max}, the expression for transducer gain must be differentiated with respect to the real and imaginary parts of the generator and load immittance and the four derivatives set equal to zero. They may then be substituted into the transducer gain equation to give the maximum available power gain. This is not a difficult operation, but since the technique of obtaining G_{max} by the Linvill method is the one used in later design examples, only the results of the differentiation are presented now.

The imaginary parts of the generator and load that maximize the power gain of an unconditionally stable two-port are:

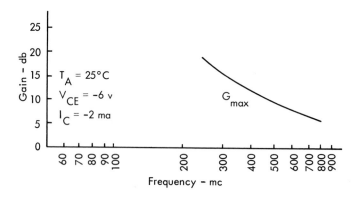

Fig. 4. G_{max} versus frequency.

$$B_g = -\text{Im}(y_{11}) + \frac{\text{Im}(y_{12}y_{21})}{2\text{Re}(y_{22})} \tag{32}$$

$$B_L = -\text{Im}(y_{22}) + \frac{\text{Im}(y_{12}y_{21})}{2\text{Re}(y_{11})} \tag{33}$$

The real parts of the generator and load that maximize the power gain of an unconditionally stable two-port are:

$$G_g = \frac{1}{2\text{Re}(y_{22})}\left\{[2\text{Re}(y_{11})\,\text{Re}(y_{22}) - \text{Re}(y_{12}y_{21})]^2 - |y_{12}y_{21}|^2\right\}^{1/2} \tag{34}$$

$$G_L = \frac{1}{2\text{Re}(y_{11})}\left\{[2\text{Re}(y_{11})\,\text{Re}(y_{22}) - \text{Re}(y_{12}y_{21})]^2 - |y_{12}y_{21}|^2\right\}^{1/2} \tag{35}$$

Substituting these values in the equation for transducer gain gives the expression for G_{max}:

$$G_{max} = \frac{|y_{21}|^2}{2\text{Re}(y_{11})\,\text{Re}(y_{22}) - \text{Re}(y_{12}y_{21}) + \left\{[2\text{Re}(y_{11})\,\text{Re}(y_{22}) - \text{Re}(y_{12}y_{21})]^2 - |y_{12}y_{21}|^2\right\}^{1/2}} \tag{36}$$

Maximum Available Gain. If the effect of the inverse feedback of the two-port is neglected, then the power gain obtained when the input and output are conjugately matched to the generator and load is the maximum available gain MAG. As might be expected, the expression G_{max} is meaningless unless the active device is unconditionally stable. Since the effect of the inverse feedback ratio will be neglected, the condition of unconditional stability is already satisfied. And, since G_{max} was obtained under the conditions of conjugate match at both ports, it is only necessary to substitute $y_{12} = 0$ in the G_{max} expression to obtain the equation for MAG. This substitution into Eq. (36) yields:

$$\text{MAG} = \frac{|y_{21}|^2}{4\text{Re}(y_{11})\,\text{Re}(y_{22})} = \frac{|h_{21}|^2}{4\text{Re}(h_{11})\,\text{Re}(h_{22})} \tag{37}$$

This term, because it involves easily measurable parameters, is used as a figure of merit for transistor performance. It is best to use MAG only in this sense.

To relate this form of power gain back to the device parameters, the equivalent circuit of Fig. 5 is used. As is evident from this equivalent circuit, the common-emitter input impedance at high frequencies is essentially r_b'. Since the effect of internal feedback is neglected, the following derivation may be performed:

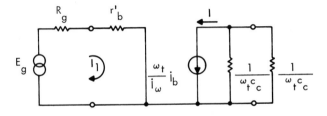

Fig. 5. High-frequency simplified equivalent circuit neglecting reverse internal feedback.

$$P_{AVS} = \frac{E_g{}^2}{4R_g} = \frac{E_g{}^2}{4r_b{}'} \tag{38}$$

where $R_g = r_b{}'$ under the condition of conjugate match.

but

$$I_1 = \frac{E_g}{2r_b{}'} \tag{39}$$

and

$$E_g{}^2 = 2r_b{}'^2 I_1{}^2 = 4r_b{}'^2 I_1{}^2 \tag{40}$$

so

$$P_{AVg} = \frac{I_1{}^2 4(r_b{}')^2}{4r_b{}'} = I_1{}^2 r_b{}' \tag{41}$$

The maximum available output power is:

$$E_{Load} = \frac{-I}{2\omega_t C_c} \tag{42}$$

$$P = E_L{}^2 \omega_t C_c = \frac{I^2(\omega_t C_c)}{4(\omega_t C_c)^2} \tag{43}$$

The resulting power gain is

$$MAG = \frac{I^2}{4\omega_t C_c} \frac{1}{I_1{}^2 r_b{}'} = \frac{\left(\frac{I}{I_1}\right)^2}{4r_b{}'\omega_t C_c} \tag{44}$$

But $(I/I_1)^2$ is actually the current gain squared, which according to Fig. 5 is:

$$\left|\frac{\omega_t}{j\omega}\right|^2 = \frac{\omega_t{}^2}{\omega^2} \tag{45}$$

Substituting Eq. (45) into Eq. (44) gives

$$MAG = \frac{\omega_t}{\omega^2 \, 4r_b{}' \, C_c} \tag{46}$$

The familiar expression for f_{max} is easily obtained from MAG; at f_{max}, MAG $= 1$, so:

$$1 = \frac{\omega_t}{\omega^2 \, 4r_b{}' \, C_c} = \frac{f_t}{(2\pi) f^2 4r_b{}' \, C_c} = \frac{f_t}{8\pi r_b{}' \, C_c \, f^2} \tag{47}$$

Solving for f, and calling this f_{max}:

$$f_{max} = \sqrt{\frac{f_t}{8\pi r_b{}' \, C_c}} \tag{48}$$

Forward-to-reverse Gain Ratio. Before leaving the subject of MAG it is well to mention another interesting and very similar expression called the forward-to-reverse gain ratio. It has just been shown that the MAG in the forward direction is:

$$MAG_F = \frac{|y_{21}|^2}{4g_{11} g_{22}} \tag{49}$$

The subscript F is used to denote forward MAG. A similar expression exists in the reverse direction:

$$MAG_R = \frac{|y_{12}|^2}{4g_{22}\, g_{11}} \qquad (50)$$

The ratio of these two equations yields the forward-to-reverse gain ratio.

$$MAG_{F\text{-}R} = \frac{|y_{21}|^2}{|y_{12}|}$$

This expression is useful in specifying an upper bound on the useful frequency range. For example, on the 2N2415 this is set at $MAG_{F\text{-}R} = 20$ db at 800 mc. This means that the difference in the forward and reverse gain has degenerated to 20 db at 800 mc, a ratio of 100 to 1. This limit is completely arbitrary and could have been set at any desired value. Any higher-frequency application for the 2N2415 would mean:

1. the gain is essentially impedance gain only, and
2. the noise figure is becoming equal to the gain.

These conditions will not, in general, be true for other transistors, but the concept of limiting the upper frequency of *primary application* in this way is a simple and useful way to compare transistors in the upper-frequency regions.

Unilateral Power Gain. Neutralization of internal reverse feedback can be achieved by an external network as shown in Fig. 6. The a and p subscripts denote active and passive parameters. The composite network will have these terms:

$$y_{11c} = y_{11a} + y_{12p} \qquad (51)$$

$$y_{22c} = y_{22a} + y_{12p} \qquad (52)$$

$$y_{21c} = y_{21a} - y_{12p} \qquad (53)$$

$$y_{12c} = y_{12a} - y_{12p} \qquad (54)$$

When $|y_{12a}| = |y_{12p}|$, the value of y_{12c} is 0, and with a conjugate match of source and load to y_{11c} and y_{22c} respectively, the value of power gain is:

$$G_U = \frac{|y_{21a} - y_{12p}|^2}{4(g_{11a} + g_{12p})(g_{22a} + g_{12p})} \qquad (55)$$

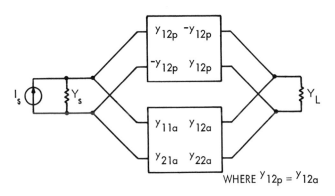

WHERE $y_{12p} = y_{12a}$

Fig. 6. A unilateralized two-port.

In other words, G_U is the power gain obtained when a network is used to just offset the internal feedback to develop a unilateral composite structure. The transducer gain can be treated in the same way. It is easy to see this expression as the unilateral transducer gain G_{TU}.

$$G_{TU} = \frac{4 \, |y_{21a} - y_{12p}|^2 \, G_S \, G_L}{|(Y_S + y_{11a} + y_{12p})(Y_L + y_{22a} + y_{12p})|^2} \tag{56}$$

Neutralized Power Gain. If the condition

$$|y_{12a}| = |y_{12p}| \tag{57}$$

is not completely established, the resulting structure will be only partially unilateral because only part of the internal feedback is compensated. Under these conditions the composite admittance parameters are substituted into any of the previous power gain expressions and the gain is referred to as neutralized gain G_N.

Maximum Stable Power Gain. A special type of power gain term should be mentioned. It has been shown that G_{max} is only defined when the transistor is unconditionally stable. It is unconditionally stable if $C < 1$, where the inherent stability factor C is defined by

$$C = \frac{|y_{12}y_{21}|}{2g_{11}g_{22} - \mathrm{Re}(y_{12}y_{21})} \tag{58}$$

C is shown vs frequency in Fig. 7. At the exact frequency where $C = 1$, the transistor is on the threshold between potential instability and unconditional stability. The following derivation illustrates the interesting fact that G_{max} at this point ($C = 1$) is given by

$$G_C = \frac{|y_{21}|}{|y_{12}|} \tag{59}$$

The derivation is as follows:

$$G_{max} = \frac{2 \, [1 - (1 - C^2)^{1/2}] \, |y_{21}|^2}{[4g_{11}g_{22} - 2\mathrm{Re}(y_{12}y_{21})]C^2} = \frac{|y_{21}|^2}{2g_{11}g_{22} - \mathrm{Re}(y_{12}y_{21})} \tag{60}$$

But if $C = 1$, then

$$2g_{11}g_{22} - \mathrm{Re}(y_{12}y_{21}) = |y_{12}y_{21}| \tag{61}$$

Substituting this into the previous expression gives:

$$G_C = \frac{|y_{21}|}{|y_{11}|} = G_{max} \text{ at the frequency where } C = 1$$

This gain factor serves as a useful figure of merit when specified with the frequency at which $C = 1$. Figure 8 shows that the 2N2415 has a $G_C = 18.5$ db at 245 mc.

POWER GAIN CONSIDERATIONS

Consider the comparison of the power gain G_p and the transducer gain G_T. The transducer gain is the ratio of power the transistor delivers to the load over the power the generator would deliver to that load, were the load conjugately matched to the generator. If we conjugately match the input of the LAN to the generator, then G_p becomes G_T. If the input and source are not quite conjugately matched, then G_p will be slightly greater than G_T for identical output levels.

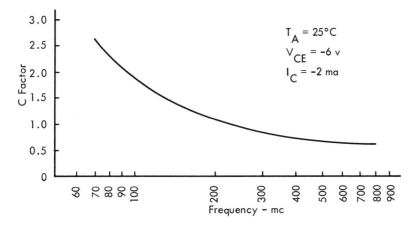

Figure 7

Power gain G_p is dependent on the transistor two-port parameters and the load. Therefore, to be complete, a specification of G_p must be accompanied by the value of M_L, the general form of the real part of the load immittance. Transducer gain must have the source and load specified to be meaningful.

The value of G_{max} is dependent only on the device parameters and, when the device is unconditionally stable, gives an accurate indication of the upper gain limit of a transistor. It should be possible to achieve this value minus insertion loss of interstages. However, as the gain y_{21}/y_{12} is approached, the inherent stability decreases. In other words, moving back in frequency along the G_{max} line of Fig. 8, the inherent stability is decreasing so that at the value y_{21}/y_{12}, the critical factor is unity.

The transistor is then on the threshold of potential instability. Since G_{max} requires a conjugate match to input and output it is quite clear that if any change anywhere in the circuit occurs then actual oscillation will occur. Therefore, because of the random nature of these disturbances in any parameter of the system, there is a practical limit to how close y_{21}/y_{12} may be approached. Figure 8 shows the

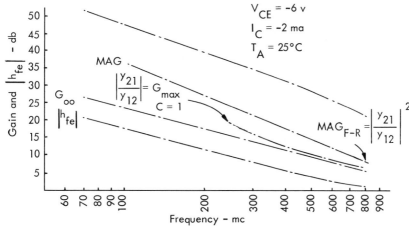

Figure 8

comparison of $|h_{fe}|$, G_{oo}, G_{max}, MAG, and MAG_{F-R} for the common-emitter 2N2415. Curves for the common-base connection may be developed in a similar way.

STABILITY CONCEPTS

There are many approaches to the analysis of amplifier stability. One approach is based on the study of the conditions that cause the (transducer) gain to become infinite. Another approach is to examine the nature of the components of the transient response of the system; in other words, we are interested in whether the system has any natural frequencies. Still another technique is due to Nyquist. Each of these approaches has its own advantages, yet all are common because all the information about the stability of a system is contained in the characteristic equation describing that system.

In the case of the gain analysis, the characteristic equation (or a form of it) appears in the denominator of the gain equation. The examination of the transient response resolves to a problem of locating the roots of the system equation (characteristic equation) and deciding on the basis of the location of the roots whether the response to a transient will die out or not. When the Nyquist technique is used, one examines the locus of the value of E_{out}/E_{source} corresponding to the locus of s in the complex frequency plane. However, the denominator of E_{out}/E_{source} is the familiar characteristic equation of the system. Therefore, one of the most natural ways of examining stability is to examine the characteristic equation describing the system.

SYSTEM STABILITY

There are many ways of obtaining the characteristic equation of a system. Consider the active two-terminal pair shown in Fig. 9. Assume that we characterize this network by y parameters. The matrix is:

$$I_1 = y_{11} E_1 + y_{12} E_2 \tag{62}$$

$$I_2 = y_{21} E_1 + y_{22} E_2 \tag{63}$$

$$I_1 = - Y_g E_1 \tag{64}$$

$$I_2 = - Y_L E_2 \tag{65}$$

Now substituting these back into the matrix set

$$0 = (y_{11} + Y_g) E_1 + y_{12} E_2 \tag{66}$$

$$0 = y_{21} E_1 + (y_{22} + Y_L) E_2 \tag{67}$$

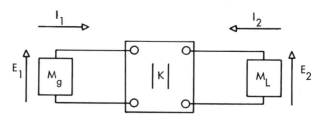

Fig. 9. A general active two-terminal pair with no external signal.

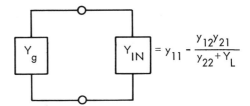

Fig. 10. Input node immittance.

Now, for the condition in which $E_1 = E_2 \neq 0$, the solution of this set is

$$(y_{11} + Y_g)(y_{22} + Y_L) - y_{12}y_{21} = 0 \tag{68}$$

This is the system determinant or characteristic equation. It should be obvious that this is also the sum of the input admittance from the input node equated to zero. See Fig. 10.

TESTS FOR STABILITY

If a testing procedure is to be effective in determining whether a characteristic equation represents a stable system or not, it must be simple, quick, and not yield any more information than necessary. It can be shown that if any roots of the characteristic equation exist in the right half of the complex frequency plane, the system will be unstable. Since the terms y_{11}, y_{12}, y_{21}, y_{22}, Y_g, and Y_L may all be expressed as functions of the complex frequency variable s, the characteristic equation is of the form $F(s) = 0$. Now if the system represented by $F(s)$ is stable, then $F(s)$ must have no roots in the right-half plane. In other words, it must be a Hurwitz polynomial. A polynomial of the form

$$F(s) = A_0 + A_1 s + A_2 s^2 + A_3 s^3 + \ldots A_{n-1}s^{n-1} + A_n s^n \tag{69}$$

is Hurwitz if:
1. all the coefficients are positive and real,
2. there are no missing terms in s, and
3. it contains no roots on the j-axis or in the right-half plane.

The first two conditions may be checked by inspection. If these are satisfied, then testing may be continued to determine whether there are any right-half plane roots.

One way to test a polynomial for Hurwitz character is to form a determinant of its coefficients as shown in Fig. 11. The indices of the letter A in each row decrease by one, element by element from left to right. The indices of A in each column increase by two, element by element from top to bottom. Letters with negative indices or indices greater than n are replaced by zeros. If, and only if, each of the principal minors of the determinant is *positive* (if any of them is zero, imaginary roots are indicated), the polynomial is Hurwitz.

A_1	A_0	0	0	. . . 0
A_3	A_2	A_1	A_0	. . . 0
A_5	A_4	A_3	A_2	. . . 0
A_7	A_6	A_5	A_4	. . . 0
.	.	.	.	.
.	.	.	.	.
.	.	.	.	.
0	0	0	0	0

Fig. 11. Determinant of coefficients of Eq. (69).

The above tests simply indicate whether there are any roots on the $j\omega$ axis or whether there are any roots in the right-half plane. If the Hurwitz test shows all principal minors to be positive, the system is stable. If no roots are in the right-half plane and any roots are on the imaginary axis, the system is critically stable. If any roots are in the right-half plane, one of the principal minors will turn up negative and the system is unstable.

As an example of this type of test, consider the system polynomial of Eq. (70).

$$4s^2 + 5s + 1 = 0 \qquad (70)$$

Forming the determinant as outlined above gives:

$$\begin{vmatrix} 5 & 1 \\ 0 & 4 \end{vmatrix} \qquad \begin{array}{l} \text{first minor:}\ \ 5 > 0 \\ \text{second minor:}\ 20 > 0 \end{array}$$

The principal minors are all greater than zero, so Hurwitz character is indicated. This type of test is very attractive because of its simplicity and because it offers no more information than is necessary.

A more detailed method of establishing the Hurwitz character of a given polynomial is known as the "continued fraction expansion method." The criteria for Hurwitz character are that the coefficients of the quotients are all positive, and that the process of division does not terminate prematurely. If it does terminate prematurely, j-axis zeros are indicated and the system must be considered unstable. This method of testing consists of forming the polynomial

$$Q(s) = \frac{M(s)}{N(s)}$$

where $M(s) =$ an even function of s

$N(s) =$ an even function of s

Note: If $N(s)$ is of higher power, use $\dfrac{N(s)}{M(s)}$

Testing the polynomial of Eq. (70),

$$
\begin{array}{r}
4/5s \\
5s \,\overline{)\, 4s^2 + 1} \\
-4s^2 \qquad\quad 5s \\
\overline{\;\; 1 \,\overline{)\, 5s}} \\
-5s \\
\overline{0}
\end{array}
$$

Hurwitz character is again indicated as all coefficients are positive and there are no j-axis zeros.

TRANSISTOR INHERENT STABILITY

It now becomes necessary to differentiate between active device stability and system stability. At least three different authors have shown that the criterion for active device stability is given by Eq. (71).

$$ 2\mathrm{Re}(y_{11})\,\mathrm{Re}(y_{22}) - \mathrm{Re}(y_{12}\,y_{21}) > |\,y_{12}\,y_{21}\,| \tag{71} $$

This is quite obviously a necessary condition for stability since the real part of the immittance which maximizes the power gain of a two-port would be negative if

$$ |\,y_{12}\,y_{21}\,| > 2\mathrm{Re}(y_{11})\,\mathrm{Re}(y_{22}) - \mathrm{Re}(y_{12}\,y_{21}) \tag{72} $$

The value of the real part of the source impedance which maximizes the power gain is

$$ \mathrm{Re}(Z_g) = \frac{1}{2\mathrm{Re}(y_{22})}\big\{[2\mathrm{Re}(y_{11})\,\mathrm{Re}(y_{22}) - \mathrm{Re}(y_{12}\,y_{21})]^2 - |\,y_{12}\,y_{21}\,|^2\big\}^{1/2} \tag{73} $$

Recalling the expression for the maximum available power gain of an unconditionally stable two-port to be

$$ G_{\max} = \frac{|\,y_{21}\,|^2}{2\mathrm{Re}(y_{11})\,\mathrm{Re}(y_{22}) - \mathrm{Re}(y_{12}\,y_{21}) + \big\{[2\mathrm{Re}(y_{11})\,\mathrm{Re}(y_{22}) - \mathrm{Re}(y_{12}\,y_{21})]^2 - |\,y_{12}\,y_{21}\,|^2\big\}^{1/2}} \tag{74} $$

if

$$ 2\mathrm{Re}(y_{11})\,\mathrm{Re}(y_{22}) - \mathrm{Re}(y_{12}\,y_{21}) = |\,y_{12}\,y_{21}\,| \tag{75} $$

which is the same as stating that the frequency of measurement* is f_c'' (or for that matter f_c'), then it is easy to see that $G_{\max}$ reduces to

$$ G_{\max} = \frac{|\,y_{21}\,|}{|\,y_{12}\,|} = G_c \tag{76} $$

It is also very obvious that the power gain†

$$ G_p' = \frac{|\,y_{21}\,|^2}{2\,[2\mathrm{Re}(y_{11})\,\mathrm{Re}(y_{22}) - \mathrm{Re}(y_{12}\,y_{21})]} \tag{77} $$

---

*f_c'' is defined here as the upper critical frequency at which the device is between unconditional stability and potential instability. A similar definition for the lower frequency yields f_c'. This is identical to the frequency at which Linvill's critical factor is unity.

†G_p' is used here to emphasize again that this power gain is obtained from the general power gain expression by conjugate match to y_{22} (not y_{out}). It is identical to Linvill's P_{oo}/P_{io}.

at the frequency f_c'' reduces to:

$$G_p' = \frac{|y_{21}|}{2\,|y_{12}|} \tag{78}$$

Therefore, forming the ratio of Eqs. (76) and (78),

$$\frac{G_{max}}{G_p'} = \frac{|y_{21}|}{|y_{12}|}\frac{2\,|y_{12}|}{|y_{21}|} = 2 \tag{79}$$

This shows that the power gain G_p at f_c'' is exactly 3 db from the maximum available gain obtainable at f_c''. Furthermore, it will never be more than 3 db away from G_{max}.

Unconditional stability simply means that if the inequality of Eq. (71) is satisfied by the device itself, no load or source immittance can ever be found that will cause the system in which it is used to oscillate. Consequently, if this inequality is not satisfied, the device is termed potentially unstable, which means it is possible to find external immittances that will make the system oscillate. It is important to reemphasize that the terms "unconditionally" or "inherently stable" and "potentially unstable" refer to the active *device,* whereas a *system* is referred to as being either stable or unstable.

VARIOUS STABILITY FACTORS

To make clear the relationships among the stability terms that are in common usage, it is necessary to derive the terms presented by Stern and Linvill. Since Linvill approaches the problem with the aid of a unique gain chart, and since the chart will be used in the design examples that follow, his stability factor is presented first.

Linvill defines a "critical factor":

$$C = 2\,\frac{P_{oo}}{P_{io}}\frac{|y_{12}|}{|y_{21}|} \tag{80}$$

and shows graphically that its interpretation is as indicated in Fig. 12. It is clear from this figure that if C is > 1, then the device characterized by that particular set of y parameters has a region (oscillatory region) in which power output is possible for negative power input.

One way to discover how the equation for C came about is to consider the expression

$$2\mathrm{Re}(y_{11})\,\mathrm{Re}(_{22}) - \mathrm{Re}(y_{12}\,y_{21}) \; > |\,y_{12}\,y_{21}| \tag{81}$$

This has been shown to be the criterion for device stability. Now dividing through by $|\,y_{12}\,y_{21}|$ we get

$$\frac{2\mathrm{Re}(y_{11})\,\mathrm{Re}(y_{22}) - \mathrm{Re}(y_{12}\,y_{21})}{|\,y_{12}\,y_{21}|} > 1 \tag{82}$$

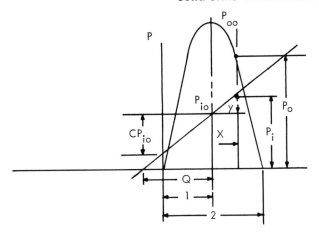

Fig. 12. Two-dimensional power gain model.

Now inverting
$$\frac{|\, y_{12}\, y_{21}\,|}{2\mathrm{Re}(y_{11})\,\mathrm{Re}(y_{22}) - \mathrm{Re}(y_{12}\, y_{21})} < 1 \qquad (83)$$

If this expression is satisfied by the device, then it is unconditionally stable. If it is not satisfied, the device is potentially unstable. To facilitate reference to this expression, the letter C may be used and an equality substituted for the "less than" sign:

$$\frac{|\, y_{12}\, y_{21}\,|}{2\mathrm{Re}(y_{11})\,\mathrm{Re}(y_{22}) - \mathrm{Re}(y_{12}y_{21})} = C \qquad (84)$$

Recalling that:
$$G_{oo} = \frac{|\, y_{21}\,|^2}{4\mathrm{Re}(y_{11})\,\mathrm{Re}(y_{22}) - 2\mathrm{Re}(y_{12}y_{21})} \qquad (85)$$

it is clearly seen that

$$C = \frac{|\, y_{21}\,|^2}{4\mathrm{Re}(y_{11})\,\mathrm{Re}(y_{22}) - 2\mathrm{Re}(y_{12}y_{21})} \; \frac{2\,|\, y_{12}\,|}{|\, y_{21}\,|} \qquad (86)$$

$$= \frac{|\, y_{12}y_{21}\,|}{2\mathrm{Re}(y_{11})\,\mathrm{Re}(y_{22}) - \mathrm{Re}(y_{12}y_{21})} \qquad (87)$$

$$= 2G_{oo}\frac{|\, y_{12}\,|}{|\, y_{21}\,|} \qquad (88)$$

Stern defines a stability factor that includes the effect of the load and source and is customarily presented as in Fig. 13. The modified y matrix will now be

$$y = \begin{vmatrix} y_{11} + Y_g & y_{12} \\ y_{21} & y_{22} + Y_L \end{vmatrix}$$

The stability criterion equation will now be of the form

$$2(g_{11} + G_g)(g_{22} + G_L) - \mathrm{Re}(y_{12}y_{21}) > |\, y_{12}y_{21}\,| \qquad (89)$$

Now let
$$L = |\, y_{12}y_{21}\,|$$
$$M = \mathrm{Re}(y_{12}y_{21})$$

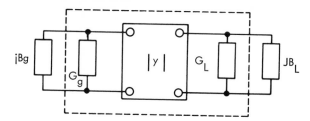

Fig. 13. Model used to demonstrate Stern's K factor.

Eq. (89) becomes

$$2(g_{11} + G_g)(g_{22} + G_L) - M > L \qquad (90)$$

$$(g_{11} + G_g)(g_{22} + G_L) > \frac{L + M}{2} \qquad (91)$$

Now the inequality sign may be disposed of in the same way as before, as shown in Eq. (92):

$$(g_{11} + G_g)(g_{22} + G_L) = K\left(\frac{L+M}{2}\right) \qquad (92)$$

In Eq. (92):

if $K > 1$, the system as loaded is unconditionally stable

if $K < 1$, the system as loaded is potentially unstable

Stern's stability factor K has the same implication as Linvill's factor C (although they are inverse) as far as the terms "potential instability" and "unconditional stability" go, except that Stern brings the real part of the load and source into the stability equation. Thus, his K factor is not entirely a property of the device. On the other hand, the real part of the load and source are usually not varied when tuning the circuit. Thus, including them in the stability expression is a practical thing to do and K might more logically be called the actual stability factor of the circuit, while Linvill's C factor could be called an intrinsic stability factor of the device. Comparison of Eqs. (93), (94), and (95) clearly shows the interrelationships of these concepts:

stability criterion: $\quad 2g_{11}g_{22} - \mathrm{Re}(y_{12}y_{21}) > |\,y_{12}y_{21}\,| \qquad (93)$

Linvill's C factor: $\quad 2g_{11}g_{22} - \mathrm{Re}(y_{12}y_{21}) = \dfrac{1}{C}|\,y_{12}y_{21}\,| \qquad (94)$

Stern's K factor: $\quad 2(g_{11} + G_g)(g_{22} + G_L) - K\mathrm{Re}(y_{12}y_{21}) = K|\,y_{12}y_{21}\,| \qquad (95)$

BIBLIOGRAPHY

Bagley, J. H.: The Measurement of Transistor Characteristics at VHF, report presented at International Convention of Transistors and Associated Semiconductor Devices, May 21, 1959.

Cote, A. J., and J. B. Oakes: "Linear Vacuum-tube and Transistor Circuits," McGraw-Hill Book Company, Inc., New York, 1961.

Gärtner, W. W.: "Transistors: Principles, Design, and Applications," D. Van Nostrand Company, New Jersey, 1960.

Gibbons, J. F.: The Design of Alignable Transistor Amplifiers, *Stanford Electronics Lab Tech. Rep. No. 106,* May 7, 1956.

Johnson, G. D.: The Relationship Among Stability, Sensitivity, Gain, and Bandwidth in Tuned Transistor Amplifiers, Unpublished thesis presented to the Southern Methodist University Graduate School, August 12, 1962.

Lathi, B. P.: Optimal Design of Multi-stage Tuned-transistor Amplifiers Considering Gain, Stability, and Sensitivity, *Stanford Electronics Lab Tech. Rep. No. 1603-1,* July 11, 1960.

Linvill, J. G.: The Theory of Two-ports, report presented at International Convention on Transistors and Associated Semiconductor Devices, May 21, 1959.

Linvill, J. G., and J. F. Gibbons: "Transistors and Active Circuits," McGraw-Hill Book Company, Inc., New York, 1961.

Pritchard, R. L.: Electric-network Representation of Transistors — A Survey, *IRE Trans.,* vol. CT-3, March, 1956.

Pritchard, R. L.: Frequency Response of Theoretical Models of Junction Transistors, *IRE Trans.,* vol. CT-9, September, 1962.

Pritchard, R. L.: Frequency Variations of Junction-transistor Parameters, *Proc. IRE,* vol. 42, May, 1954.

Pritchard, R. L.: High-frequency Power Gain of Junction Transistors, *Proc. IRE,* vol. 43, September, 1955.

Pritchard, R. L.: Modern High-frequency Transistors, *IRE-AIEE U. of Penna. Transistor Conf.,* 1957.

Pritchard, R. L.: Transistor Equivalent Circuits, report presented at the International Convention on Transistors and Associated Semiconductor Devices, London, May 22, 1959.

Rollett, J. M.: Stability and Power-gain Invariants of Linear Two-ports, *IRE Trans.,* vol. CT-9, pp. 29–32, March, 1962.

Scanlan, J. O., and J. S. Singleton: The Gain and Stability of Linear Two-port Amplifiers, *IRE Trans.,* vol. CT-9, September, 1962.

5

High-frequency Amplifier Design Using Admittance Parameters

by George Johnson, Peter Norris, Frank Opp

INTRODUCTION

High-frequency amplifier design using two-port theory is demonstrated by measuring the y parameters of a silicon epitaxial mesa transistor. Since the two-port parameters of any Linear Active Network (LAN) completely describe its power gain and stability, curves of inherent stability and power gain are developed and presented. This information satisfies the first need of a designer: a complete and accurate description of the gain capability of the linear active network over the frequency range of interest.

A design technique, originated by J. G. Linvill, is described in some detail. This technique includes unique charts* and graphical representations useful in the analysis of relationships among power gain, stability, and sensitivity. A numerical example is presented which uses this design technique.

ADMITTANCE PARAMETER CHARACTERIZATION

In general, any of the six sets of two-port parameters may be used to describe the linear active network. Most common of these, of course, are the h and y parameters. In high-frequency work the y parameters are generally accepted as the most useful description of LAN; at lower frequencies the h parameters are commonly used. The parameter choice is also influenced by the type of measuring instrument and the accuracy with which it can measure the parameter in question. For this discussion a consistent set of y_e data was measured and is contained in Figs. 3 through 6 which are found later in this chapter.

The General Radio Type 1607-A Transfer Function and Immittance Bridge, a coaxial null-type instrument, was selected because of its wide range of frequency

---

.*These charts are adapted from J. G. Linvill and L. G. Schimpf, "The Design of Tetrode Transistor Amplifiers," Bell System Tech. J., vol. 35, pp. 813–840, July 1956, with permission of the authors and the Bell Telephone Laboratories.

applicability, its accuracy, and because no test jigs are required for the measurements. The measuring procedure and bridge description along with its line losses and other error sources are described in the GR Instruction Manual and will not be described here. Accuracy equations found in the instruction book are repeated in Table 1 for convenience. The fixed error may be reduced approximately one order of magnitude by the use of appropriate accessories and line-loss corrections.

Table 1. Bridge Accuracy

Parameter	Accuracy
y_{11} or y_{22}	$2(1 + \sqrt{y_{11}/20})\% + 0.4$ mmhos
y_{21} or y_{12}	$2.5(1 + \sqrt{y_{21}/20})\% + 0.5$ mmhos

POWER GAIN AND STABILITY

Before developing the power flow concepts, it is necessary to review the various forms of power gain and to describe in general the concept of stability. This will establish the proper perspective for the material that follows.

Figure 1 shows a general four-terminal network. Although the network is characterized in terms of y parameters, any consistent set of parameters will work. Table 2 shows the various power ratios which may be defined for this network. Note that the term "power gain" has a definite meaning. Notice also that the term "maximum available gain" is meaningful only when the transistor is unconditionally stable. This is obvious since the gain obtainable from a transistor that is potentially unstable is unbounded.

Neutralization can be achieved by modifying the y_{12} parameter with a parallel network, as shown in Fig. 2. The a and p subscripts denote active and passive parameters.

Neutralized power gain is not described by any particular ratio in Table 2 and no specific equation is given since any of the above gains can be neutralized gains. In many amplifier circuits, neutralization of inverse feedback is applied only as far as necessary to achieve the stability figure desired, to reduce the input variation for a given output variation, or to achieve a specified power gain. Therefore, any of the gain equations are applicable if the composite parameters of the networks are used. These parameters are defined by the following equations:

$$y_{12c} = y_{11a} + y_{12p}$$

$$y_{22c} = y_{22a} + y_{12p}$$

$$y_{21c} = y_{21a} - y_{12p}$$

$$y_{12c} = y_{12a} - y_{12p}$$

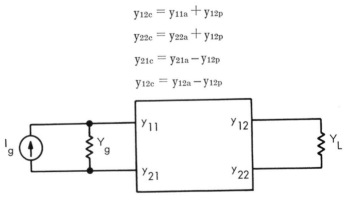

Fig. 1. A general two-port.

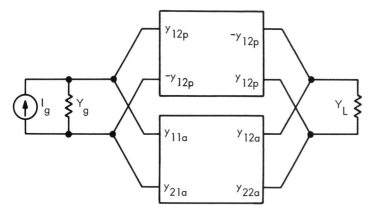

Fig. 2. A neutralized two-port.

When external feedback is applied to the point of reducing y_{12c} to zero, the following expression results:

$$G_U = \frac{|y_{21} - y_{12}|^2}{4(g_{11} + g_{12})(g_{22} + g_{12})}$$

It is now evident that the G_U in Table 2 is not the unilateral gain of the transistor, but the gain of the composite network. Now consider the meaning of the gain expression if the external unilateralizing network is not added. Let us assume internal feedback does not exist. The G_{max} term and G_U become equal and are expressed by:

$$G_U = \frac{|y_{21}|^2}{4g_{11}g_{22}}$$

This is a somewhat meaningless expression since at frequencies sufficiently low to make y_{12} small and difficult to measure, the effect of y_{12} is still important and causes potential instability. Furthermore, at higher frequencies it is erroneous to assume that y_{12} does not exist. Before this is demonstrated, however, another power gain term should be described. Define this gain the same way G_P was defined, except let the load be the conjugate of y_{22}, i.e., not Y_{out}. The expression will be of the following form:

$$\frac{P_{oo}}{P_{io}} = G_{oo} = \frac{|y_{21}|^2}{4g_{11}g_{22} - 2\text{Re}(y_{12}y_{21})}$$

Table 2. Power Ratios for a General Two-port

EXPRESSION	SYMBOL	DESCRIPTION	EQUATION
Power Gain	G_P	Pwr. Delivered to Load / Pwr. Delivered to Input	$\dfrac{\lvert y_{21}\rvert^2 \operatorname{Re}(Y_L)}{\left\lvert Y_L + y_{22} \right\rvert^2 \operatorname{Re}\left(y_{11} - \dfrac{y_{12}y_{21}}{y_{22} + Y_L} \right)}$
Transducer Gain	G_T	Pwr. Delivered to Load / Max. Pwr. Available from source	$\dfrac{4\operatorname{Re}(Y_g)\operatorname{Re}(Y_L)\,\lvert y_{21}\rvert^2}{\lvert (y_{11}+Y_g)(y_{22}+Y_L)-y_{12}y_{21}\rvert^2}$
Max. Available Gain	G_{max}	Max. Pwr. Available at output / Max. Pwr. Available from source	$*\ \dfrac{\lvert y_{21}\rvert^2}{2g_{11}g_{22}-\operatorname{Re}(y_{12}y_{21})+\{[2g_{11}g_{22}-\operatorname{Re}(y_{12}y_{21})]^2-\lvert y_{12}y_{21}\rvert^2\}^{1/2}}$
Neutralized Pwr. Gain	G_N	(See Text)	(See Text)
Unilateral Pwr. Gain	G_U	(See Text)	$\dagger\ \dfrac{\lvert y_{21c}\rvert^2}{4g_{11c}g_{22c}}$

$*\,g_{11}$ is the $\operatorname{Re}(y_{11})$ and has no relation to the two-port parameter G_{11}.

$\dagger$ The subscript c implies "composite."

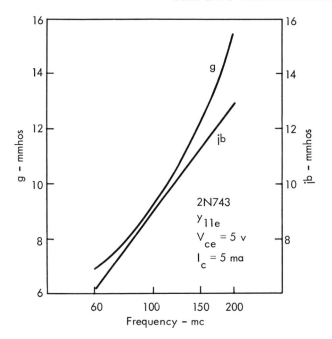

Fig. 3. y_{11e} vs. frequency (typical data).

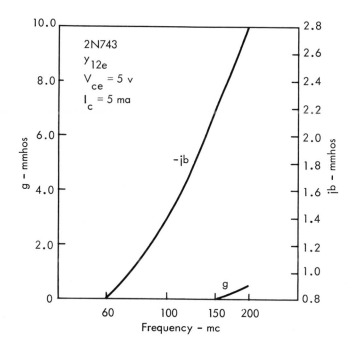

Fig. 4. y_{12e} vs. frequency (typical data).

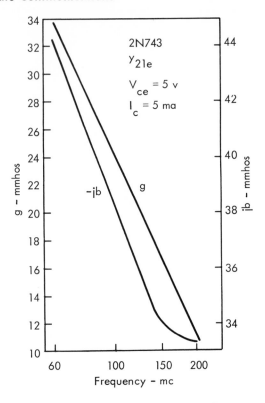

Fig. 5. y_{21e} **vs. frequency (typical data).**

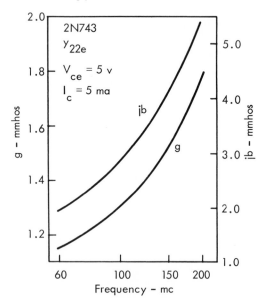

Fig. 6. y_{22e} **vs. frequency (typical data).**

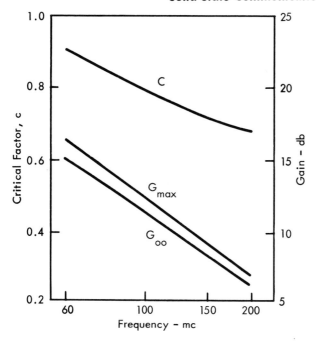

Fig. 7. 2N743 common-emitter, critical factor, and gain vs. frequency.

Note that the expression includes the existence of the y_{12} component, and just as in G_P, this expression has nothing to do with the driving source R_g. Figure 7 shows a plot of G_{oo} and G_{max}. Note that for the stage in this range G_{max} is approximately equal to G_{oo}. This will be described further in the later sections.

At least three different authors have shown the criterion for active device stability, which is expressed by:

$$2g_{11}g_{22} - \mathrm{Re}(y_{12}y_{21}) > |y_{12}y_{21}|$$

This may be seen by inspecting the equation for the source resistance which maximizes the power gain:

$$\mathrm{Re}(Z_g) = \frac{1}{2\mathrm{Re}(y_{22})}\left\{[2(g_{11})(g_{22}) - \mathrm{Re}(y_{12}y_{21})]^2 - |y_{12}y_{21}|^2\right\}^{1/2}$$

Now, if

$$2g_{11}g_{22} - \mathrm{Re}(y_{12}y_{21}) < |y_{12}y_{21}|$$

then the $\mathrm{Re}(Z_g)$ is a negative quantity and forces an unstable condition.

A BRIEF DESCRIPTION OF THE LINVILL TECHNIQUE

The need for a more comprehensive description of the general process of power flow through a two-port has been clearly indicated by the fact that active devices can be potentially unstable. To describe this power flow process, the following section shows that the equation for output power in mathematical form is sufficient to describe the geometric shape of a parabola of revolution. Similarly, the input power equation is shown to be a geometric plane. Using this representation, we show how these geometrical representations may be combined to evaluate graphically the power gain of the two-port. A unique aspect of this interpretation is that both positive and negative input power flow are indicated. Thus device stability is explicitly indicated, and the region of instability is clearly defined.

A stability term called the critical factor c is related to this combined geometric concept of power gain and indicates the slope of the input power plane. If this slope is too great, there is a region of instability. The c factor is thus an indication of inequality of the familiar stability criterion:

Stability criterion: $2g_{11}g_{22} - \text{Re}(y_{12}y_{21}) > |y_{12}y_{21}|$

The new stability equation: $2g_{11}g_{22} - \text{Re}(y_{12}y_{21}) = \frac{1}{c}|y_{12}y_{21}|$

Values of c simply show the degree of unconditional stability ($c < 1$), or potential instability ($c > 1$). When $c > 1$, there is a source or load termination which causes the transistor to oscillate. It is clear the c factor is an important characteristic "parameter" of the transistor because:

a. The frequencies at which $c > 1$ define the frequency range of potential instability.

b. Its manifestation on the Linvill chart allows a load selection which will always result in stable amplifier operation.

c. When $c < 1$, the factor

$$K_G = 2\left[\frac{1 - \sqrt{1-c^2}}{c^2}\right]$$

when multiplied by G_{oo} gives G_{max}, which is the maximum available gain obtainable in an unneutralized circuit.

There are other attractive properties of this analysis procedure. First, it is possible to construct sensitivity curves on the Linvill chart. Sensitivity δ is defined as the percent change in input immittance to the percent change in output immittance and indicates the degree of "non-unilateralness." This has great significance in multi-stage, i-f strip design. When these δ contours are constructed they define an area in which a given load can be placed that satisfies gain and sensitivity requirements. Other methods relating mismatch to gain loss require a few calculations, but sensitivity contours and gain curves on a Linvill chart neatly relate gain, stability, alignability, and bandwidth in one picture. A second advantage of this method is that an input immittance chart or overlay may be used to read input immittance for a given load. Although it is easily calculated, the use of this overlay speeds up the analysis of input immittance brought about by varying loads, and reduces complex algebraic manipulation.

Although sensitivity contours and input immittance overlays are not discussed here to any great extent, it should be made clear that they exist and provide the circuit designer with a powerful analytic tool as well as a complete picture of tuned amplifier performance.

The following section presents a brief development of the charts and concepts, a step-by-step design procedure, and an example design using a silicon epitaxial mesa transistor in a single-tuned 60-mc i-f amplifier stage.

GRAPHICAL PRESENTATION OF POWER GAIN

For the four-terminal network shown in Fig. 8, the power P_o delivered to the load, and the network input power P_i, are expressed as functions of the load Y_L. Working from the network equations:

$$I_1 = y_{11}E_1 + y_{12}E_2 \tag{1}$$

$$I_2 = y_{21}E_1 + y_{22}E_2 \tag{2}$$

and defining:

$$E_1 = 1 + jO$$

$$E_2 = (L + jM) \frac{-y_{21}}{2\mathrm{Re}(y_{22})}$$

Now P_o and P_i may be obtained as functions of the network parameters, and L and M may be obtained by substituting the expression for E_1 and E_2 into the network equations:

$$P_o = L \frac{|y_{21}|^2}{2\mathrm{Re}(y_{22})} - \frac{(L^2 + M^2)|y_{21}|^2}{4\mathrm{Re}(y_{22})} \tag{3}$$

$$P_i = \mathrm{Re}(y_{11}) + L\,\mathrm{Re}\left[\frac{y_{21}y_{12}}{2\mathrm{Re}(y_{22})}\right] + M\,\mathrm{Im}\left[\frac{y_{21}y_{12}}{2\mathrm{Re}(y_{22})}\right] \tag{4}$$

L, M, and Y_L are related by:

$$I_2 = -Y_L E_2$$

and Eq. (2):

$$I_2 = y_{21}E_1 + y_{22}E_2 = -Y_L E_2$$

Again using the E_1 and E_2 expressions, we have:

$$Y_L + y_{22} = \frac{2\mathrm{Re}(y_{22})}{L + jM} = G_2 + jB_2 \tag{5}$$

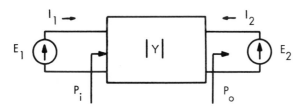

Fig. 8. Power flow directions.

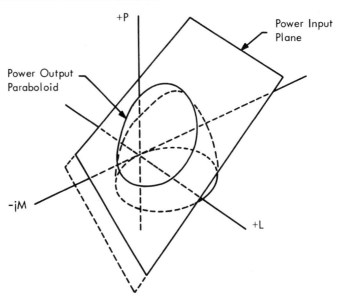

Fig. 9. Power surfaces.

Therefore, any value of Y_L can be simulated by varying L and M. If these expressions are plotted in the LMP coordinate system, the surface P_o is a paraboloid and P_i is a plane. These surfaces are shown in Fig. 9.

Since we are only concerned with passive load admittance, only the positive P_o surface is shown. The intersection of P_o and the L-M plane is a circle centered at L = 1, M = 0, of radius 1. This circle represents zero output power. The input plane can assume any position relative to P_o, its exact position determined by the parameter values used. The P_i and the L-M plane intersect in a straight line at $P_i = 0$. The amplifier gain, stability, and bandwidth can be determined by examining the relative positions of P_o and P_i. All of the necessary design information can be placed within the $P_o = 0$ circle in the L-M plane. No attempt is made to prove any of the procedures or statements given. For those who are interested, the references given provide a complete mathematical development.

At this point several quantities should be defined. To clarify these definitions, Fig. 10 shows a section of the two surfaces in question.

1. The input power plane is defined by its gradient and elevation at L = 1, M = 0. P_i at this point is labeled

$$P_{io} = \frac{2\mathrm{Re}(y_{11})\,\mathrm{Re}(y_{22}) - \mathrm{Re}(y_{12}y_{21})}{2\mathrm{Re}(y_{22})} \tag{6}$$

The gradient is equal to

$$Gr = \left| \frac{y_{12}y_{21}}{2\mathrm{Re}(y_{22})} \right| e^{j\theta} \tag{7}$$

where $\theta = \arg\,(-y_{12}y_{21})^*$.

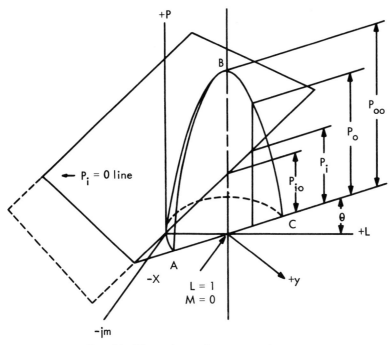

Fig. 10. Dimensions of power surface.

The ABC plane used in Fig. 10 contains the centerline of the paraboloid and makes an angle θ with the L-M plane. The intersection of this cutting plane and the L-M plane is called the gradient line. This line orients the input power in the L-M plane.

2. P_{oo} is the maximum output power and occurs at $L = 1$, $M = 0$, which corresponds to $Y_L = y_{22}$.

3. P_o is any output power and P_i is any input power.

4. A new coordinate system xy in the L-M plane has x along the gradient line and y normal to it with the origin at $L = 1$, $M = 0$.

5. The critical factor c is a measure of the transistor inherent stability. If the surfaces in Fig. 10 are viewed with a line of sight along y, the coordinate system can be reduced to two dimensions as shown in Fig. 11.

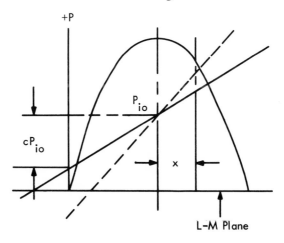

Fig. 11. Two-dimensional

projection.

As long as $c < 1$, P_i is positive for all positive values of P_o and the device is stable. If the input power plane is positioned such that it intersects the L-M plane as indicated by the dotted line in Fig. 11, negative P_i's are possible for positive P_o's. In this region both P_o and P_i flow from the network, and it, therefore, must be generating power. This condition can only occur if $c > 1$. Therefore, for $c < 1$, the transistor is unconditionally stable and there are no passive terminations which can cause the transistor to oscillate. For $c > 1$, the system is potentially unstable and certain passive terminations can cause oscillations. The c factor in terms of the network y parameters is:

$$c = \frac{|\, y_{21} y_{12}\,|}{2\,\mathrm{Re}\,(y_{11})\,\mathrm{Re}\,(y_{22}) - \mathrm{Re}\,(y_{21} y_{12})}$$

$$= 2 \left(\frac{P_{oo}}{P_{io}}\right) \left|\frac{y_{12}}{y_{21}}\right| \tag{8}$$

6. Constant gain contours appear as circles in the L-M plane. In terms of x and y:

$$\frac{P_i}{P_{io}} = 1 + cx$$

$$1 - \frac{P_o}{P_{oo}} = x^2 + y^2$$

Letting:

$$g = \frac{P_o/P_i}{P_{oo}/P_{io}}$$

the constant gain equation becomes:

$$1 - g + \left(\frac{g_c}{2}\right)^2 = \left(x + \frac{g_c}{2}\right)^2 + y^2 \tag{9}$$

For $c < 1$, g can have any value between 0 and K_G:

$$K_G = 2\,\frac{1 - \sqrt{1 - c^2}}{c^2} \tag{10}$$

The maximum gain will occur at a point $x = -\dfrac{cK_G}{2}$ along the gradient line. For

$c > 1$, g can have any value between 0 and infinity.

The sensitivity is expressed by:

$$\delta = \frac{dY_{in}/Y_{in}}{dY_L/Y_L} = \left|\frac{Y_L}{y_{22} + Y_L}\right| \cdot \left|\frac{g_{11}}{y_{11}}\right| \cdot \frac{K}{\left|\dfrac{y_{22} + Y_L}{g_{22}} + \dfrac{g_{11}}{y_{11}} K e^{j\theta}\right|} \tag{11}$$

where: $K = \dfrac{y_{12} y_{21}}{g_{11} g_{22}}$

$\theta = \arg\,(-y_{12} y_{21})\,*$

The portion of the L-M plane contained within the $P_o = 0$ circle is called the Linvill chart. Any point on this chart represents a gain and value of Y_L. This chart is similar to a Smith chart in the manner of the Y_L presentation. In fact, just three

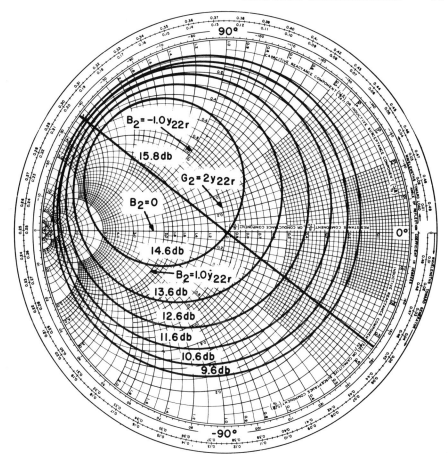

Fig. 12. 2N743 60-mc Linvill chart.

modifications convert the Smith to the Linvill chart, Fig. 12. First, a 180° rotation is required; second, the conductance-susceptance normalization factor is now the real part of the output admittance; and third, the wavelength and reflection angle graduations are replaced by angular graduations as shown in Fig. 12. A general admittance point on this chart is:

$$G_2 + jB_2 = Y_L + y_{22}$$

Therefore, as stated before, all passive Y_L values are displayed.

LINVILL CHART PREPARATION

The preparation of the Linvill chart to show transistor performance at a particular frequency requires these steps:

1. Obtain the real and imaginary parts of y_{11}, y_{22}, y_{21}, and y_{12}.

2. Complete:

$$\frac{P_{oo}}{P_{io}} = \frac{|y_{21}|^2}{4\text{Re}(y_{11})\,\text{Re}(y_{22}) - 2\text{Re}(y_{12}y_{21})}$$

$$C = 2\left(\frac{P_{oo}}{P_{io}}\right)\left|\frac{y_{12}}{y_{21}}\right|$$

$$\theta = \arg(-y_{21}y_{12})\,*$$

3. Draw the gradient line at the angle θ from the $B_2 = 0$ line.
4. If $c > 1$, draw a line perpendicular to the gradient through a point a distance $x = -1/c$ from the center of the circle. This line represents $P_i = 0$ and divides those terminations that cause oscillation from those that allow stable performance. If $c < 1$, this line is outside the chart.
5. If $c < 1$, calculate:

$$K_G = 2\,\frac{1 - \sqrt{1 - c^2}}{c^2}$$

the equation:
$$G_{max} = K_G\left(\frac{P_{oo}}{P_{io}}\right) \tag{12}$$

yields the maximum mismatch gain. Using:

$$1 - g + \left(\frac{cg}{2}\right)^2 = \left(x + \frac{cg}{2}\right)^2 + y^2$$

calculate and plot other constant-gain contours of interest.

LINVILL CHART CALCULATIONS EXAMPLE

To show the 2N743 60-mc performance, a Linvill chart, Fig. 12, has been prepared following the steps previously outlined:

1. The common-emitter y parameters at this frequency are:

$$y_{ie} = (6.8 + j\,6.1)\,10^{-3} = 9.13 \times 10^{-3}\;\underline{/41.9°}$$
$$y_{oe} = (1.24 + j\,1.92)\,10^{-3} = 2.28 \times 10^{-3}\;\underline{/57.15°}$$
$$y_{fe} = (33.6 - j\,44.2)\,10^{-3} = 55.5 \times 10^{-3}\;\underline{/-52.75°}$$
$$y_{re} = (-j\,0.81)\,10^{-3} = 0.81 \times 10^{-3}\;\underline{/-90°}$$

2. Calculate the following:

$$\frac{P_{oo}}{P_{io}} = \frac{|y_{fe}|^2}{4\text{Re}(y_{ie})\,\text{Re}(y_{oe}) - 2\text{Re}(y_{fe}y_{re})}$$

$$= \frac{55.5^2}{4(6.8)(1.24) - 2\text{Re}(33.6 - j\,44.2)(-j\,0.81)}$$

$$= \frac{(55.5)^2}{33.72 + 71.5}$$

$$= 29.2,\text{ or } 14.65\text{db}$$

$$c = 2 \left(\frac{P_{oo}}{P_{io}} \right) \left| \frac{y_{re}}{y_{fe}} \right|$$

$$= 2(29.2) \left(\frac{0.81}{55.5} \right)$$

$$= 0.854$$

The angle θ is easily found by the following steps:

$$y_{fe}y_{re} = (33.6 - j\,44.2)(-j\,0.81)\,10^{-6}$$

$$= (-35.8 - j\,27.2)\,10^{-6}$$

$$-(y_{fe}y_{re}) = (35.8 + j\,27.2)\,10^{-6}$$

$$(-y_{fe}y_{re})^* = (35.8 - j\,27.2)\,10^{-6}$$

$$= 45 \times 10^{-6} \; \underline{/-37.2^\circ}$$

$$\theta = -37.2^\circ$$

3. The gradient line is therefore drawn at an angle of $\theta = -37.2^\circ$ to the $B_2 = 0$ line.
4. Since $c < 1$, the $P_i = 0$ line lies outside the chart boundaries.
5. The constant gain circles can now be calculated and plotted. If $c < 1$, which it is in this case, the first calculation should be with $g = K_G$.

From Eq. (10),

$$K_G = 2 \frac{1 - \sqrt{1 - (0.854)^2}}{(0.854)^2}$$

$$= 1.31$$

Therefore from Eq. (12),

$$G_{max} = (1.31)(29.2)$$

$$= 38.4, \text{ or } 15.8\text{db}$$

Table 3 contains information for plotting other gain circles.

Table 3. Constant Gain Circles

g		Center	Radius
Numeric	db	$gc/2$	$\sqrt{1 - g + (gc/2)^2}$
1.31	+1.17	−0.569	0
1.0	0	−0.427	0.427
0.793	−1	−0.342	0.569
0.63	−2	−0.269	0.662
0.5	−3	−0.215	0.739
0.398	−4	−0.170	0.794
0.318	−5	−0.137	0.837

The gain circles can now be plotted on the Linvill chart. For example, to plot the 0.793 (P_{oo}/P_{io}) circle, locate the center on the gradient line at a distance of −0.342 from the center of the chart. With this center and a radius of 0.569, draw the circle. All distances are normalized to the unity radius circle. For $c > 1$, a portion of the gain circles will be off the chart, but this fact does not change the above procedure.

GAIN DESIGN PROCEDURES

1. Select Y_L based on a specified value of δ. Equation (11) can be simplified if $Y_L >> y_{22}$:

$$\delta = \frac{|\, y_{21}y_{12}\, |}{|\, y_{11}Y_L - y_{21}y_{12}\, |} \tag{13a}$$

If $\delta << 1$,

$$\delta = \frac{|y_{\,21}y_{12}|}{|\, y_{11}\, |\, |\, Y_L\, |} \tag{13b}$$

2. Locate the G_2 circle on the Linvill chart corresponding to the above Y_L value.
3. Find the maximum gain on this G_2 circle. This gain will occur at the point of tangency of the G_2 and a gain circle and indicates the jB_2 value necessary.
4. Draw a gain circle 3 db lower than the gain indicated in step 2. The intersections of this circle with the G_2 circle represent the half-power points.
5. Move along the G_2 circle and find the total susceptance change necessary to move from one intersection to the other.
6. To produce the required output stage bandwidth, let:

$$\frac{\Delta B}{\Delta \omega} = 2C_L$$

Select the inductance to produce the required load using the above capacitance from:

$$B_L = \omega C_L - \frac{1}{\omega L}$$

7. Calculate the Y_{in} for the collector load which yields maximum gain.
8. Match the generator admittance to the complex conjugate of Y_{in}.
9. Calculate Y_{out}, the output admittance, for this match at the input. Solve for C_{out}.
10. Transform the amplifier load to yield the required Y_L as specified by the sensitivity requirement.

GAIN DESIGN EXAMPLE

Using the 60-mc y parameters given previously, design a stage for maximum gain under the conditions:

$$\delta \leq 0.3$$

$$R_2 = R_1 = 50\Omega$$

$$BW_{3db} \geq 10 \text{ mc}$$

where R_2 and R_1 are the load and source impedances, respectively, not to be confused with the Y_L determined from the charts, or Y_{in}^*.

1. Select the $|Y_L|$ necessary for δ less than 0.3. Solving for $|Y_L|$ from Eq. (13),

$$|Y_L| \geq \frac{|y_{21}y_{12}|}{|y_{11}|\,\delta}$$

Using the y parameters given previously and $\delta = 0.3$,

$$|Y_L| \geq \frac{4.93 \times 10^{-3}}{0.3} \geq 16.4 \times 10^{-3}\,\text{mhos}$$

2. Locate the G_2 circle:

$$G_2 \geq \left(1 + \frac{|Y_L|}{y_{22r}}\right) y_{22r}$$

$$\geq \left(1 + \frac{16.4}{1.24}\right) y_{22r}$$

$$\geq 14.2 y_{22r}$$

3. The Linvill chart shows that the highest possible gain is about 2 db less than P_{oo}/P_{io} and that the G_2 and B_2 values necessary are:

$$G_2 = 14.2 y_{22r}$$

$$B_2 = -2 y_{22r}$$

4. Draw a gain circle 3 db below the circle tangent to the $14.2y_{22r}$ point found above. This is the $0.318\ (P_{oo}/P_{io})$ circle.

5. Figure 13 shows an enlarged picture of the G_2 gain circles. The total

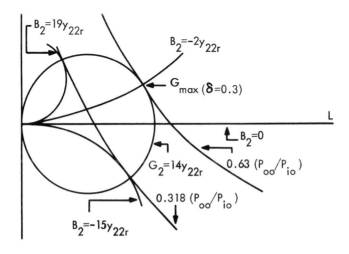

Fig. 13. Gain diagram.

susceptance change is:

$$\Delta B = 15 y_{22r} - (-19 y_{22r})$$

$$= 34 y_{22r}$$

$$= (34)(1.24)10^{-3}$$

$$= 42.2 \times 10^{-3} \text{ mhos}$$

6. Assuming a BW_{3db} of 20 mc for both the input and the output network, let:

$$\Delta \omega = BW_{3db} = (2\pi)(20 \text{ mc})$$

$$C_L = \frac{1}{2}\frac{\Delta B}{\Delta \omega} = \frac{42.2 \times 10^{-3}}{40\pi \times 10^6} = 168 \text{ pf}$$

Solve for B_L:

$$B_2 = -2 y_{22r} = y_{22i} + B_L$$

$$B_L = -2 y_{22r} - y_{22i} = (-2.48 - 1.92)10^{-3}$$

$$= -4.40 \times 10^{-3}$$

$$= \omega C_L - \frac{1}{\omega L}$$

Substituting into this expression $C_L = 168$ pf, $\omega = (2\pi)(60 \text{ mc})$, and $B_L = -4.4 \times 10^{-3}$ yields:

$$L_2 = 0.04 \ \mu h$$

7. The input admittance is:

$$Y_{in} = y_{11} - \frac{y_{12} y_{21}}{y_{22} + Y_L}$$

$$Y_{in} = \left\{ 6.8 + j6.1 - \left[\frac{(33.6 - j44.2)(-j0.81)}{1.24 + j1.92 + (13.2)1.24 - j4.4} \right] \right\} 10^{-3}$$

$$= (8.6 + j7.9)10^{-3}$$

8. Therefore $\quad\quad\quad\quad Y_g = (8.6 - j7.9)10^{-3}$

9. The output admittance for this Y_g is:

$$Y_{out} = y_{22} - \frac{y_{12} y_{11}}{y_{11} + Y_g}$$

$$= \left\{ 1.24 + j1.92 - \left[\frac{(33.6 - j44.2)(-j0.81)}{6.8 + j6.1 + 8.6 - j7.9} \right] \right\} 10^{-3}$$

$$= (3.3 + j4.0)10^{-3} \text{ mhos}$$

$$C_{out} = \frac{B_{out}}{\omega}$$

$$= \frac{4.0 \times 10^{-3}}{(2\pi)(60 \times 106)}$$

$$= 10.6 \text{ pf}$$

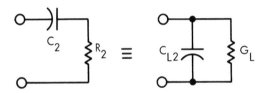

Figure 14

10. The load R_2 must now be transformed as shown in Figs. 14 and 15 below:

$$C_{L2} = C_2 \frac{1}{1 + 1/Q^2}$$

Solving for Q,

$$Q = \sqrt{1/G_L R_2 - 1}$$

$$= \frac{1}{\omega C_2 R_2}$$

$$= \sqrt{\frac{1}{(16.4 \times 10^{-3})(50)} - 1}$$

$$= 0.469$$

$$\omega C_2 = \frac{1}{(0.469)(50)} = 0.0426 \text{ mhos}$$

$$C_2 = 113 \text{ pf}$$

Use $C_2 = 110$ pf

$$C_{L2} = 110 \left(\frac{1}{1 + 1/0.22} \right)$$

$$= 19.8 \text{ pf}$$

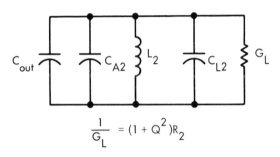

$$\frac{1}{G_L} = (1 + Q^2)R_2$$

Figure 15

The total load capacitance C_L which was determined from the selectivity requirement is:

$$C_L = C_{A2} + C_{L2} + C_{out}$$

where C_{A2} is additional capacitance required to give C_L. Then:

$$C_{A2} = C_L - C_{L2} - C_{out}$$
$$= 168 - 19.8 - 10.6$$
$$= 138 \text{ pf}$$

A variable capacitor supplies this additional capacitance.

The 50-ohm generator impedance is matched to Y_{in}^* in the same manner.

$$Y_{in} = (8.5 + j7.4)\, 10^{-3}$$

$$Q = \sqrt{\left(\frac{1}{(8.5)(50) \times 10^{-3}}\right) - 1}$$
$$= 1.16$$

$$\omega C_1 = \frac{1}{(1.16)(50)}$$
$$= 0.0173 \text{ mhos}$$
$$C_1 = 45.7 \text{ pf}$$

Use $C_1 = 47$ pf;

$$C_2 = 47\frac{1}{1 + 1/(1.16)^2}$$
$$= 26.9 \text{ pf}$$

The transistor capacitance is:

$$C_{in} = \frac{B_{in}}{\omega}$$
$$= 20 \text{ pf}$$

Choosing an input circuit $Q = 3$ will result in an amplifier bandwidth of approximately 13 mc. For this circuit:

$$Q = \frac{B_T}{2G_{in}}$$

where:

$$B_T = \omega(C_{in} + C_2 + C_{A1})$$

and C_{A1} is the additional capacitance.

$$B_T = 2QG_{in}$$
$$= (2)(3)(8.6 \times 10^{-3})$$
$$= 51.6 \times 10^{-3}$$
$$\omega C_{A1} = B_T - \omega(C_{in} + C)$$
$$= 51.6 \times 10^{-3} - (3.77 \times 10^8)(26.9 + 20)10^{-12}$$
$$C_{A1} = 89.5 \text{ pf}$$

Again use a variable capacitor to supply this capacitance.

$$L_1 = \frac{1}{\omega^2 C_T}$$

$$= \frac{1}{(3.77 \times 10^8)^2 (1.35 \times 10^{-10})}$$

$$= 0.052 \ \mu h$$

The circuit diagram is shown in Fig. 16 and the measured performance is given in Table 4. Measured gain, bandwidth, and input admittance agree very well with the computed values. The input admittance was also measured for $G_L = 24$ mmhos to indicate the input-output isolation. Single-stage amplifiers do not generally require this much isolation, but multi-stage amplifiers demand it. Multi-stage design follows the same general procedure with the exception that Y_{in} calculated at maximum gain must now be transformed by an appropriate matching network to the correct collector load. This procedure is followed for as many stages as required. The input stage is then matched to the generator impedance.

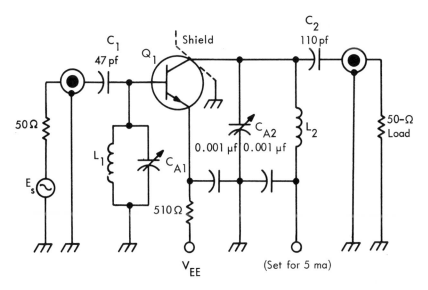

Components

L_1=1 1/2T, #14 wire, 1/4" dia

L_2=2T, #14 wire, 1/4" dia

C_{A1}, C_{A2}=Arco 465
(or equivalent) 45–380 pf

Q_1=2N743

δ(alignability)=0.3

Typical performance

G_T=11.5 db

BW≅10 mc

Fig. 16. 2N743 60-mc amplifier.

Table 4. Amplifier Performance

2N743 60-mc AMPLIFIER $I_c = 5$ ma $V_{ce} = 5$ volts				$G_L = 16$ mmhos		$G_L = 24$ mmhos	
UNIT	GAIN db	f_{HIGH} mc	f_{LOW} mc	G_{in} mmhos	B_{in} mmhos	G_{in} mmhos	B_{in} mmhos
81	12.2	64.8	55.2	5.53	5.84	5.13	5.35
82	12.1	64.8	55.2	8.55	8.2	8.0	7.61
83	11.2	64.8	55.0	9.53	9.45	8.93	8.85
85	12.0	64.8	54.9	6.95	7.46	6.92	6.75
86	11.2	64.8	54.9	8.93	7.73	8.34	7.35
88	12.1	64.8	54.3	9.62	8.2	9.17	7.68
93	11.2	64.8	54.8	10.62	8.85	10.3	8.33
95	10.8	64.8	55.2	7.8	5.46	7.46	5.2
96	10.0	65.0	55.2	8.85	5.82	8.4	5.65
98	11.3	64.9	55.2	7.7	6.1	7.4	5.8

BIBLIOGRAPHY

1. Gibbons, J. F.: "The Design of Alignable Transistor Amplifiers," *Stanford Electronics Lab Technical Report,* No. 106; May 7, 1956.
2. Pritchard, R. L.: "Modern High-Frequency Transistors — A Survey," A paper presented at the 1957 IRE-AEE University of Pennsylvania Transistor and Solid State Circuits Conference, Feb. 15, 1962.
3. Scanlan, J. O., and J. S. Singleton: "The Gain and Stability of Linear Two-Port Amplifiers," *IRE Transactions on CT,* Vol. CT-9, No. 3, Sept. 1962.
4. Rollett, J. M.: "Stability and Power Gain Invariants of Linear Two-Ports," *IRE Transactions on CT,* pp. 29–32, March 1962.
5. Linvill, J. G.: "The Theory of Two-Ports," International Convention on Transistors and Associated Semiconductor Devices, May 21, 1959.
6. Pritchard, R. L.: "High-Frequency Power Gain of Junction Transistors," *Proceedings IRE,* Vol. 43, No. 9, Sept. 1955.
7. Gärtner, W. W.: *Transistors: Principles, Design and Application,* D. Van Nostrand Company, New Jersey, 1960.
8. Cote, A. J., and J. B. Oakes, *Linear Vacuum-Tube and Transistor Circuits,* McGraw-Hill, New York, 1961.
9. Linvill, J. G., and J. F. Gibbons: *Transistors and Active Circuits,* McGraw-Hill, New York, 1961.

6

Small-signal UHF Amplifier Design

by George Johnson

INTRODUCTION

This chapter describes the design procedure for a 450-mc RF amplifier. Admittance parameters are used to describe the linear active network (LAN). A Linvill Chart of the LAN is used to select load and source terminations for a specified gain. Admittance-impedance charts are used to design coupling networks. Amplifier construction is discussed and experimental results of gain measurements are shown to compare well with predicted values.

POWER GAIN-STABILITY DESCRIPTION OF THE LAN

In order to get a complete description of the LAN at 450 mc, a set of y data was measured using the General Radio Transfer Function Bridge. Since the full set of y data completely characterized the LAN, its gain and stability properties may be accurately indicated. The accuracy of the y data is determined by "T-bridge" and is not subject to jig errors* (as such) because no jig is required with the T-bridge. The admittance parameters that are used in the design example are those of a germanium epitaxial mesa transistor.

$$y_{ie} = 29.7 + j14.3 = 33 \ \underline{/\ 25.8°} \text{ mmhos}$$

$$y_{re} = -0.38 - j2.0 = 2.0 \ \underline{/\ 259.2°} \text{ mmhos}$$

$$y_{fe} = -10.3 - j50.2 = 51.3 \ \underline{/\ 258.4°} \text{ mmhos}$$

$$y_{oe} = 0.93 + j5.31 = 5.39 \ \underline{/\ 80.0°} \text{ mmhos}$$

---

*There are, however, certain precautions which should be taken in nulling the bridge and minimizing lead length between the header and the face of the T-bridge socket. Lead length for the above data was $\cong 1.7$ millimeters. Data above were taken with the fourth lead grounded.

One of the most important properties of the device is its inherent stability.* The device may be either potentially unstable or unconditionally stable. The criterion for unconditional stability is given by Eq. (1).

$$2g_{11}g_{22} - \text{Re}(y_{12}y_{21}) > |y_{12}y_{21}| \tag{1}$$

where g_{11} is $\text{Re}(y_{11})$

This expression may be modified slightly to make it more explicit. The quantity C is defined as a degree of inequality and is called the stability factor. Equation (2) shows this relation.

$$2g_{11}g_{22} - \text{Re}(y_{12}y_{21}) = \frac{1}{C}|y_{12}y_{21}| \tag{2}$$

If the value of C is less than unity, then Eq. (1) is satisfied and the device is unconditionally stable. This means that no complex input or output termination may be found which will cause the LAN to oscillate. If C is greater than unity, then the converse is true. The value of C for the device described by the above y parameters is:

$$C = \frac{|y_{21}y_{12}|}{2g_{11}g_{22} - \text{Re}(y_{12}y_{21})}$$

$$= \frac{105}{2(29.5)(0.93) - (-97)}$$

$$= \frac{105}{152.1}$$

$$= 0.69$$

The stability factor is less than unity; therefore, the device is unconditionally stable at 450 mc. And because C is considerably less than unity, the amplifier will be very stable. Now consider the gain of the LAN. The value of h_{fe} at 450 mc is:

$$h_{fe} = \frac{y_{fe}}{y_{ie}}$$

$$= \frac{51.3 \ /\underline{258.4°}}{33 \ /\underline{25.8°}}$$

$$= 1.56 \ /\underline{232.6°}$$

$$= 3.87 \text{ db}$$

The resulting value of f_t (assuming 6 db/octave roll-off)† is:

$$f_t = (1.56)(450)$$

$$= 700 \text{ mc}$$

---

*Inherent stability refers specifically to the device stability without external circuitry. Actual stability, on the other hand, takes into consideration the total external shunt conductances of g_{11} and g_{22}. It is therefore not independent of the circuit as is the inherent stability factor C.

†This is a good assumption since the numeric value of h_{fe} at the frequency is almost 2.

The power gain G_{oo} is defined in the following way:

$$G_{oo} = \frac{\text{Power delivered to Re } (Y_L)}{\text{Power delivered to input of two-port}}$$

where Y_L is conjugately matched to y_{22}

The value of G_{oo} may be calculated for the LAN by using the following expression:

$$G_{oo} = \frac{|y_{21}|^2}{4g_{11}g_{22} - 2\text{Re}(y_{12}y_{21})}$$

$$= \frac{C}{2}\left|\frac{y_{21}}{y_{12}}\right|$$

$$= \frac{0.69}{2}\left|\frac{51.3}{2.0}\right|$$

$$= 8.7 \text{ or } 9.4 \text{ db}$$

Had C been greater than unity, the value of G_{max} would have been unbounded. However, since $C = 0.69$, G_{max} is finite and may be calculated by evaluating K_G and multiplying by G_{oo}:

$$K_G = \frac{2(1 - \sqrt{1-c^2})}{c^2}$$

$$= 1.15$$

$$G_{max} = (K_G)(G_{oo})$$
$$= (1.15)(8.7)$$
$$= 10 \text{ db}$$

These calculations indicate that the LAN at 450 mc will be unconditionally stable, will have an h_{fe} of about 4 db ($f_t \cong 700$ mc), and will have a G_{max} of 10 db.

The display of the gain and stability of the LAN is uniquely combined in a graphic representation devised by Linvill. The calculations and constructions of this system are presented in Appendix I to this chapter. The finished Linvill Chart is shown in Fig. 5. It is essentially a plot of gain on a field of output admittance (in terms of $G_2 \pm jB_2$). The utility of such a chart is two-fold. First, it shows exactly what complex load will result in G_{max}. Second, it shows that no load which may be selected would cause instability.

LOAD CALCULATION

The evaluation of the load to obtain G_{max} of 10 db is done as follows:

$$G_2 + jB_2 = G_L + jB_L + y_{22}$$

Solving for G_L:

$$G_L = G_2 - y_{22r}$$
$$= 3y_{22r} - y_{22r}$$
$$= 1.86 \times 10^{-3} \text{ mhos}$$

Now, evaluating the reactive part:

$$B_L = B_2 - y_{22i}$$
$$= 0.7y_{22r} - y_{22i}$$
$$= -4.65 \times 10^{-3} \text{ mhos}$$

The load should be $1.86 - j4.65$ mmhos to yield 10 db gain.

OUTPUT NETWORK DESIGN

The load of 50 ohms must be transformed to $1.86 - j4.65$ mmhos. This may be done with the aid of an admittance-impedance chart. Appendix II discusses this type of chart and its use. One possible form of the network is shown in Fig. 1. It was chosen because the capacitor offers d-c isolation and impedance matching.

Locate the 50-ohm load on the impedance coordinate system, using a scale factor of one unit as 200 ohms or 0.5×10^{-2} mhos. This is located on the horizontal axis at $R = 0.25$. The value of the series capacitive reactance is added as a vertical line down from 0.25. The amount of reactance necessary to transform 50 ohms to 540 ohms is obtained by moving down from 50 ohms to the constant conductance circle marked $G = -0.37$.

$$G = \frac{200\,\Omega}{0.37}$$
$$= 540\,\Omega$$

At this point the transformation from 50 to 540 ohms is completed, but as can be seen, the terminal value is rather capacitive. In order to neutralize this it is clearly necessary to add $-jB$ to the $+jB$ already present due to the transformed value of the series capacitor. If a transformation from 50 ohms to 1.86 mmhos instead of $1.86 - j4.65$ mmhos had been desired, the amount of shunt inductance would have been indicated by:

$$B = (-1.1)(0.5 \times 10^{-2})$$
$$= -0.55 \times 10^{-2} \text{ mhos}$$

However, the Linvill Chart indicates that a complex load is necessary to achieve the value G_{max}, so locating the desired load point:

$$\text{Real part: } \frac{1.86 \times 10^{-3}}{0.5 \times 10^{-2}} = 0.37 \text{ units}$$

$$\text{Imaginary part: } \frac{-4.65 \times 10^{-3}}{0.5 \times 10^{-2}} = -0.93 \text{ units}$$

Now instead of stopping at the horizontal axis, the process is continued until the point $0.37 - j0.93$ is reached. The above discussion is made clearer by Fig. 2.

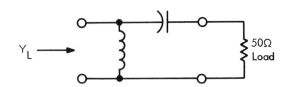

Fig. 1. Load resistance transforming network.

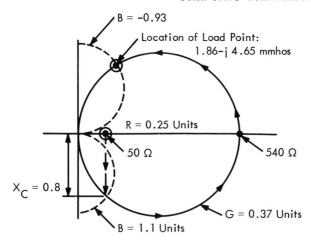

Fig. 2. Impedance-admittance chart for output network.

Solving for the value of X_c gives:

$$X_c = (0.8)(200)$$
$$= 160\ \Omega$$
$$C = 2.2\ pf\ at\ 450\ mc$$

Now solving for the amount of shunt inductance necessary to move to desired load point on the constant-conductance circle, $G = 0.37$.

$$X_L = \frac{200}{2.03} = 98\ \Omega \quad (\text{where } 2.03 = 1.1 + 0.93)$$

$$L = 0.034\ \mu h\ at\ 450\ mc$$

The resulting network shown in Fig. 3 performs the desired impedance transformation at 450 mc.

To allow tuning of the above network, a shunt capacitance is added. It is calculated by selecting a fractional bandwidth of 0.1.

$$FBW = 0.1 \qquad (45\ mc)$$
$$Q_L = 10$$
$$= (540)(6.28)(450 \times 10^6)C$$

$$C = \frac{10}{(540)(6.28)(450 \times 10^6)}$$

$$= 6.5\ pf$$

Fig. 3. Load resistance transforming network.

The inductance required to resonate with 6.5 pf is 0.02 μh at 450 mc. The network appears as in Fig. 4.

INPUT NETWORK DESIGN

Before designing the input networks, the value of the input immittance must be obtained for the specified load. This may be calculated using Eq. (3).

$$Y_{in} = y_{11} - \frac{y_{12}y_{21}}{y_{22} + Y_L} \qquad (3)$$

where $Y_L = 1.86 - j4.65$ mmhos

However, a quicker way has been devised which not only reduces the amount of complex algebra but allows a much more rapid analysis of input immittance for changing load conditions. Its application is discussed in Appendix III so that the design sequence presented so far will not be interrupted.

As demonstrated in Appendix III,

$$Y_{in} - y_{11} = G_1 + jB_1 \qquad (4)$$

By placing a quadrant chart over the Linvill Chart (Fig. 5) and rotating it so that its real axis lies along the gradient line, we may evaluate the input impedance. Reading the values of:

$$\frac{G_1}{\left|\dfrac{y_{12}y_{21}}{2y_{22r}}\right|} = 0.52$$

and

$$\frac{B_1}{\left|\dfrac{y_{12}y_{21}}{2y_{22r}}\right|} = -0.39$$

$$\left|\frac{y_{12}y_{21}}{2y_{22r}}\right| = \frac{105 \times 10^{-6}}{(2)(0.93 \times 10^{-3})}$$

$$= 56.5 \times 10^{-3}$$

which are indicated by the point of maximum gain, we may calculate the value of Y_{in}. Substituting in Eq. (4):

$$Y_{in} = (0.52)(56.5 \times 10^{-3}) - j(0.39)(56.5 \times 10^{-3}) + 29.7 \times 10^{-3} + j14.3 \times 10^{-3}$$
$$= 59.1 \times 10^{-3} - j7.7 \times 10^{-3}$$

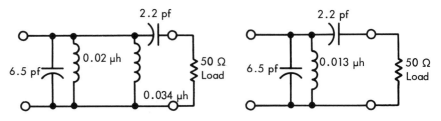

Fig. 4. Complete output network.

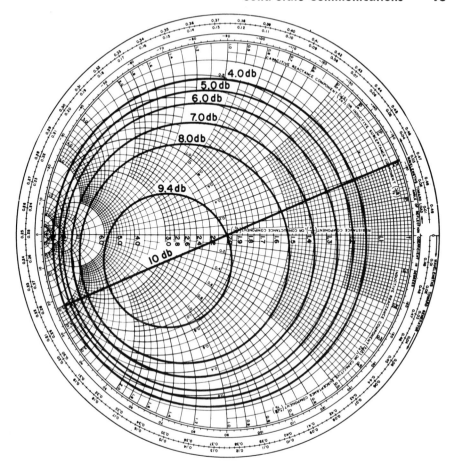

Fig. 5. Linvill chart.

Therefore the input admittance of the terminated stage at 450 mc is as shown in Fig. 6. The input network to match the generator to this admittance will be as shown in Fig. 7. And the complete input circuit with d-c return for the base and d-c block for the input will take the form shown in Fig. 8.

In designing the input network, use 1 unit = 50 ohms or 0.02 mmhos. The input admittance is $59.1 - j7.7$ mmhos, which becomes $2.9 - j0.385$ units. Locating this on the admittance chart establishes the starting point. Notice that the input admit-

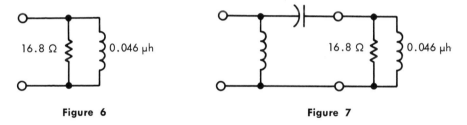

Figure 6   **Figure 7**

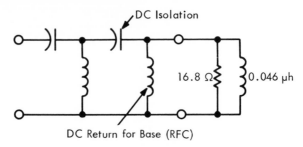

Figure 8

tance is automatically converted to a series combination simply by reading the rectangular coordinates at this point.

The first component in the desired network is a series C which requires a move straight down the chart from $2.9 - j0.385$ until the constant-conductance circle of 1 is intersected. This is the value to which 16.8 ohm is transformed. The value of X_c required is:

$$X_c = (0.58)(50)$$
$$= 29\,\Omega$$
$$C = 12 \text{ pf at } 450 \text{ mc.}$$

Moving around the constant-conductance circle from $B = 1.25$ to $B = 0$ requires a shunt inductance to be added to the network. Its value is:

$$X_L = \frac{50}{1.25}$$

$$= 40\,\Omega$$
$$L = 0.014\,\mu\text{h at } 450 \text{ mc.}$$

The admittance-impedance chart of Fig. 9 pictures the above discussion. The completed network is as shown in Fig. 10. The completed circuit is shown in Fig. 11.

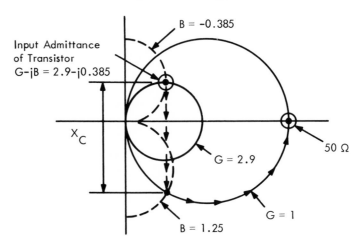

Figure 9. Input circuit design.

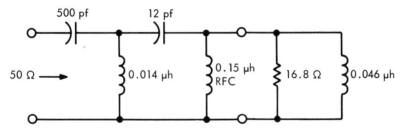

Fig. 10. Input network.

EXPERIMENTAL RESULTS

Average power gain was measured at 8.6 db. The output tank Q_L is 10 and the Q_U of the inductor is 100, so the insertion loss of the network is 1 db. Since G_{max} was 10 db, this indicates that the typical power gain should have been about 9 db. The difference between 8.6 db and 9 db is probably due to small but finite losses in the input network and to experimental and measurement errors. Bandwidth measured on the amplifier was 48 mc. This compared to the design bandwidth of 45 mc. The difference is probably due to the slight differences in actual Y_{Yr} value in the output circuit because of the tolerances of standard value capacitances used in the transforming networks.

Noise figure was about 6 db. The coincidence of best noise figure and best gain was quite close.

The construction of this circuit was straightforward. A brass two-section box approximately 3″ x 2″ x 1″ was used. The coils were made of copper strips approximately ½″ wide, 1/32″ thick and 1″ long. Silvered miniature air-variable capacitors were used in the tanks. Care was taken to minimize the lead inductance by modifying the TO-18 Teflon* socket. Most of the Teflon was removed so that only a thin disc, approximately the chassis thickness, remained. The bypass and decoupling 500-pf capacitors were high-quality r-f ribbon types.

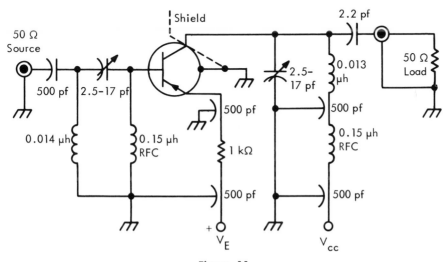

Figure 11

*Trademark of DuPont Corporation.

APPENDIX I: POWER FLOW IN A GENERAL TWO-PORT

A general two-port is defined and used to demonstrate power flow. The input power is derived and shown to be a plane. The output power is derived and shown to be a paraboloid. The combination of these two surfaces describes power gain. Potential instability and unconditional stability are defined and demonstrated graphically.

Consider the general two-port of Fig. 12. The choice of h parameters is arbitrary; any consistent set of parameters could be used. The choice of generators shown in Fig. 12 is for h parameters. Had y parameters been used, the output generator would have been a current generator but its complex identity would have been of the same form. The input current generator may be normalized to $1 + j0$ amps. The value of the output generator may be changed by varying a or b. In this way any load condition may be simulated.

Define the system of coordinates as shown in Fig. 13. The term P_o is output power. The form of the mathematical equation representing output power is a paraboloid. It is convenient to choose a new set of rectangular coordinates L and M to describe this paraboloid.

Define P_{oo} as the maximum power output from the model of Fig. 12 if the effect of h_{12} is neglected. It occurs as shown in Fig. 13 at L, M = 1, 0. Under these conditions it is obvious that:

$$P_o = \mathrm{Re}\,(-E_2{}^*I_2)$$

The general form of the power to the load is:

$$P_o = \mathrm{Re}\,(-E_2{}^*1_2)$$

where

$$-E_2 = (L + jM)\left(\frac{h_{21}}{2h_{22r}}\right)$$

Therefore the dimension for $(L + jM)$ is amps, and of course the dimension of $h_{21}/2h_{22r}$ is ohms.

Thus

$$-E_2 = (L + jM)\left(\frac{h_{21}}{2h_{22r}}\right)$$

$$= (\mathrm{amps})\,(\mathrm{ohms}) = \mathrm{volts}$$

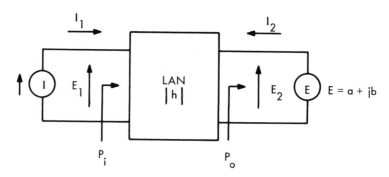

Fig. 12. Two-port power flow model.

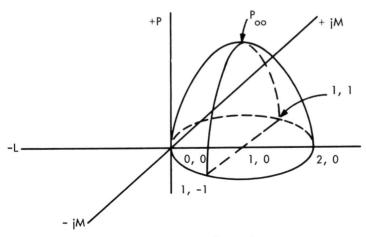

Fig. 13. Power out description.

If E_2, the "generator-load" component, is less than the output voltage produced at the output port by the signal at the input port, then the generator actually represents an IR drop rather than an EMF. If it is an IR drop it may be considered as being identical to a passive immittance.

Now writing the expression for P_o,

$$I_2 = h_{21}(1 + jO) + h_{22}(L + jM)\left(-\frac{h_{21}}{2h_{22r}}\right)$$

and

$$P_{oo} = \frac{|h_{21}|^2}{4h_{22r}}$$

Since

$$P_{oo} = |E_2|^2 Y_{Lr} = E_2{}^2 h_{22r} = \frac{|h_{21}|^2}{4h_{22r}}$$

then

$$|E_2|^2 \text{ must be:}$$

$$|E_2|^2 = \frac{|h_{21}|^2}{4(h_{22r})^2}$$

$$|E_2| = \frac{|h_{21}|}{2h_{22r}}$$

The value P_{oo} occurs at $L + jM = 1 + j0$ so it is clear that an appropriate choice for the variables a and jb is:

$$E_2 = a + jb = (L + jM)\left(-\frac{h_{21}}{2h_{22r}}\right)$$

Therefore

$$P_o = \mathrm{Re}(E_2{}^*)(I_2)$$

$$= \mathrm{Re}\left\{\frac{(h_{21})^*(L - jM)}{2h_{22r}}\left[h_{21} - \frac{(L + jM)(+h_{21})h_{22}}{2h_{22r}}\right]\right\}$$

$$= \frac{L|h_{21}|^2}{2h_{22r}} - \frac{(L^2 + M^2)|h_{21}|^2}{4h_{22r}}$$

The input power is given by:

$$P_i = Re(E_1{}^*)(I_1)$$

$$E_1 = h_{11}I_1 + h_{12}E_2$$

$$= h_{11}(1 + j0) + h_{12}(L + jM)\left(\frac{-h_{21}}{2h_{22r}}\right)$$

$$P_i = h_{11}(1 + j0)(1 + j0) + h_{12}(1 + j0)(L + jM)\left(\frac{-h_{21}}{2h_{22r}}\right)$$

$$= h_{11r} - L\,Re\left(\frac{h_{12}h_{21}}{2h_{22r}}\right) + M Im\left(\frac{h_{12}h_{21}}{2h_{22r}}\right)$$

This is the equation of a plane in the coordinate system of Fig. 13. Figure 14 shows this general relationship. Cutting the model of Fig. 14 along the plane ABC yields Fig. 15.

It is quite apparent from this figure that the maximum power gain occurs at a distance d to the left of the 1.0 point. The following derivations can be made using geometry and Fig. 15.

$$\frac{f}{e} = 2\left(\frac{1 - \sqrt{1 - c^2}}{c^2}\right) = K_G$$

$$d = \frac{CK_G}{2}$$

$$C = 2\frac{P_{oo}}{P_{io}}\left|\frac{h_{12}}{h_{21}}\right| = \frac{|h_{21}||h_{12}|}{2h_{11r}h_{22r} - Re(h_{12}h_{21})}$$

and when $C < 1$:

$$G_{max} = K_G\frac{P_{oo}}{P_{io}}$$

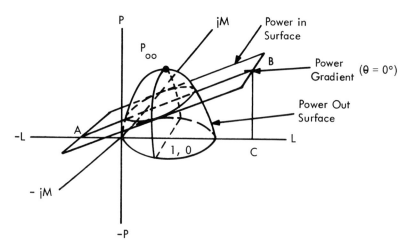

Fig. 14. Power gain model.

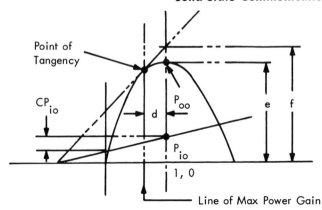

Point of Tangency

CP$_{io}$

P$_{oo}$

d

e   f

P$_{io}$

1, 0

Line of Max Power Gain

Fig. 15. Two-dimensional view of power gain model.

The Linvill Chart. The L-M plane has been discussed and shown to be a way of representing a wide variety of load conditions for the two-port. The actual load admittance must be related to this L-M plane. This may be done by considering the following expressions:

$$I_2 = I_1 h_{21} + E_2 h_{22}$$

$$= (1 + j0) h_{21} - (L + jM) \left(\frac{+h_{21}}{2h_{22r}} \right) h_{22}$$

$$= - Y_L E_2$$

$$Y_L E_2 = Y_L \frac{L + jM}{2h_{22r}} h_{21}$$

$$Y_L \frac{L + jM}{2h_{22r}} h_{21} + \frac{L + jM}{2h_{22r}} h_{22} h_{21} = h_{21}$$

$$Y_L + h_{22} = \frac{2h_{22r}}{L + jM} = G_2 + jB_2$$

In the L-M plane the real and imaginary parts, G_2 and jB_2, are mutually orthogonal circles. This kind of a plot is shown in Fig. 16.

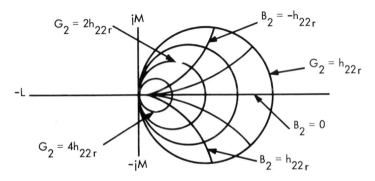

$G_2 = 2h_{22r}$ jM $B_2 = -h_{22r}$

$G_2 = h_{22r}$

-L

$B_2 = 0$

$G_2 = 4h_{22r}$ -jM $B_2 = h_{22r}$

Fig. 16. $G_2 + jB_2$ in the LM plane.

APPENDIX II: LOSSLESS MATCHING TECHNIQUES

There are many ways to realize practical matching networks. The efficiency of modern synthesis is astounding, but in many cases its realization techniques are too detailed for simple matching problems. The method described here deals with coupling networks that are made from lumped, linear, constant-valued elements. It makes use of immittance charts which reduce the calculations of components to simple evaluation of reactance into inductance or capacitance. With a reactance-frequency chart or reactance slide rule, these calculations are eliminated and the whole problem reduces to simply reading the values of the network components.

The Admittance-Impedance Chart. Consider the Cartesian coordinate system of Fig. 17. This system defines all impedance functions that have positive real parts. This chart may be transformed into a system of orthogonal circles that have a common tangent point at 0. This transformed system represents all admittance functions which have positive real conductance values, and is shown in Fig. 18. Superimposing these charts results in Fig. 19.

From these charts it is obvious that

$$Z = R + jX = \frac{1}{Y} = \frac{1}{G + jB}$$

As a result it is also obvious that the problem of converting a series combination to a parallel combination of real and imaginary terms is accomplished simply by locating the parallel combination on the appropriate orthogonal circles and reading the R and X values indicated. A general chart of this type is shown in Fig. 19.

The Real Source-Load Transformation. Consider the problem of transforming 50 ohms to 450 ohms. The procedure is to systematically "build" the immittance matching network by first adding a series component of the appropriate value and then adding a shunt component of the appropriate value. The dual chart shown in Fig. 19 is used to decide what these values are. When a series component is added, the R-X part of the chart is used. Then when a shunt element is added, the orthogonal admittance coordinate system is used. Since they are superimposed as in Fig. 19, the change from one chart to the other is simply a change in the type of motion, either rectangular or circular. Since it is in normalized form, the first step is to decide on a scale factor which will put both the load and source on the

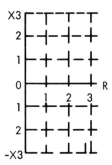

Fig. 18. Orthogonal admittance coordinate system.

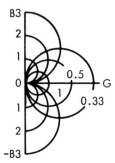

Fig. 17. Rectangular impedance coordinate system.

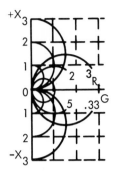

Fig. 19. Admittance impedance system.

chart. For the above values of 50 ohms and 450 ohms this scale factor may be chosen as

$$1 \text{ unit} = 100 \ \Omega \ (\text{or } 0.01 \text{ mhos})$$

Starting with the 50-ohm load and using the rectangular system of coordinates, locate the point 0.5, which is:

$$\frac{50 \, \Omega}{100 \, \Omega/\text{unit}} = 0.5 \text{ units}$$

This point is located at ① in Fig. 20. A value of series capacitive reactance may be added to 50 ohms by moving straight down from the 50 ohms point, ① , to point ② The amount of this capacitive reactance determines the resistance transformation. Since 450 ohms or 4.5 units is the desired value, the amount of X_c must extend down to the constant-conductance circle of 0.22 units. Point ② is then considered as being on the circle system shown in Fig. 18. This converts the series combination of R and C to a parallel combination. Adding shunt inductance to resonate with this shunt capacitance will not change the shunt real part, so going from ② to ③ must be along the constant-conductance circle (0.22 units). Of course, this circle was chosen so that ③ would be 450 ohms. Notice that moving

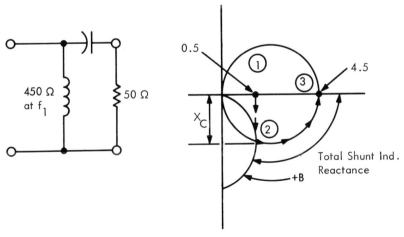

Fig. 20. Series capacitance L-section.

from ② to ③ on the constant-conductance circle requires the addition of a shunt $-B$ to counteract the value of $+B$ at ② . This is an inductive susceptance. Addition of such a susceptance completes the transformation.

Another network will also perform this transformation. Figure 21 shows the path followed when a series coil is used rather than a series capacitor.

Complex Load-Source Transformation. There is no essential difference in the technique if both load and source are complex. Consider the following example:

$$\text{Input} = R_s + jX_s$$
$$\text{Load} = G + jB$$

The chart looks like Fig. 22.

APPENDIX III: INPUT IMMITTANCE

It is evident that a relation between the input impedance of the general two-port and the L-M plane exists. This may be shown by:

$$E_1 = I_1h_{11} + E_2h_{12} = Z_{in}$$

Since the general current is $1 + j0$, then $E_1/1 + j0$ is Z_{in}.

$$Z_{in} = (1 + j0)h_{11} + (L + jM)\frac{-h_{21}}{2h_{22r}}h_{12}$$

$$Z_{in} - h_{11} = R_1 + jX_1 = (L + jM)\frac{-h_{12}h_{21}}{2h_{22r}}$$

$$\frac{R_1 + jX_1}{Gr} = (L + jM)e^{-\theta}$$

where Gr is the gradient and θ is the angle of the gradient.

The values $\dfrac{R_1}{Gr}$ and $\dfrac{jX_1}{Gr}$ can be conveniently thought of as the coordinates

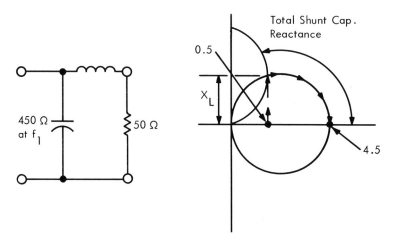

Fig. 21. Series inductance L-section.

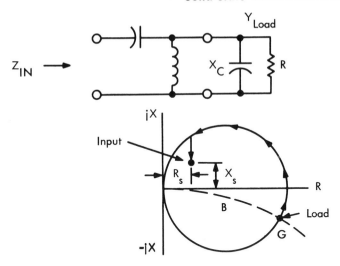

Fig. 22. Complex load-source chart.

of a rectangular grid which can be put over the L-M plane. Reading the value of $R_1/|Gr|$ and $jX_1/|Gr|$ it is possible to solve for Z_{in} using

$$Z_{in} - h_{11} = R_1 + jX_1$$

This equation is perfectly general. Had the characterization of the LAN been in y parameters, the equation would have been written

$$Y_{in} - y_{11} = G_1 + jB_1$$

The rectangular grid is shown in Fig. 23.

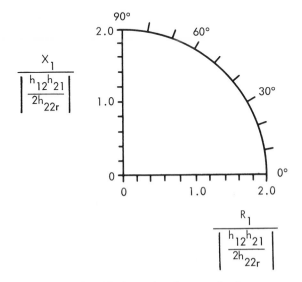

Fig. 23. Input immittance chart.

7

Field-effect Transistors for Low-level Circuits

by L. J. Sevin and Stan Holcomb

A SIMPLIFIED THEORY

A Field-effect Transistor (FET) is essentially a semiconductor current path whose resistance is controlled by applying an electric field perpendicular to the current. The electric field results from reverse biasing a P-N junction.

When a P-N junction is reverse biased a "depletion" or space-charge layer develops on both sides of the junction. That is, the current carriers on either side of the junction are swept across and away from the junction, leaving regions that contain a net charge but no free current carriers except those generated by heat. The current-carrier density determines how well a semiconductor will conduct current; therefore, the space-charge region on either side of a P-N junction will be very low in conductivity.

Resistance of a Semiconductor Bar. Consider a bar of semiconductor silicon crystal having the dimensions shown in Fig. 1, excess impurity concentration P, and ohmic (non-rectifying) contacts at each end. The approximate resistance

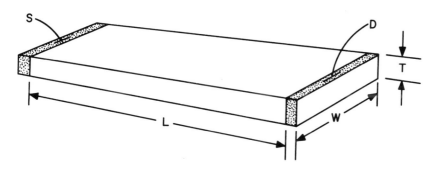

Figure 1

R_o between terminals S and D is:

$$R_o = \frac{L}{(q\mu)PWT}$$

where
q = electron charge
μ = majority carrier mobility

The factor $q\mu P$ in the denominator is a good approximation for the conductivity σ of the semiconductor material if the doping level is such that the minority carrier density is negligible. Since the dimensions of the bar are fixed, the resistance of the bar must be controlled by controlling the conductivity.

Silicon Bar with P-N Junctions. Figure 2 shows a P-type bar of silicon which has had N-type impurities introduced into opposite sides, forming P-N junctions. The two N regions are electrically connected and a bias voltage (V_{GS}) is applied to the two junctions. The N regions are called gates and the space between the gates is called the channel. The resistance R_o is modulated by depleting carriers from parts of the channel.

Another view is that the effective thickness of the bar in Fig. 1 can be changed by a transverse electric field produced by the bias voltage V_{GS}. If the doping level in the gates is purposely very large compared to that in the channel, the carrier-depleted or "space-charge" zone will extend principally into the channel. Figure 3 is a graph of the net charge density, electric field, and potential through a cross-section of the channel for a given V_{GS}. Uniform charge density and ideal step junctions are assumed. The shaded areas above and below the zero concentration axis are equal, because the depleted regions on either side of the junction must contain equal net charge. The electric field and potential plots shown in Fig. 3 are obtained by performing successive integrations.

Behavior of Space-charge Layer With Channel Current. The simple field-effect structure of Fig. 2 is reproduced in Figs. 4(a) and (b) with an expanded vertical scale to allow a more graphic description of the behavior of the space-charge layer with an applied drain-to-source voltage. In Fig. 4(a), as the voltage V_{DD} is increased from zero to small values, the current rises linearly with V_{DS}. At small currents, the channel between the drain and source behaves as a linear resistor, but as current increases the parts of the channel near the junctions become significantly negative with respect to the source terminal. Since the N gates are connected externally to the source, the junctions are reverse biased and the space-charge

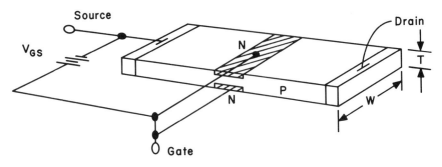

Figure 2

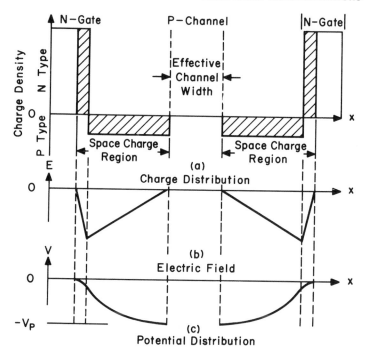

Figure 3

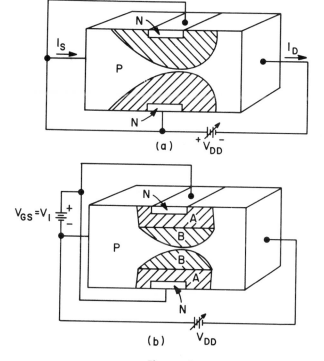

Figure 4

layers are extended into the channel, lowering the channel conductance. The electrical behavior of Fig. 4(a) is plotted in Fig. 5; note that the relatively constant slope at low voltages becomes less linear with increasing applied voltage. At some V_{DS} the space-charge layers extend into the channel until they almost meet, as shown by the shaded areas in Fig. 4(a); this corresponds approximately to the voltage at the "knee" of the $V_{GS} = 0$ curve in Fig. 5. Shockley[1] called this voltage the pinch-off voltage. Above the pinch-off voltage the drain current saturates; i.e., it increases very little for further increases in drain-to-source voltage. The fact that reverse bias on the P-N junction is greatest at the drain end gives the space-charge layers their characteristic wedge shape. Most of the potential drop in the channel is confined to the short span where the space-charge layers nearly meet; this is the active or control part of the device. The remainder of the drain-to-source voltage is dropped across the bulk channel resistance between the two terminals and this active part.

In Fig. 4(b) a fixed reverse bias, $V_{GS} = V_1$, is applied to the gates. With no channel current, there is no electric field component tangent to the junction and the space-charge layer extends uniformly part of the way into the channel (region A). When a drain current flows, both tangential and normal components of electric field are present, creating the wedge-shaped space-charge region B. The ratio of the thicknesses of regions A and B depends on the magnitude of the external reverse bias; higher values of V_{GS} increase the thickness of A relative to B. Obviously, less channel current is required to produce pinch-off as V_{GS} increases. In Fig. 5, the $V_{GS} = V_1$ curve has the same shape as the zero bias curve except that pinch-off occurs at a lower drain-to-source voltage and a lower drain current. The reverse bias on the junction required to bring the two space-charge layers together is the sum of the externally applied bias V_{GS} and the internal self bias due to current flow through the channel resistance. From this it seems that the external bias required to bring the two space-charge layers together should be capable of reducing the drain current to the reverse saturation current of the P-N junction. However, this pinch-off condition never occurs. In practice, the drain current approaches some irreducible minimum greater than the diode reverse saturation current.

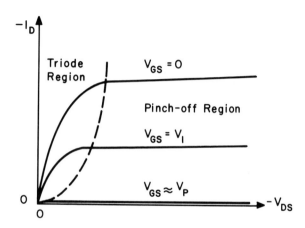

Figure 5

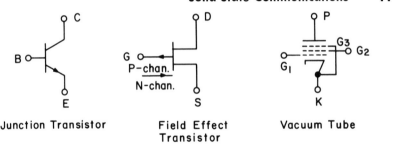

Junction Transistor   Field Effect Transistor   Vacuum Tube

Figure 6

Figure 5 is a set of curves that look remarkably like the output characteristics of a pentode vacuum tube, the drain, source, and gate terminals being analogous to the plate, cathode, and grid terminals respectively. The symbol adopted for the field-effect transistor is compared to those of the junction transistor and the triode vacuum tube in Fig. 6. Although the FET has only three terminals, its electrical behavior is closer to the pentode tube than to the triode tube.

Operation in the Pinch-Off Region. Aside from some suggested gain-control applications (which apparently have not been fully explored at this time) little use has been found for the FET operation in the triode or voltage saturation region. Because of the relatively high saturation voltage of the present device, it has not made an efficient switch. It has so far been most useful as an active element operating in the pinch-off region in linear applications, and it is here that we will place our emphasis.

At this point it is convenient to re-define the pinch-off voltage V_p as that gate-to-source voltage which should reduce the drain current to the reverse saturation current of the gate-channel diode. In practice, this voltage must be extrapolated from the behavior of drain current with gate-to-source voltage at drain currents significantly greater than zero.

The expression for the saturation drain current as a function of gate-to-source voltage derived by Shockley[1] is:

$$I_D = I_{DSS}\left[1 - 3\,\frac{V_{GS}}{V_p} + 2\left(\frac{V_{GS}}{V_p}\right)^{3/2}\right] \qquad (1)$$

The term I_{DSS} (per 56 IRE 28.S1) is the saturation drain current with zero gate-to-source bias voltage at any drain-to-source voltage in the pinch-off region below breakdown. Equation (1) was derived assuming a step junction, and is correct for both P-channel and N-channel devices since V_{GS} and V_p carry the same sign. The plot of Eq. (1) in Fig. 7 is the common-source forward transfer characteristic of the FET analogous to the common-cathode transconductance curve of a vacuum tube. This curve is in good agreement (except at low I_D) with transfer curves of practical field effects made by the alloy process; alloy junctions closely approximate step junctions.

Equation (1) must be modified to take into account the diode reverse saturation and leakage current, I_{GSS}:

$$I_D = (I_{DSS} + I_{GSS})\left[1 - 3\,\frac{V_{GS}}{V_p} + 2\left(\frac{V_{GS}}{V_p}\right)^{3/2}\right] - I_{GSS} \qquad (2)$$

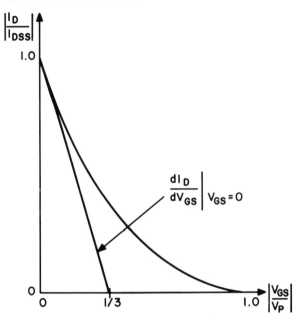

Figure 7

The disagreement between this expression and the behavior of practical devices is most marked at very low values of I_D. In practice, I_D cannot be reduced to I_{GSS} by the reverse bias on the gate-to-channel diode; as a result, D_p can be extrapolated from the measurement of V_{GS} at two or more values of I_D, or by measurement of the slope dI_D/dV_{GS} (forward transconductance), of the transfer curve at some value of V_{GS} (preferably $V_{GS} = 0$).

From Eq. (2):

$$\frac{dI_D}{dV_{GS}}\bigg|\ V_{GS} = 0 = -\frac{3}{V_p}\ (I_{DSS} + I_{GSS}) \tag{3}$$

I_{GSS} can usually be neglected when compared to I_{DSS}. Equation (3) implies that a tangent drawn to a transfer curve at $V_{GS} = 0$ as in Fig. 7 will intersect the $I_D = 0$ axis at $1/3\ V_p$.

The derivation of Eq. (1) was done with the assumption that carrier mobility remains constant with reverse gate bias, i.e., the longitudinal electric field in the channel does not exceed a critical value (around 1000 v/cm) above which Ohm's law no longer holds.[2] This assumption is apparently valid for alloy field-effect transistors, but not for FET's made by a diffusion process. The longitudinal electric field in the channel of diffused types can exceed 1000 v/cm, and the carrier mobility then becomes proportional to the square root of the electric field. Dacey and Ross[3] derived an expression for the drain current behavior with gate-to-source voltage in the pinch-off region for the "square root" mobility case:

$$I_D = I_{DSS} \left\{ 4 \left[1 - \left(\frac{V_{GS}}{V_p}\right)^{1/2} \right]^3 - 3 \left[1 - \left(\frac{V_{GS}}{V_p}\right)^{1/2} \right]^4 \right\}^{1/2} \tag{4}$$

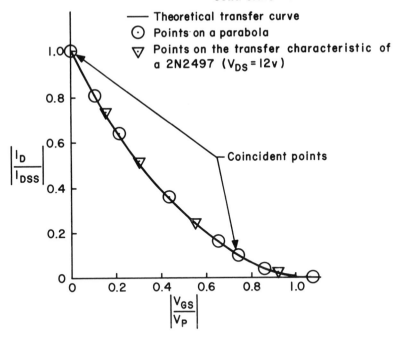

Fig. 8. Approximating the transfer curve with a parabola.

This is a more complicated expression than Eq. (1), but it agrees very well with the transfer characteristics of practical diffused type FET's. As in the case of Eq. (1), it fails at very low drain currents. An even better approximation to measured transfer curves is given by a simple parabola, properly "force-fitted" to Eq. (4). Figure 8 shows a plot of Eq. (4) with the points describing a force-fitted parabola superimposed. The force-fitting technique consists of selecting two points at which parabola and Eq. (4) are forced to coincide. The particular points selected, $I_D = I_{DSS}$ and $I_D = 0.1\ I_{DSS}$, give excellent results and are convenient for measurement. The parabola yields a slightly higher V_p than Eq. (4), i.e., 1.06/1, but the normalized transfer curve of a 2N2497 P-channel planar (diffused) FET plotted in Fig. 8 shows that the parabola is a better approximation at low currents.

The equation of the parabola in Fig. 8 is:

$$I_D = I_{DSS} \left(\frac{V_{GS}}{V_p} - 1 \right)^2 \qquad (5)$$

Taking into account the effect of I_{GSS}:

$$I_D = (I_{DSS} + I_{GSS}) \left(\frac{V_{GS}}{V_p} - 1 \right)^2 - I_{GSS} \qquad (6)$$

Because virtually all of the FET's presently being marketed are made by some type of diffusion, this simple approximation can be a very powerful engineering tool for circuit design.

STATIC CHARACTERISTICS

Gate Cutoff Current. By connecting the drain to the source and reverse biasing the gate-channel diode, a measure of the direct-current input impedance and an indication of the quality of the diode can be obtained. A circuit for the measurement of this gate cutoff current I_{GSS} is shown in Fig. 9. The voltage used in this measurement is 10 volts, the gate being positive with respect to the channel for a P-channel device. If this voltage were increased in magnitude, a point would be reached at which the gate-channel diode would break down. Figure 10 shows the typical exponential variation of I_{GSS} with temperature. Static values of short-circuit input impedance are in the thousands of megohms near zero degrees centigrade.

Breakdown Voltages. For a better understanding of breakdown voltage terminology, consider the typical drain characteristics presented in Figs. 11, 12, and 13 for the 2N2497, 2N2498, and 2N2499 respectively. These are curves of drain current I_D as a function of drain-source voltage V_{DS} for the common-source configuration with gate-to-source voltage V_{GS} as a running parameter. It will be noted that the gate bias voltage is of opposite polarity to that of the drain supply voltage; hence, for ordinary bias conditions, a greater potential difference exists across the gate-drain diode than exists across the gate-source diode. This implies that gate-drain diode breakdown will occur before gate-source diode breakdown. By disconnecting the source from the drain in Fig. 9 and applying a current source of $-10\ \mu a$ to the drain, the drain-gate breakdown voltage BV_{DGO} can be determined under the conditions stated on the data sheet. The smallest voltage specified for the three types of units mentioned above is -20 volts.

Since the point at which the source is connected to the channel is physically removed from the drain connection, the source can be connected to the gate in the latter measurement without appreciably changing the value of the breakdown voltage. This connection yields BV_{DSS}, the breakdown voltage from drain to source with the gate shorted to the source. Typical values of BV_{DSS} for the three units are obvious from the break on the $V_{GS} = 0$ curves in Figs. 11, 12, and 13.

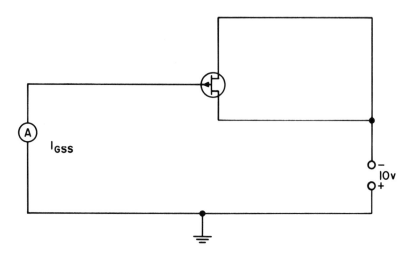

Fig. 9. Gate cutoff current test circuit.

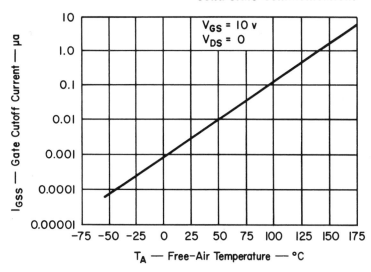

Fig. 10. Gate cutoff current vs. free-air temperature.

The break in the drain characteristic curves occurs at lower drain voltages as the gate voltage is increased; that is, the drain-gate breakdown voltage is almost constant and independent of drain-source current. Equation (7) states the relationship suggested above:

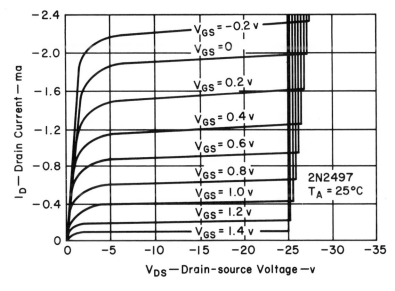

Fig. 11. Common-source drain characteristics.

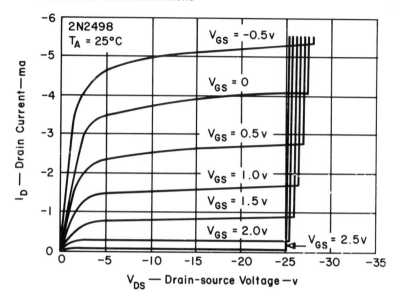

Fig. 12. Common-source drain characteristics.

$$BV_{DG} = BV_{DSX} + V_{GS} \cong a \text{ constant} \tag{7}$$

where the subscript X denotes the value of BV_{DS} for a particular value of V_{GS}. Substituting BV_{DGO} for the constant, Eq. (7) becomes

$$BV_{DSX} = BV_{DGO} - V_{GS} \tag{8}$$

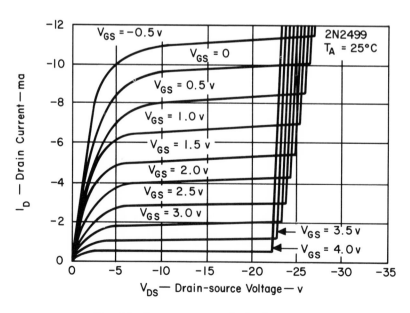

Fig. 13. Common-source drain characteristics.

Using the specified minimum BV_{DGO} and values of gate voltage, a curve can be plotted on the drain characteristic as suggested in Fig. 14. In the area to the right of this curve, breakdown is likely to occur. The useful area on the drain characteristic lies, therefore, between this curve and some characteristic curve resulting from a slight forward gate bias. Signals on the gate which cause the gate-source diode to go into forward conduction are clipped because of the sudden drop in input impedance, but the drain current is not severely affected. If the signal causes the drain-gate diode to break down, the signal is again clipped by conduction between the drain and the gate.

Saturation Drain Current $I_{D(on)}$. I_{DSS} is the IEEE standard symbol for the drain current at zero gate-to-source bias at any drain voltage (see the $V_{GS} = 0$ curve in Fig. 14). I_{DSS}, when measured at a specified drain voltage in the pinch-off or current saturation region, is called $I_{D(on)}$. If the output characteristics are relatively flat in the pinch-off region (i.e. the output impedance is very high), I_{DSS} can be approximated by $I_{D(on)}$.

The first page of the 2N2497 series data sheet is reproduced in Fig. 15 to aid this discussion. The test conditions given for $I_{D(on)}$ are $V_{DS} = 10$ and $V_{GS} = 0$. Notice that there is a 3-to-1 variation in $I_{D(on)}$ at 25 °C for a given type number. $I_{D(on)}$ is strongly temperature dependent; the temperature dependence for the 2N2497 series is shown in Fig. 16. The silicon channel has a positive temperature coefficient of resistance due to decreased carrier mobility as temperature rises, but the carrier concentration at the doping levels involved remains fairly constant with temperature.[4] The total charge removed from the depletion regions depends only on the transverse electric field. Therefore, as temperature rises, it takes less current to cause sufficient voltage drop in the channel to produce pinch-off.

Pinch-off Voltage V_p. The data sheet gives a parameter $I_{D(off)}$, called the "pinch-off current," which is a measure of how much gate bias is required to reduce the drain current below a specified value. For example, the data sheet guarantees that a 2N2497 with a reverse gate bias of 5 volts will have a drain current of not

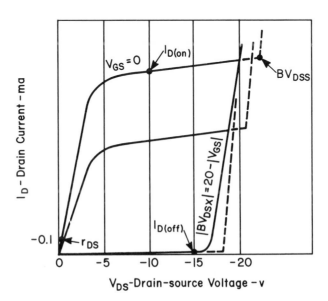

Figure 14

TYPES 2N2497, 2N2498, 2N2499, 2N2500
P-CHANNEL DIFFUSED PLANAR SILICON FIELD-EFFECT TRANSISTORS

TYPES 2N2497, 2N2498, 2N2499, 2N2500
BULLETIN NO. DL-S 633519, MAY 1963
REPLACES BULLETINS NO. DL-S 622727 AND DL-S 622749, JUNE 1962

FOR SMALL-SIGNAL, LOW-NOISE APPLICATIONS

- Guaranteed 10 cps Noise Figure (2N2500)
- High Input Impedance (>5 megohms at 1 kc)
- High Nuclear Radiation-Damage Resistance

*mechanical data

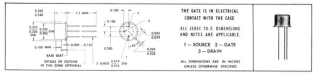

THE GATE IS IN ELECTRICAL
CONTACT WITH THE CASE

ALL JEDEC TO-5 DIMENSIONS
AND NOTES ARE APPLICABLE.

1 — SOURCE   2 — GATE
3 — DRAIN

ALL DIMENSIONS ARE IN INCHES
UNLESS OTHERWISE SPECIFIED

*absolute maximum ratings at 25°C free-air temperature (unless otherwise noted)

Gate Current . . . . 10 ma
Total Device Dissipation at (or below) 25°C Free-Air Temperature (See Note 1) . . . . . 0.5 w
Total Device Dissipation at (or below) 25°C Case Temperature (See Note 2) . . . . . . 1.5 w
Storage Temperature Range . . . . −195°C to +300°C

*electrical characteristics at 25°C free-air temperature (unless otherwise noted)

	PARAMETER	TEST CONDITIONS	2N2497 MIN	2N2497 MAX	2N2498 MIN	2N2498 MAX	2N2499 MIN	2N2499 MAX	2N2500 MIN	2N2500 MAX	UNIT
BV_{DGO}	Drain-Gate Breakdown Voltage (See Note 3)	$I_D = -10\ \mu a$, $I_S = 0$	−20		−20		−20		−20		v
I_{GSS}	Gate Cutoff Current	$V_{GS} = 10$ v, $V_{DS} = 0$		0.01		0.01		0.01		0.01	μa
I_{GSS}	Gate Cutoff Current	$V_{GS} = 10$ v, $V_{DS} = 0$ $T_A = 150°C$		10		10		10		10	μa
$I_{D(on)}$	Zero-Gate-Voltage Drain Current	$V_{DS} = -10$ v, $V_{GS} = 0$	−1	−3	−2	−6	−5	−15	−1	−6	ma
$I_{D(off)}$	Pinch-Off Drain Current	$V_{DS} = -15$ v, $V_{GS} —$ (See Note 4)		−10		−10		−10		−10	μa
r_{DS}	Static Drain-Source Resistance	$I_D = -100\ \mu a$, $V_{GS} = 0$		1000		800		600			ohm
$|y_{is}|$	Small-Signal Common-Source Input Admittance			0.2		0.2		0.2		0.2	μmho
$|y_{fs}|$	Small-Signal Common-Source Forward Transfer Admittance	$V_{DS} = -10$ v, $I_D —$ (See Note 5) $f = 1$ kc	1000	2000	1500	3000	2000	4000	1000	2200	μmho
$|y_{rs}|$	Small-Signal Common-Source Reverse Transfer Admittance			0.1		0.1		0.1		0.1	μmho
$|y_{os}|$	Small-Signal Common-Source Output Admittance			20		40		100		20	μmho
$|y_{fs}|$	Small-Signal Common-Source Forward Transfer Admittance	$V_{DS} = -10$ v, $I_D —$ (See Note 5) $f = 10$ mc	900		1350		1800		900		μmho
C_{iss}	Common-Source Short-Circuit Input Capacitance	$V_{GS} = 0$, $V_{DS} = -10$ v $f = 140$ kc		32		32		32		32	pf

*operating characteristics at 25°C free-air temperature

			2N2497	2N2498	2N2499	2N2500	
NF	Spot Noise Figure	$V_{DS} = -5$ v, $I_D = -1$ ma $f = 1$ kc, $R_G = 1$ MΩ	3	3	4	1	db
		$V_{DS} = -5$ v, $I_D = -1$ ma $f = 10$ cps, $R_G = 10$ MΩ				5	db

NOTES: 1. Derate linearly to 175°C free-air temperature at the rate of 3.3 mw/C°.
2. Derate linearly to 175°C case temperature at the rate of 10 mw/C°.
3. This parameter corresponds closely to BV_{DSS} (the Drain-Source Breakdown Voltage for $V_{GS} = 0$). BV_{DSX} (the Drain-Source Breakdown Voltage for other values of V_{GS}) may be calculated from: $|BV_{DSX}| \cong |BV_{DGO}| - |V_{GS}|$.

	2N2497	2N2498	2N2499	2N2500
NOTE 4: $V_{GS} =$	5 v	6 v	8 v	6 v
NOTE 5: $I_D =$	−1 ma	−2 ma	−5 ma	−1 ma

*Indicates JEDEC registered data.

TEXAS INSTRUMENTS
INCORPORATED
SEMICONDUCTOR-COMPONENTS DIVISION
POST OFFICE BOX 5012 • DALLAS 22, TEXAS

Figure 15

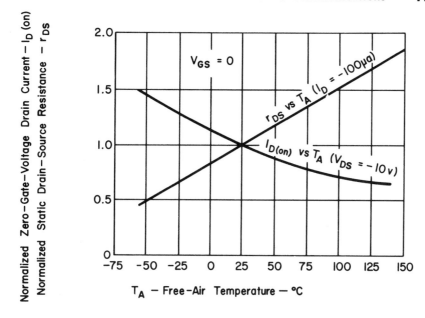

Fig. 16. Normalized zero-gain-voltage drain current and static drain-source resistance vs. free-air temperature.

more than 10 microamps. While the values of $I_{D(on)}$ and $I_{D(off)}$ give information about the transfer curves near its end points, they do not necessarily convey any useful information about the region between. And after all, this is the region in which the FET is usually operated. It is essential, then, to be able to describe the behavior of the field-effect, particularly its forward transfer characteristic, in the pinch-off region. To use a parabola for the transfer curve as described in the previous section, one must know the limits on extrapolated pinch-off voltage for each device number. Some TI data sheets do not specifically state extrapolated pinch-off voltages, but the necessary data for extracting this information are provided.

Consider the transfer curves in Fig. 17, which show parts of parabolas having as end points the maximum and minimum I_{DSS} given by the data sheet, and the maximum and minimum extrapolated pinch-off voltages, as yet undetermined. The curves are correct for P-channel devices at room temperature. The data sheet also guarantees maximum and minimum values of $|Y_{fs}|$, the small-signal forward transconductance (measured at 1 kc), which is simply dI_D/dV_{GS} when $\Delta V_{DS} = 0$. The test conditions given for $|Y_{fs}|$ show that the measurement is made at a drain current corresponding to the minimum I_{DSS} for each type, these points being intersected by the dotted line drawn from $I_{DSS(min)}$ in Fig. 17.

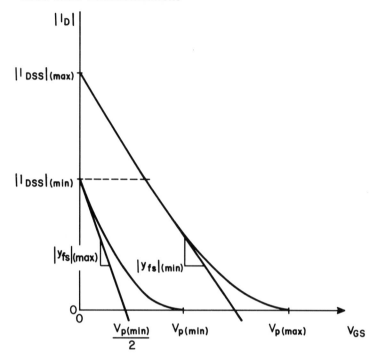

Figure 17

From Eq. (5):

$$\frac{dI_D}{dV_{GS}} = \frac{2I_{DSS}}{V_p}\left(\frac{V_{GS}}{V_p} - 1\right) = Y_{fs} \tag{9}$$

Evaluated at $I_D = I_{DSS}$:

$$\frac{dI_D}{dV_{GS}}\bigg|_{I_D = I_{DSS}} = -\frac{2I_{DSS}}{V_p} \tag{10}$$

Equation (10) implies that the tangent drawn to the transfer curve at $I_D = I_{DSS}$ intersects the $I_D = 0$ axis at $1/2\ V_p$; this is analogous to Eq. (3) for alloy field-effects. Equation (10) can be used to determine the minimum pinch-off voltage:

$$|V_{p(min)}| = \frac{2\,|\,I_{DSS}\,|_{(min)}}{|\,Y_{fs}\,|_{(max)}} \tag{11}$$

In Fig. 18, the maximum $|Y_{fs}|$ tangent to the left-hand characteristic curve at $I_D = I_{DSS(min)}$ is shown intersecting the abscissa at $V_{GS} = 1/2\ V_{p(min)}$. To determine $V_{p(max)}$, Eq. (9) must be evaluated for the right-hand curve at $I_D = I_{DSS(min)}$. To do this, V_{GS} at this current must be found from Eq. (5):

$$V_{GS}\bigg|_{I_D = |\,I_{DSS}\,|_{(min)}} = V_{p(max)}\left(1 - \sqrt{\frac{I_{DSS(min)}}{I_{DSS(max)}}}\right) \tag{12}$$

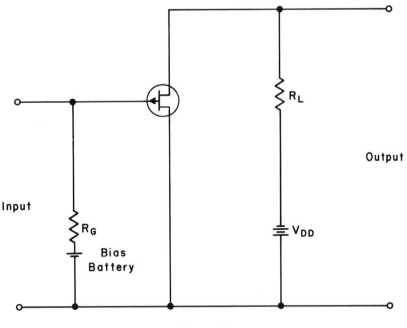

Figure 18

Substituting into Eq. (9) and solving for $\left| V_{p(max)} \right|$:

$$\left| V_p \right|_{(max)} = \frac{2 \left| I_{DSS} \right|_{(max)}}{\left| Y_{fs} \right|_{(min)}} \sqrt{\frac{I_{DSS(min)}}{I_{DSS(max)}}} \qquad (13)$$

When these pinch-off voltages are to be evaluated from the data sheet parameters at data sheet test conditions, $I_{D(on)}$ is substituted everywhere for I_{DSS} in Eqs. (11) and (13).

BIASING FOR STABLE A-C OPERATION

The simplest method of biasing a device is to employ a fixed bias, which consists of determining from the d-c characteristics of the device what value of bias voltage or current is required to establish the desired operating conditions. This type of bias is shown in Fig. 18. Fixed bias is only useful if the temperature is going to be held nearly constant (room temperature) and if some provision is made for readjustment when the original device is replaced.

A type of bias that offers some relief from the restrictions imposed by the fixed-bias method is the self-bias method, shown in Fig. 19. With this type of biasing, the bias voltage is the drop in a resistor placed in series with the source. The drop is produced by the device's own operating current, hence the term self-bias. Since self-bias is a form of negative feedback, the operating conditions are stabilized by the device's own gain and reasonable stability is achieved for a three-to-one $I_{D(on)}$ variation if the drain current I_D is selected about half the minimum $I_{D(on)}$. Stability is usually good enough for the average small-signal stage if the temperature variation is restricted to $\pm 20^\circ$C, about room temperature.

But when large-temperature-range operation, or large-signal operation, or small-signal operation from a high-voltage supply, or any combination thereof is required,

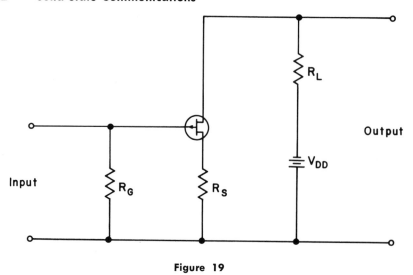

Figure 19

greater stability can be obtained from the circuit in Fig. 20. This increased stability is achieved without loss in device dynamic operating range by forward-biasing the gate and compensating by adding more source resistance, thus increasing the negative feedback. The fixed forward bias is achieved economically with the resistive divider R_1 and R_2.

By using a parabola to approximate the forward transfer characteristic of the FET, a graphical design procedure can be worked out that ensures stable operation of the circuit in Fig. 20 under "worst case" conditions arising from either environmental changes or device substitution.

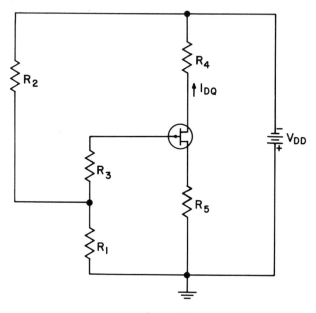

Figure 20

To determine the quiescent drain current I_{DQ} in an amplifier circuit like that in Fig. 20 it is only necessary to sum the voltage around the loop containing the gate and source terminals of the FET; the equation thus obtained will yield the operating point when it is plotted on a graph of the forward transfer characteristic. The circuit of Fig. 20 can be reduced to an equivalent circuit as in Fig. 21 by making the following substitutions:

$$R_D = R_4$$

$$R_S = R_5$$

$$R_G = R_3 + \frac{R_1 R_2}{R_1 + R_2}$$

$$V_A = V_{DD} \frac{R_1}{R_1 + R_2}$$

Writing Kirchoff's law around the gate-source loop and solving for I_D,

$$I_D = \frac{V_A + I_{GSS}(R_G + R_S) + V_{GS}}{R_S} \qquad (14)$$

Figure 22 shows Eq. (14) plotted onto a typical transfer curve to locate I_{DQ}. If all devices were identical and their parameters independent of temperature, Eq. (14) would contain all the information necessary for bias design, and that would be that. But rather wide variation in parameters must be taken into account, especially where circuits are to be mass produced. Of course, this problem is not unique to FET's; it arises with all active electronic devices.

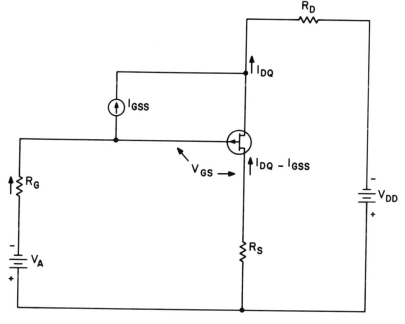

Figure 21

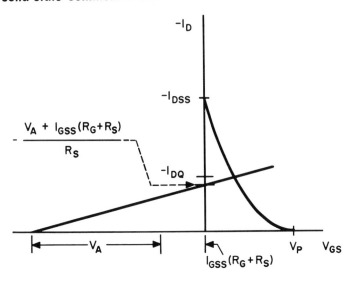

Figure 22

The effect of parameter variations on the operating point is shown by Fig. 23. These two transfer curves have the worst-case maximum and minimum values of I_{DSS} and V_p as their end points. The temperature variation of I_{DSS} must be taken into account, so that the worst-case maximum I_{DSS} would occur at the lowest ambient temperature (see Fig. 16), while the worst-case minimum occurs at the highest channel temperature. The overlines and underlines on the quantities in Fig. 23 indicate the worst-case maximum and minimum values, respectively.

From Fig. 23 and Eq. (14), the maximum I_{DQ} is:

$$|\bar{I}_{DQ}| \leq \frac{V_A + I_{GSS}(R_G + R_S) + V_{GS}}{\underline{R}_S} \tag{15}$$

The conservative minimum I_{GSS} is, of course, zero, so that the minimum value of I_{DQ} is:

$$\underline{I}_{DQ} \geq \frac{V_A + \underline{V}_{GS}}{\bar{R}_S} \tag{16}$$

The resistor tolerances and the tolerance on V_A can be written into the equations with the following substitutions:

$$\bar{R}_S = R_S(1 + m)$$

$$\underline{R}_S = R_S(1 - n)$$

$$\bar{V}_A = V_A(1 + p)$$

$$\underline{V}_A = V_A(1 - q)$$

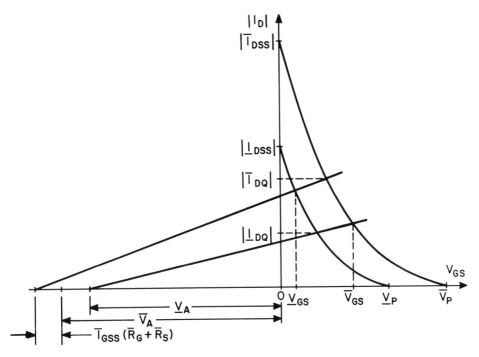

Figure 23

Combining Eq. (15) and (16) and solving for V_A:

$$V_A \geq \frac{\overline{I}_{GSS}(R_G + R_S)(1 + m)^2 + \overline{V}_{GS}(1 + m) - \underline{V}_{GS}K(1-n)}{(1-q)(1-n)K - (1+p)(1+m)} \qquad (17)$$

where:
$$K = \frac{\overline{I}_{DQ}}{\underline{I}_{DQ}}$$

For Eq. (17) to have any solution at all,

$$K > \frac{(1+p)(1+m)}{(1-q)(1-n)} \qquad (18)$$

This is the minimum variation to which the quiescent drain current can possibly be held with these resistor tolerances and power supply variations. How severe a limitation this is can be seen by evaluating p and q from the resistive divider (R_1 and R_2) in Fig. 20.

For $R_1 \ll R_2$

$$V_A(1 + p) = V_{DD}(1 + r)\frac{R_1(1 + m)}{(R_1 + R_2)(1-n)} \qquad (19)$$

$$V_A(1 - q) = V_{DD}(1-r)\frac{R_1(1-n)}{(R_1 + R_2)(1 + m)} \qquad (20)$$

where r is the plus and minus power supply tolerance; e.g., for $V_{DD} = 28 \pm 10\%$, $r = 0.1$. Dividing Eq. (19) by Eq. (20):

$$\frac{1+p}{1-q} = \frac{1+r}{1-r}\left(\frac{1+m}{1-n}\right)^2 \tag{21}$$

And finally, substituting Eq. (21) back into Eq. (18),

$$K > \frac{1+r}{1-r}\left(\frac{1+m}{1-n}\right)^3 \tag{22}$$

This is a rather startling result. Of course, the possibility of all worst-case conditions occurring simultaneously is rather remote, but it is easy to see how the use of 10 per cent composition resistors can lead to trouble. The best (but not the most economical) solution is to use precision resistors with equal temperature coefficients, at least for R_1 and R_2.

Equation (17) demonstrated in no uncertain manner the need for the gate bias voltage, V_A. Without this external forward bias, one might as well use a potentiometer for R_S and encase the whole circuit in an oven.

The biasing problems implied by Eqs. (17) and (22) are not peculiar to field-effect transistors, but also occur with equal severity in junction transistors and to a lesser extent in vacuum tubes. Competent circuit design using any of these devices requires about the same amount of care and effort.

Equation (17) yields the value of V_A necessary to maintain the quiescent drain current within specified limits in terms of transistor parameters and resistance and supply tolerances. These limits are usually dictated by the nature of the application (or sometimes by a specification writer's whim); whether the limits are realistic or not can be checked quickly with Eq. (18). The minimum quiescent drain current can be determined if the minimum allowable output peak signal swing ($V_{pk(min)}$) is known:

$$\underline{I}_{DQ} \geq \frac{V_{pk(min)}}{R'_L} \tag{23}$$

where

$$R'_L = \frac{R_D R_L}{R_D + R_L}$$

R_L is the equivalent output load resistor and R_D is the drain load resistor in Fig. 20.

The maximum drain current I_{DQ} must not cause the FET to operate in the triode region; that is,

$$\underline{V}_{DQ} = \underline{V}_{DD} - \overline{I}_{DQ}(\overline{R}_D + \overline{R}_S) \text{ must not be less than } \overline{V}_p - V_{GS} + V_{pk(min)} \tag{24}$$

On a plot of V_{DS} vs I_D characteristics, a drain-to-source voltage equal to $V_p - V_{GS}$ marks the boundary between the triode and the pinch-off region at every drain current. A conservative minimum value of V_{GS} in Eq. (24) is zero; its value at $I_D = I_{DSS}$.

Another consideration in biasing an FET is that the maximum drain-to-gate voltage must not exceed BV_{DGO}, the drain-to-gate breakdown voltage. This condition can be expressed using Fig. 21 and noting that the drain-to-gate voltage is the sum of the drain-to-source and source-to-gate voltages:

$$\overline{V}_{DD} - \underline{I}_{DQ}(R_D + R_S)(1-n) + V_{pk(min)} - \overline{V}_{GS} \leq BV_{DGO} \qquad (25)$$

A more useful form of this equation results from solving for $(R_D + R_S)$:

$$R_D + R_S \geq \frac{\overline{V}_{DD} - BV_{DGO} + V_{pk(min)} - \overline{V}_{GS}}{\underline{I}_{DQ}(1-n)} \qquad (26)$$

Let us illustrate the use of this information by biasing an FET amplifier stage. An arbitrary set of conditions and requirements will be set down. These in turn will dictate the order of steps in the design procedure; the order will not necessarily remain the same under different conditions and requirements.

BIAS DESIGN EXAMPLE

1. *Conditions and requirements:*
   Supply voltage: 28 vdc $\pm 5\%$
   A-C load resistance: 10 kilohms
   Operating temperature range: -55 to $+100°C$
   Minimum output signal: 1 volt rms
2. *Determination of* $\underline{I}_{DQ}$:

A drain load resistor can often be chosen arbitrarily, especially if (as here) no output resistance requirement is made of the amplifier. It is common practice in transistor circuitry to use a value twice the a-c load, or 20 kilohms. The equivalent a-c load resistor R_L is 6.7 ohms.
   Then from Eq. (23):

$$\underline{I}_{DQ} \geq \frac{1.41 \text{ v}}{6.67 \text{ K}\Omega} = 0.21 \text{ ma}$$

To prevent the FET from operating near cut-off, and hence in a high-distortion region when I_{DQ} approaches $\underline{I}_{DQ}$, about 50% will be added to this value. That is, $I_{DQ} = 0.3$ ma.

3. *Device selection:*
   Device selection at this point is mostly an educated guess, but it must be done now to keep the procedure relatively simple. The procedure is then continued on a trial basis; if the design does not prove to be practical, another device must be selected and the procedure must be repeated, beginning with this step. The value of I_{DQ} solved for in the previous step provides some basis for device selection. It seems reasonable to expect at this point that the quiescent drain current should not have to exceed the minimum value of $I_{D(on)}$ given for the 2N2497, which we will select.

4. *Resistor selection:*
   Equation (22) indicates that the use of precision resistors is in order in a "worst case" design. The temperature coefficient of resistance of TI deposited carbon resistors depends on the resistance, but for values up to 150 kilohms in the CD 1/2 MR type, a conservative value of $-0.03\%/C°$ can be used; for values from 150 kilohms to 2 megohms, $-0.04\%/C°$ is a good approximation.
   R between 0 and 150 k:

$$1 + m = 1.025$$
$$1 - n = 0.975$$

R between 150 kilohms and 2 megohms:

$$1 + m = 1.03$$
$$1 - n = 0.97$$

Assuming that both resistors to be used in the voltage divider for V_A will be less than 150 kilohms:

$$1 + p = 1.12$$
$$1 - q = 0.88$$

5. *Determination of* R_S*:*

Having made the device and resistor selections, the next step is to find the lower limit on R_S imposed by Eq. (26). BV_{DGO} is given directly by the data sheet, while V_{GS} will be assumed to be zero.

$$R_S \geq \frac{29.4 - 20 + 1.41}{0.3\,(0.975)} - 20 \text{ kilohms} = 17 \text{ kilohms}$$

$$R_S = 18 \text{ kilohms will be used.}$$

6. *Determination of* $\bar{I}_{DQ}$*:*

Solving Eq. (24) for $\bar{I}_{DG}$:

$$I_{DQ} < \frac{V_{DD} - \overline{V}_p - V_{pk(min)}}{(R_D + R_S)(1 + m)}$$

$\overline{V}_p$ can be evaluated using Eq. (13) and information supplied by the data sheet. For the 2N2497, $\overline{V}_p = 3.46$ volts.

$$\bar{I}_{DQ} \leq 0.55 \text{ ma}$$

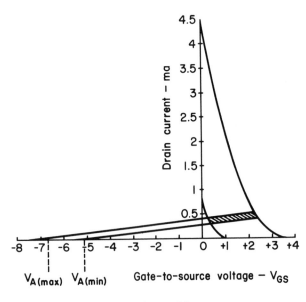

Figure 24

7. V_A *and* R_G:

In Fig. 24 two transfer curves obtained using the parabola approximation are plotted. The end points of the lower curve are V_p from Eq. (11) and $I_{D(on)}$. $I_{D(on)}$ for the 2N2497 at $V_{DS} = 10$ volts and 25°C is 1 ma; at 100°C it drops to 0.75 ma (see Fig. 18). The end points of the upper curve are $\bar{I}_{D(on)}$ and $\bar{V}_p$ $I_{D(on)}$ at -55°C is 4.5 ma. Equations (15) and (16) are plotted on these transfer curves as load lines. The slope of the upper load line is $\dfrac{1}{R_S(1+m)}$. The shaded area includes all possible operating points for any device type 2N2497 operating in this circuit within these ambient temperature extremes.

The intersection of the lower load line with the zero drain current axis yields the lower limit on V_A:

$$V_A \geq \frac{5.2 \text{ v}}{1-q} = 5.9 \text{ v}$$

The upper load line intersects the $I_D = 0$ axis at the upper limit of V_A plus the maximum allowable voltage drop across R_G and R_S due to $\bar{I}_{GSS}$:

$$V_A(1+p) + \bar{I}_{GSS}(R_G + R_S)(1+m) \leq 7.3 \text{ v}$$

I_{GSS} at 100°C is 0.75 μamps. Solving for R_G:

$$R_G \leq 887 \text{ kilohms}$$

The resistance values of the completed circuit (Fig. 20) are:

$R_1 - 6.49$ k, CD 1/2 MR	$R_3 - 820$ k, CD 1/2 MR
$R_2 - 24$ k, CD 1/2 MR	$R_4 - 20$ k, CD 1/2 MR
	$R_S - 18$ k, CD 1/2 MR

All or part of R_5 may be bypassed with a capacitor to obtain the desired gain and low-frequency cut-off.

The value of R_G is disappointingly low; however, this is to be expected when operating temperatures much higher than room ambient are encountered. For example, if the upper operating temperature limit had been 50°C, I_{GSS} (see Figs. 19 and 24) would have been 0.05 microamps and $R_G = 13$ megohms would have worked in the circuit.

MATCHING FOR STABLE D-C OPERATION

Since FET parameters are temperature sensitive, the best way to compensate for this effect is to use them as matched pairs in the differential amplifier connection, Fig. 25.

A simple analysis of the circuit on the basis of equivalent input drift will indicate which parameters should be matched. The total equivalent input voltage drift is

$$\frac{\Delta \text{Vin}}{\Delta T} = \frac{\Delta(V_{GS1} - V_{GS2})}{\Delta T} + \frac{\Delta(I_{G1} - I_{G2})}{\Delta T}(R_G + R_S) \qquad (27)$$

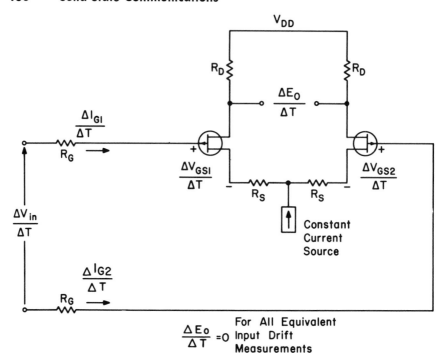

Figure 25

where $\dfrac{\Delta(V_{GS1}-V_{GS2})}{\Delta T}$ is the equivalent input voltage drift of the FET pair and

$\dfrac{\Delta(I_{G1}-I_{G2})}{\Delta T}$ is the equivalent input current drift of both the circuit and

the FET pair.

Thus, the equivalent input drift of the circuit will be reduced if the FET's are

matched so that $\dfrac{\Delta(V_{GS1}-V_{GS2})}{\Delta T}$ and $\dfrac{\Delta(I_{G1}-I_{G2})}{\Delta T}$ are made small.

This poses the question: Which measurements or combinations of measurements will be most effective in selecting matched pairs? For the equivalent input current matching the answer is very simple since gate current is saturation current and is greatest at high temperatures. Thus, if FET's with small differences in gate current

at the highest temperature needed are paired, $\dfrac{\Delta(I_{G1}-I_{G2})}{\Delta T}$ will be minimized.

Examples of gate current vs temperature are shown in Fig. 26.

Matching of the individual equivalent input voltage drifts $\dfrac{\Delta V_{GS}}{\Delta T}$ may be

accomplished for one drain current by holding the drain current constant, varying the temperature, and recording the change in V_{GS} for each unit.

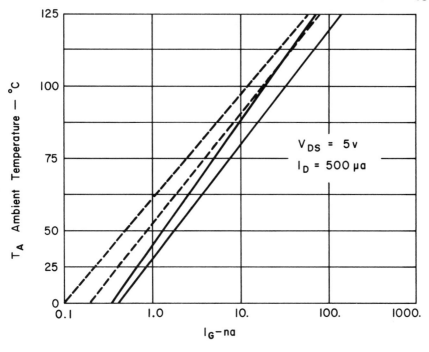

Figure 26

This method would guarantee the paired FET's to be matched at only one set of operating conditions, i.e., V_{DS} and I_D. Also, all transistors would have to be checked vs temperature; and after pairing, they would have to be checked again to accurately determine their tracking because of the inherent reading uncertainties in the individual measurements.

In view of the difficulties and shortcomings of this matching procedure, a simpler and more perfect method was sought. This better method for matching was determined from a combination of FET theory and practical measurements by the following line of reasoning: Measurement of the equivalent input voltage drift is the measurement of the change of the d-c forward transfer characteristics with temperature and referring it to the input. This then suggests that if the d-c forward transfer characteristics of a pair of FET's can be matched, the chances are good that the temperature characteristics will be matched. To do this, more must be known about the characteristics of the forward transfer curve, i.e., I_D vs V_{GS}. This additional information is of course supplied by parabolic approximation to the static transfer characteristic introduced earlier. Thus, a hypothesis can be set forth, that if $I_{D(on)}$ matches and V_{GS} at 0.1 $I_{D(on)}$ also matches, the FET will in general match and track over a range of drain currents and temperatures.*

This scheme was used to select matched pairs from a group of FET's. The differential V_{GS} vs temperature data at drain currents of 0.5 ma, 1.0 ma, and 2 ma for five pairs were taken over a $-50°C$ temperature range and are summarized in Fig. 27. One match turned out badly, but it appears possible to match to 75 mv V_{GS} difference and obtain V_{GS} tracking of less than 300 $\mu v/°C$.

---

*Proof of this statement is supplied in the next chapter, "The Behavior of Field-effect Transistor Characteristics with Temperature."

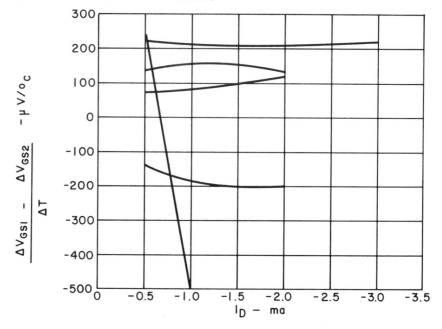

Fig. 27. Differential gate voltage tracking vs. drain current.

NOISE CHARACTERISTICS

Field-effect transistors exhibit excellent low-noise characteristics. According to Van der Ziel[5] their equivalent noise resistance is "about a factor of four better than the shot-noise resistance of a vacuum tube with comparable transconductance."

Van der Ziel lists two main sources of noise: the thermal noise of the conducting channel and the shot noise caused by the gate leakage current I_{GSS}. Figure 28 gives his noise equivalent circuit. The two voltage generators, e_s and e_d, represent the thermal noise generated in the bulk resistances, r_s and r_d, between the terminals and the active channel.

The $1/f$ noise break frequency is less than 100 cps, about half an order of magnitude lower than that of most transistors. Figure 29 is a graph of spot noise figure vs frequency for the 2N2497. The one-megohm generator resistance is not optimum at all frequencies. At lower frequencies the optimum generator resistance is higher; e.g., see Fig. 30. Figure 31 shows that, contrary to operation with junction transistors, noise figure is independent of operating current over a very wide range, and the change with drain-to-source voltage is slight.

APPLICATIONS

Since the outstanding low-level characteristics of field effects are high input impedance and low noise, they are naturally most useful at the input of a semiconductor circuit. Also, once the impedance level is reduced to that of conventional transistors, there is no reason to use FET's unless a high-impedance point recurs in the circuit. Further, it is interesting to note that the combination of field effects

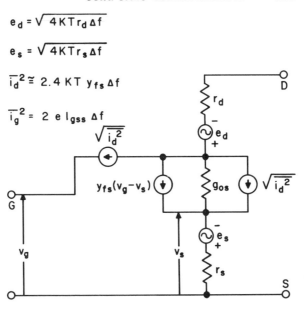

$$e_d = \sqrt{4KTr_d \Delta f}$$

$$e_s = \sqrt{4KTr_s \Delta f}$$

$$\overline{i_d^2} \cong 2.4 \, KT \, y_{fs} \Delta f$$

$$\overline{i_g^2} = 2 \, e \, I_{gss} \, \Delta f$$

Figure 28

and conventional transistors produces more power gain than either type alone, because FET's have almost infinite current gain and transistors have very large forward transfer admittance (g_m), e.g., 0.1 mho. Accordingly, all the following applications are based upon circuit combinations with conventional transistors.

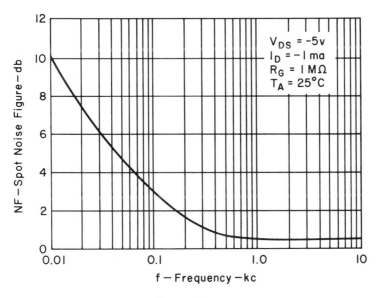

$$V_{DS} = -5v$$
$$I_D = -1 \, ma$$
$$R_G = 1 \, M\Omega$$
$$T_A = 25°C$$

NF – Spot Noise Figure – db

f – Frequency – kc

Figure 29

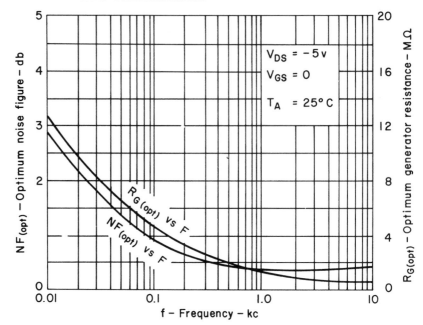

Figure 30

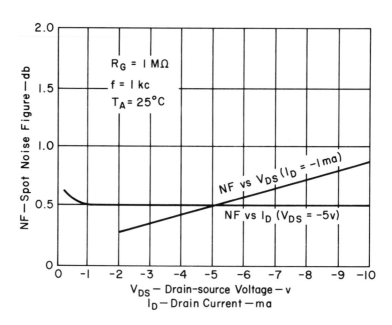

Figure 31

COMBINING CONVENTIONAL TRANSISTORS

The simple compound connection using a P-channel FET combined with a PNP transistor in Fig. 32a is equivalent to the Darlington connection. This circuit is simple and straightforward and nothing more need be said of it. The use of the circuit in Fig. 32b is somewhat obscure and requires explanation. As it stands, the source is connected to the collector so that signals applied to the gate will appear at the collector without phase inversion and near unity gain, depending upon the μ of the field effect. Thus, the connection is a simple feedback amplifier. Use has been made of this feedback in a 6-db low-noise transducer amplifier (Fig. 33) for use with very high-input-impedance low-frequency transducers. The input impedance and spot noise figure at 0.01, 0.1, 1.0, and 10 kc are shown in the accompanying table. The broad-band noise figures from 10 cycles to 10 kc with a 200-kilohm generator resistance is 1.7 db.

A simple electronic d-c millivoltmeter, Fig. 34, shows application of this compound circuit to a high-impedance low-drift d-c amplifier. The differential amplifier is made up of a pair of the simple feedback amplifiers with an approximate voltage gain of three. The field effect's operating conditions are 10 volts V_{DS} and 1 ma I_D. These conditions were selected to give a forward transconductance of 1000 to 1500 micromhos and an output impedance greater than 50 kilohms. A PNP transistor constant-current source is used to improve operating-condition stability for FET's with $I_{D(on)}$'s ranging from 1 ma to 6 ma, and to improve the common-mode rejection ratio. The circuit, when used as a d-c millivoltmeter, has an input sensitivity of 20 megohms per volt with a common-mode rejection ratio of 1000 to 1. When matched FET's are selected by the method previously discussed,

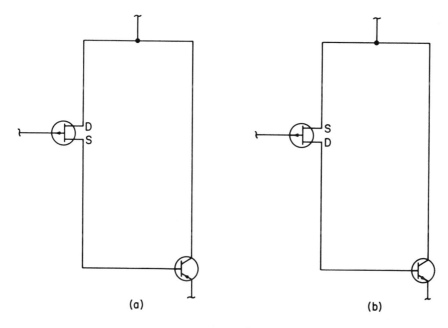

(a)   (b)

Fig. 32. Compound connection.

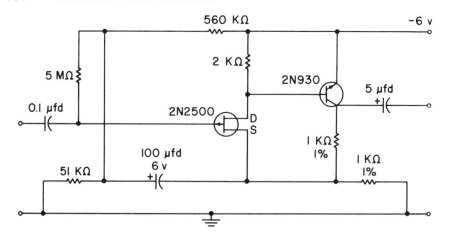

Freq. (kc)	Zin (MΩ)
0.01	180
0.1	180
1.0	27
5.0	14
10.0	3

Freq. (kc)	R_g (MΩ)	Spot Noise Figure (db)
0.01	20.0	7.0
0.1	2.0	3.0
1.0	0.2	1.5
10.0	00.02	1.2

Figure 33

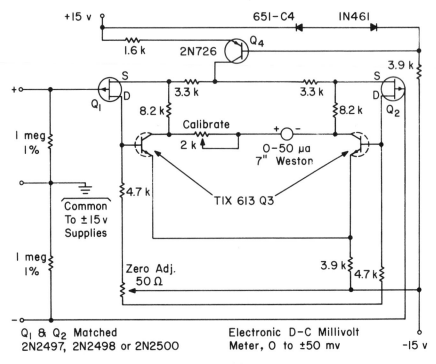

Q_1 & Q_2 Matched
2N2497, 2N2498 or 2N2500

Electronic D-C Millivolt
Meter, 0 to ±50 mv

Figure 34

reasonably good temperature characteristics can be expected even from 20-megohm gate resistors if the gate current is well matched and below 0.5 na at room temperature.

A combination of an FET and a conventional transistor to give the highest possible input impedance is the bootstrapped source follower, Fig. 35. The drain as well as the gate divider are bootstrapped in phase with the source. The primary purpose is to reduce the FET's input capacitance to a minimum so that the real part of the input impedance is all that is seen at high frequencies. Application of this combination is shown in a unity-gain high-input-impedance wideband preamplifier, Fig. 36. In this circuit, the single transistor of the preceding figure is replaced by a two-stage feedback amplifier, and the source bias resistor is replaced by a common-base current source. The typical low-frequency input impedance is approximately 100 megohms. Frequency response for various values of generator resistance is shown in Fig. 37.

A second application of the bootstrapped source follower is shown in a unity-gain temperature-stable d-c amplifier, shown in Fig. 38. Here, two of the circuits of Fig. 35 are combined to form a differential input stage where one gate serves as the feedback input and the other as the signal input. Note that driven shields are placed around the signal input FET and resistors to further reduce input capacitance. A current source is used to bias the FET's so that the circuit can accommodate a 2- to 6-ma $I_{D(on)}$ range. For good temperature stability, Q_1 and Q_2 are matched. The gain accuracy is maintained at better than 2 per cent within the band pass. The input impedance at very low frequencies is limited to 42 megohms

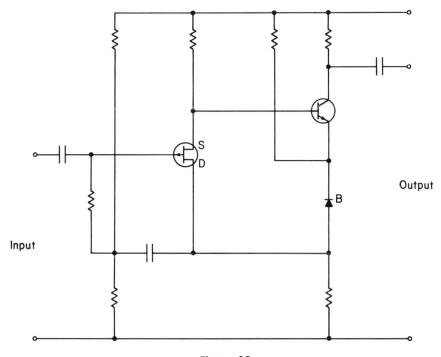

Figure 35

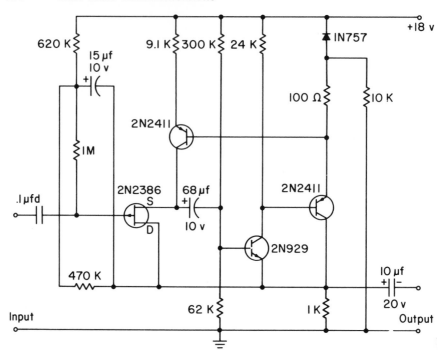

Figure 36

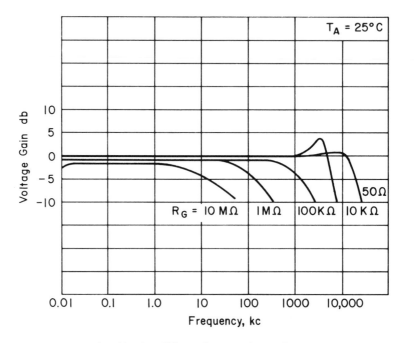

Fig. 37. Amplifier voltage gain vs. frequency.

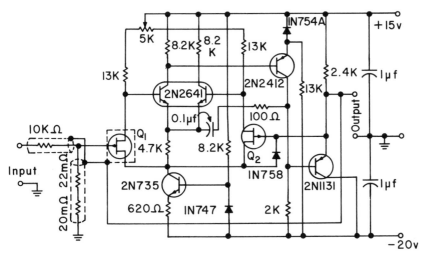

Notes: (1) Input shields are the outer conductors of RG–114/u.

   (2) Q_1 and Q_2 are Field Effect Transistors matched for $I_{D(on)}$ between 2 and 6 ma, $V_{PO} < 6v$, and $I_{GSS} < 10na$: all with 10%.

Figure 38

by the two resistors connecting the gate of the input field-effect transistor to ground. These resistors can be removed if the generator impedance provides a d-c return to ground. The input impedance will then be greater than a thousand megohms at several cycles per second.

Figure 39 contains response curves for generator resistance of 51 ohms, 33 kilohms, 100 kilohms, and 1 megohm.

Reasonably high input impedance is obtained by the direct-coupled cascode circuit, Fig. 40, but its outstanding characteristic is that the combination can be used as a single stage, having low reverse transfer and high output impedance. The low reverse transfer gives rise to a high input impedance, and its high output impedance makes possible a very large voltage gain.

An application that shows both these characteristics is the simple unity-gain high input impedance d-c amplifier, Fig. 41. Feedback is accomplished by connecting the source to the output so that for the condition of zero output for zero input voltage, the FET must operate at $I_{D(on)}$ where the output impedance of the FET alone is lowest and hence the μ is low. Feedback theory requires that the μ of the input stage be large to give this type of amplifier good gain accuracy. Thus, by using this cascode stage to replace the FET, this difficulty is corrected. At the same time, reverse transfer between drain and gate is minimized so that the input capacitance is not increased by the Miller effect; this makes possible high input impedance at high frequency. Figure 42 shows the upper cut-off frequencies for various generator resistances.

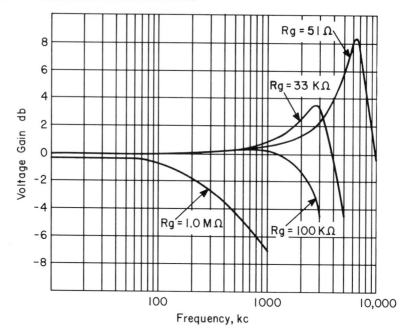

Figure 39

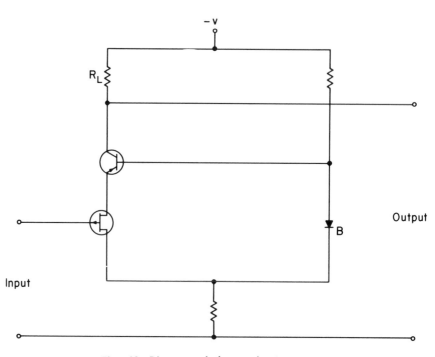

Fig. 40. Direct-coupled cascode circuit.

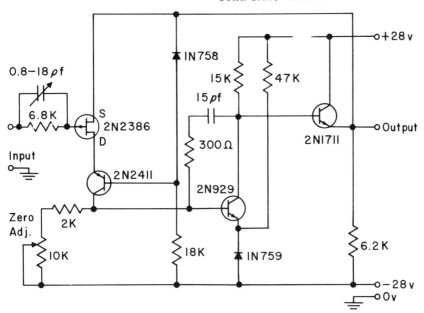

Figure 41

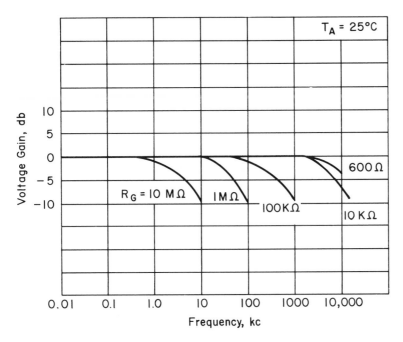

Fig. 42. Amplifier voltage gain vs. frequency.

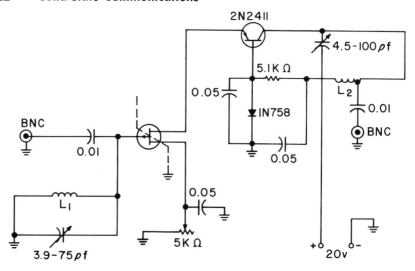

L_1, L_2 18 turns B&W 3004 Minductor; L_2 tapped 1 3/4 turns from ground.

Figure 43

The low reverse transfer of the cascode connection makes possible stable operation of a common-source FET at 10 mc in a tuned amplifier without neutralization. The tuned amplifier in Fig. 43 has measured transducer gains of 20.6 db and 25.3 db for the 2N2497 and 2N2499 respectively. The gain measurements were made for a generator resistance of 3.3 kilohms because it is very near optimum for low-noise performance as shown in Fig. 44. Note that the optimum noise figure at 10 mc is 3 db; at present, this is too large to consider FET's as low-noise devices

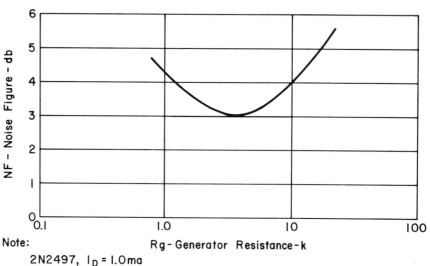

Note:

2N2497, $I_D = 1.0$ ma

2N2499, $I_D = 4.0$ ma

Fig. 44. Silicon P-channel field-effect transistors compound connection.

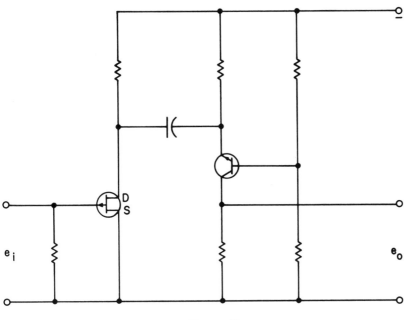

Figure 45

at radio frequencies.

The a-c coupled cascode connection, Fig. 45, has similar advantages and is uniquely suited to increasing the bandwidth of a low-noise amplifier by reducing Miller effect and permitting independent adjustment of the devices' operating conditions for optimum noise performance. In the 40-db low-noise high-input-impedance amplifier, Fig. 46, a 2N2498 is operated at 1-ma drain current while

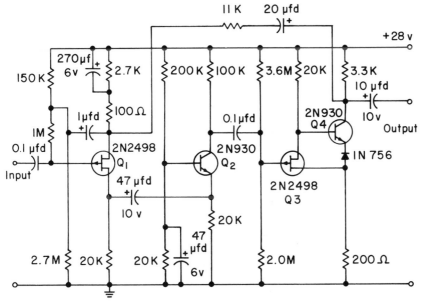

Figure 46

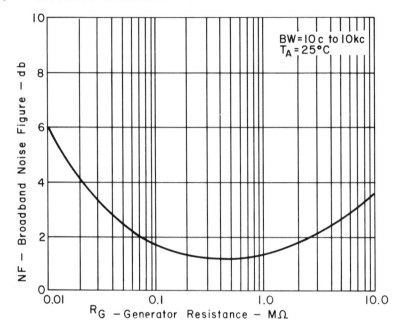

Fig. 47. Amplifier broadband noise figure vs. generator resistance.

a 2N930 is operated at 100-μa collector current. Both operating currents are optimum for the respective devices. Since the optimum generator for common-base operation is the same as for common-emitter operation, the 20-kilohm drain resistor in parallel with the 20-kilohm emitter resistor provides the 10-kilohm

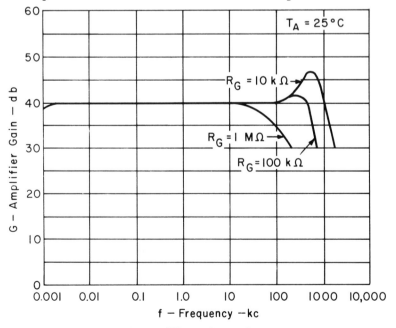

Fig. 48. Amplifier gain vs. frequency

optimum generator for the 2N390. The broadband noise figure vs generator resistance, Fig. 47, shows that the noise figure is less than 3 db over a generator resistance range of 50 kilohms to 5 megohms. The amplifier's response for generator resistances from 10 kilohms to 1 megohm is shown in Fig. 48.

BIBLIOGRAPHY

1. Shockley: "A Unipolar Field-Effect Transistor," Proc. IRE, Vol. 40, pp. 1365–1376, Nov. 1952.
2. Ryder, E. J., and W. Shockley: "Mobilities of Electrons in High Electric Fields," Physical Revue, Vol. 81, No. 1, Jan. 1, 1951.
3. Dacey, G. C., and I. M. Ross: "The Field-Effect Transistor," B.S.T.J., Vol. 34, Nov. 1955.
4. Shockley: Electrons and Holes in Semiconductors, D. Van Nostrand Co., Inc., Princeton, N. J., 1950, pp. 18–19.
5. Van Der Ziel, A.: "Thermal Noise in Field-Effect Transistors," Proc. IRE, Vol., pp. 1808–1812, August 1962.

8

Dependence of Field-effect Transistor Characteristics on Temperature

by L. J. Sevin

INTRODUCTION

The wide variation of the drain characteristics of field-effect transistors with temperature has been a serious problem in some applications, notably in d-c amplifiers. Some manufacturers' data sheets show graphs of the various FET electrical characteristics versus temperature, particularly those of the gate leakage currents I_{GSS} (not applicable to induced-channel FET's), the zero-bias drain current I_{DSS} (again not applicable to the I/C FET), the transconductance y_{fs} (or g_m), and the triode-region zero-bias channel resistance $r_{D(ON)}$. The temperature dependence of I_{GSS} is quite well understood, being the thermal saturation current of a reverse-biased P-N junction. The same can be said for g_m (with minor reservations to be explained later) and $r_{D(ON)}$: conductance varies directly and resistance inversely, with carrier mobility.

The temperature variation of I_{DSS} is another matter. Individual FET's may deviate alarmingly from the published typical behavior. For example, the TI 2N2497 data sheet shows that I_{DSS} has a negative temperature coefficient about equal to that expected of the mobility of P-type silicon (the 2N2497 is a P-channel transistor), but individual units have been found that exhibit positive temperature coefficients of I_{DSS}. Some FET's have even been found whose I_{DSS} is independent of temperature! Such loss of predictability tends to have a demoralizing influence on already harassed circuit designers.

The apparent conflict is resolved when the effect of temperatures on the barrier contact potential is taken into account. Then predictability returns, and order is restored.

THE SQUARE-LAW BEHAVIOR OF FET'S

Integrated-circuit FET's and certain P-N junction FET's exhibit very nearly a "square-law" dependence of the transfer characteristic[1,2]; the relationship describing P-N FET's is:

$$I_D = I_{DSS} \left(\frac{V_{GS}}{V_p} - 1 \right)^2 \tag{1}$$

where, by implication, V_p is the V_{GS} necessary to reduce the drain current to zero, I_D and V_{GS} are defined in Fig. 1. The effects of gate leakage current are not included in Eq. (1) and will not be considered in this discussion. V_p is related to the junction contact potential ϕ by:

$$V_p = V_{pi} - \phi \tag{2}$$

where V_{pi} is the internal voltage necessary to deplete the channel. This term is temperature independent, at least in the temperature range under consideration (250 to 400°K), since the strong electric field in the depletion region will ensure that all the donor atoms (in the P-channel) are ionized, eliminating any carrier "freeze out" as temperature lowers. The temperature dependence of V_p is determined by ϕ alone:

$$\frac{dV_p}{dT} = \frac{-d\phi}{dT} \tag{3}$$

According to Shockley[3], I_{DSS} is proportional to the square of the channel charge density and the first power of mobility, while V_p and V_{pi} are proportional to the first power of channel charge density:

$$I_{DSS} \propto \mu p^2 \tag{4a}$$

$$V_p, V_{pi} \propto p \tag{4b}$$

Since I_{DSS} is defined for $V_{GS} = 0$, then in order to cause I_{DSS} to flow it is necessary to deplete only that part of the channel not already depleted by ϕ. Therefore, I_{DSS} is proportional to V_p^2, not V_{pi}^2, or:

$$I_{DSS} = B\mu V_p^2 \tag{5}$$

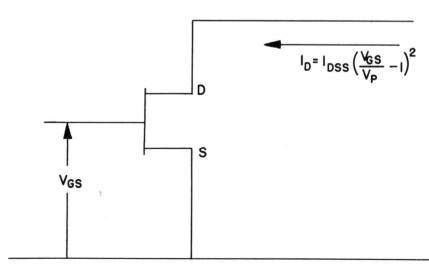

Fig. 1. A simple model.

where B encompasses the dielectric and geometry constants. Thus, there are two temperature-dependent factors in I_{DSS}, μ and V_p. For I_{DSS} to be capable of having either negative or positive temperature coefficients, the temperature dependencies of μ and V_p must be compensating, as in fact and in deed they are.

MOBILITY AND CONTACT POTENTIAL

Drift mobility exhibits an inverse power law behavior with temperature:

$$\mu = \mu_o \left(\frac{T}{T_o}\right)^{-n} \tag{6}$$

where μ_o is measured at T_o. Prince's data[4] shows that $n = 2.3$ for holes in silicon, and $n = 1.5$ for electrons in silicon.

The contact potential as a function of temperature[5] is:

$$\phi = \frac{KT}{q} \ln\left(\frac{N_a N_d}{n_i{}^2}\right) \tag{7}$$

where: K = Boltzmann's constant, $8.616 \times 10^{-5} \dfrac{eV}{K^\circ}$

  q = electronic charge, 1.6019×10^{-19} coulomb
  N_a = acceptor density on the P side of the junction, cm^{-3}
  N_d = donor density on the N side, cm^{-3}
  $n_i{}^2$ = the PN product

Now: $$n_i{}^2 = 4U^2 T^3 e^{\frac{-E_G}{KT}} \tag{8}$$

where: U = a constant, 2.42×10^{-15} cm^{-3} $(K^\circ)^{-3/2}$
  E_G = gap energy, about 1.1 ev at room temperature for silicon

Substituting Eq. (8) back into Eq. (7):

$$\phi = \frac{KT}{q}\left[\ln\left(\frac{N_a N_d}{4U^2}\right) - 3\ln T\right] + \frac{E_G}{q} \tag{9}$$

Differentiating with respect to temperature:

$$\frac{d\phi}{dT} = -3\frac{K}{q}\left[1 + \ln T - \frac{1}{3}\ln\left(\frac{N_a N_d}{4U^2}\right)\right] + \frac{1}{q}\frac{dE_G}{dT} \tag{10}$$

dE_G/dT for silicon is nearly constant above 200°K and has an approximate value of -0.28×10^{-3} ev/K° (Ref. 6). Note that $d\phi/dT$ is not a strong function of donor and acceptor densities nor of the absolute temperature, but varies as the natural logarithm of both quantities. Furthermore at the donor and acceptor densities presently used in FET's — about 2×10^{16} (or higher) for the gate impurity (N_d or N_a) and 10^{15} for the channel impurity — the term $1/3 \ln \left(\dfrac{N_a N_d}{4U^2}\right)$ in Eq.

(10) will be small compared to $1 + \ln T$. An approximate value of $d\phi/dT$ under this condition at $T = 300°K$ is -2.0 mv/K°. Then from Eq. (3), dV_p/dT is positive, and a log function of the absolute temperature; from this it is readily seen that temperature effects of mobility and contact potential on I_{DSS} oppose each other.

THE FORWARD TRANSFER CHARACTERISTICS OF
FET'S VS TEMPERATURE

Figure 2 is a graph of the transfer characteristic of a P-channel FET, with centi-grade temperature as the running parameter. I_{DO} and V_{po} are reference temperature values of I_{DSS} and V_p where $25\,°C$ is the reference temperature (T_o). The temperature coefficient of I_{DSS} is negative and that of V_p is positive; it is therefore to be expected that the I_D vs V_{GS} curves at two different temperatures should cross at some point. This expectation is fulfilled by the existence of the point Q in Fig. 2. What does not necessarily follow, however, is that the curves at three different temperatures should cross at the same point, as they apparently do in Fig. 2. The type of behavior shown in Fig. 2 is typical of most P-channel devices, but Figs. 3 and 4 show two seemingly anomalous devices; neither has a cross-over point, and one (Fig. 3) has a negative coefficient of I_{DSS} while the other (Fig. 4) has a positive coefficient.

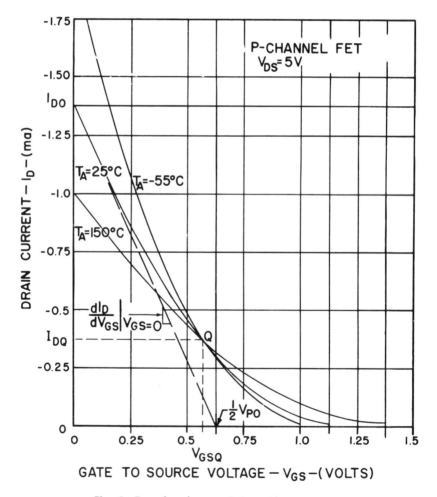

Fig. 2. Transfer characteristics with zero crossing.

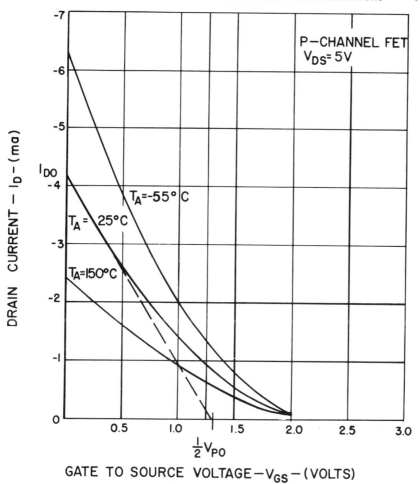

Fig. 3. Transfer characteristic with negative coefficient.

Some clue to the reasons for this behavior can be obtained by noting that the pinch-off voltage (at $T_A = T_o = 25°C$) of the device with a cross-over point (Fig. 2) lies between the pinch-off voltages of the other two devices. Admittedly, the above observation has no justification on the basis of the small sample presented, but Figs. 2, 3, and 4 are used only as an illustrative example. The observation is based on data from a much larger sample (24 devices) and at more than three temperatures, but all the data cannot be presented here for obvious reasons. The method of obtaining the pinch-off voltage from the three graphs is suggested by the square-law approximation. The tangent drawn to the transfer curves at $V_{GS} = 0$ represents the transconductance (dI_D/dV_{GS}) evaluated at $V_{GS} = 0$. By differentiating Eq. (1) with respect to V_{GS} and setting $V_{GS} = 0$, it is clear that

$$g_m = g_{max} = \frac{2\,I_{DSS}}{V_p} \qquad (11)$$

This implies that the tangent drawn at $V_{GS} = 0$ will intersect the V_{GS} axis at $V_{GS} = V_p/2$.

In Fig. 2 a bias point, Q, exists where the d-c drain current and d-c gate voltage appear to be independent of temperature. It is a simple matter to derive this bias point by differentiating Eq. (1) with respect to temperature and setting the derivative equal to zero. Proceeding in this manner:

$$\frac{dI_D}{dT} = \left(\frac{V_{GS}}{V_p} - 1 \right) \left[\frac{dI_{DSS}}{dT} \left(\frac{V_{GS}}{V_p} - 1 \right) - 2 \frac{I_{DSS}}{V_p{}^2} \right] \tag{12}$$

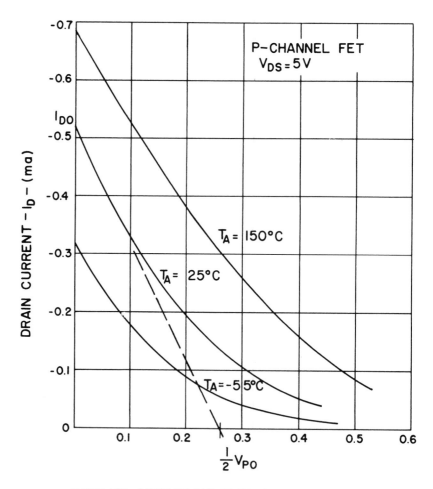

Fig. 4. Transfer characteristic with positive coefficient.

Setting Eq. (12) equal to zero, we find that

$$\frac{V_{GSQ}}{V_p} = \frac{\dfrac{dI_{DSS}}{dT}}{\dfrac{dI_{DSS}}{dT} - 2\dfrac{I_{DSS}}{V_p}\dfrac{dV_p}{dT}} \tag{13}$$

V_{GSQ} is the bias voltage from gate to source, where the temperature coefficient of the uniquely determined drain bias point current, I_{DQ}, is zero; in Eq. (13) the bias point is expressed as a fraction of the pinch-off voltage. It is generally more convenient to work with the drain current rather than the gate voltage, since good circuit practice dictates biasing with constant currents rather than with constant voltages. By subtracting one from both sides of Eq. (13) and solving for ($V_{GSQ}/V_p - 1$) in Eq. (1) we get:

$$-\sqrt{\frac{I_{DQ}}{I_{DSS}}} = \frac{2\dfrac{I_{DSS}}{V_p}\dfrac{dV_p}{dT}}{\dfrac{dI_{DSS}}{dT} - 2\dfrac{I_{DSS}}{V_p}\dfrac{dV_p}{dT}} \tag{14}$$

The minus sign is used with the radical in Eq. (14) because the plus sign yields the wrong half of the parabola; remember that Eq. (1) is a parabola with its vertex at V_p, and it is double-valued over the I_D axis. This is a snare one must always be wary of when using Eq. (1).

From Eqs. (5) and (6):

$$I_{DSS} = B\,\mu_o\left(\frac{T}{T_o}\right)^{-n} V_p^2 \tag{15}$$

then,

$$\frac{dI_{DSS}}{dT} = B\mu_o\left(\frac{T}{T_o}\right)^{-n} V_p\left(\frac{2dV_p}{dT} - \frac{n}{T}V_p\right) \tag{16}$$

Substituting Eqs. (3), (15), and (16) into Eq. (14) and squaring both sides:

$$\frac{I_{DQ}}{I_{DSS}} = \frac{4T^2}{n^2 V_p^2}\left(\frac{d\phi}{dT}\right)^2 \tag{17}$$

Now both I_{DSS} and V_p are functions of temperature; when referenced to T_o, they become I_{DO} and V_{po} respectively. That is:

$$I_{DSS} = I_{DO}\left(\frac{T}{T_o}\right)^{-n}\left[1 - \frac{\Delta\phi}{\phi_o\Delta T}(T - T_o)\right]^2 \tag{18}$$

where:

$$\left[1 - \frac{\Delta\phi}{\phi_o\Delta T}(T - T_o)\right]^2 = \left(\frac{V_p}{V_{po}}\right)^2 \tag{19}$$

Substituting Eq. (10), (18), and (19) into Eq. (17), we have finally:

$$\frac{I_{DQ}}{I_{DO}} = \frac{4T_o^n T^{2-n}}{n^2 V_{po}^2}\left[\frac{3K}{q}(1 + \ln T) + 0.28 \times 10^{-3}\right]^2 \tag{20}$$

Equation (20) is the bias point, expressed as a fraction of I_{DO}, which is the reference temperature value of I_{DSS}, where the rate of change of gate bias voltage is zero. Note that Eq. (20) is a function of temperature, but only weakly so. When I_{DQ}/I_{DO} is equal to one, the rate of change of I_{DSS} with temperature is zero, or in other words, the cross-over point is at or near $I_D = I_{DSS}$ and $V_{GS} = 0$. For P-channel FET's, using $n = 2.3$, the cross-over point will be at $I_D = I_{DSS}$ at $T = 25°C$ (298°K) on any FET having a pinch-off voltage of 0.53 volts. Equation (20) is plotted and compared to experimental data in Fig. 5. The discrepancy can be explained if it is assumed that the value of n is 2 and not 2.3. Figure 6 shows I_{DSS} vs temperature for three devices with pinch-off voltages greater than 1.5 volts, where, according to the experimental data in Fig. 5, the mobility effects should dominate I_{DSS}. The drain voltage for these measurements was 0.5 volts, so that

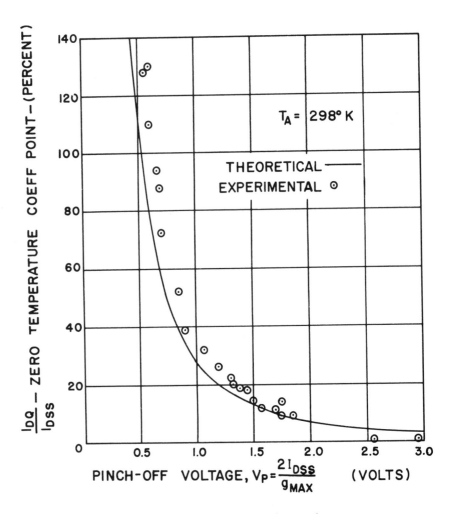

Fig. 5. Comparison of Eq. (20) with experiment.

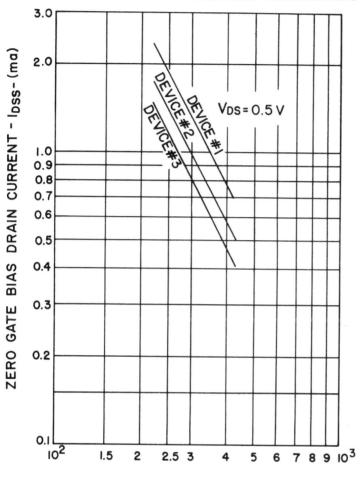

Figure 6

the field dependence of mobility[7] should be negligible. The slope of each of these three graphs is about 2. Figure 7 shows Eq. (20) plotted with $n = 2$; compared to the experimental data, the "fit" is much better. The curve for $n = 1.5$ in Fig. 7 shows the anticipated behavior of N-channel FET's, though all devices used in the experiment were P-channel. Figure 8 shows Eq. (20) plotted for $n = 2$, with centigrade temperature as the running parameter. The almost negligible shift explains why the three curves in Fig. 2 cross-over at virtually the same bias point.

The only assumption made about the FET in deriving Eq. (20) is that it obeys the square law. The curves in Fig. 7 should then be applicable to any FET that obeys the square law, regardless of construction (subject of course, to variations of n with carrier densities); this includes induced-channel FET's.

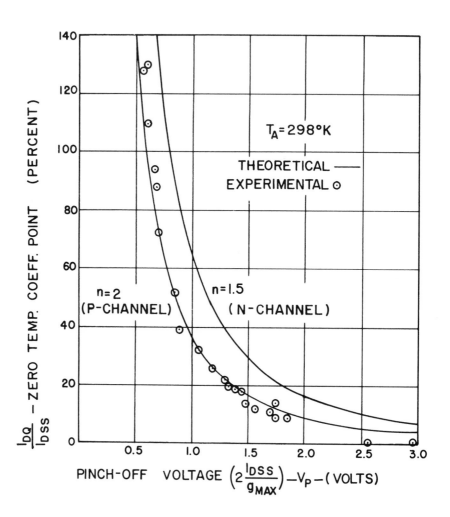

Fig. 7. Equation (20) replotted for n = 2, 1.5.

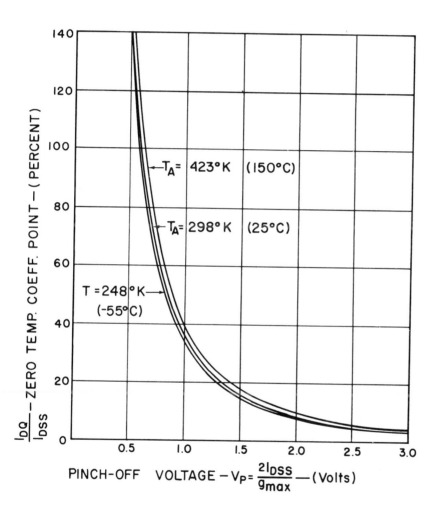

Fig. 8. Equation (20) vs. temperature.

BIBLIOGRAPHY

1. Hofstein, S. R., and F. P. Heiman: "The Silicon Insulated Gate Field-Effect Transistor," RCA Report, Air Force Contracts, AF19 (609) 8836 and AF19 (604) 8040.
2. Texas Instruments Application Report, "Theory and Application of Field Effect Transistors," April 1963.
3. Shockley, W.: "A Unipolar Field-Effect Transistor," Proc. IRE, Vol. 40, Nov. 1952, pp. 1365–1376.
4. Prince, M. B.: "Drift Mobilities in Semiconductors, II. Silicon," Phy. Rev., Vol. 93, March 15, 1954, pp. 1204–1206.
5. *Electrons and Holes in Semiconductors,* W. Shockley, D. Van Nostrand Company, Inc., Princeton, N. J., 1950, p. 307.
6. *Semiconductors,* R. A. Smith, Cambridge University Press, London, 1959, p. 352.
7. Ryder, E. J.: "Mobility of Holes and Electrons in High Electric Fields," Phy. Rev., Vol. 90, June 1, 1953, pp. 766–769.

9

Dual Transistors in Low-level Circuits

by Stan Holcomb

INTRODUCTION

The noise problems encountered in a differential direct-coupled amplifier must be considered over a frequency range that extends from dc to the upper cutoff frequency of the amplifier. The noise problems encountered at the low frequencies and at the upper cut-off frequencies have been explained, but the noise at dc, commonly called "drift," requires singular consideration. Drift is primarily a function of the transistor's temperature sensitivity characteristics and operating conditions. It can be reduced considerably by using two matched transistors in a differential connection. Therefore, the major reason for placing two transistors in one package is to improve the matching and tracking characteristics.

To explain the usefulness of dual transistors, we present the drift performance of a generalized differential amplifier as related to the matching-tracking characteristics and operating conditions of dual transistors. Then, a high-quality low-drift circuit is presented to illustrate a practical application of dual transistors.

MATCHING-TRACKING CHARACTERISTICS AND OPERATING CONDITIONS RELATED TO AMPLIFIER DRIFT

The drift in a direct-coupled d-c amplifier that has differentially connected first and second stages is primarily caused by the first stage. The magnitude of this drift is determined by the matching characteristics and the operating conditions of the dual differential transistor used in the first stage. The operating conditions have an important effect on drift even when there are very tight V_{BE} tracking and 10% h_{FE} matching specifications.

The circuit for a general direct-coupled d-c amplifier is shown in Fig. 1. A dual differential transistor is used in the first stage. The remaining stages are represented by box A. The equivalent input voltage Δv_{in}* and current drift Δi_{in} of the amplifier

*The symbol Δ is used to denote $\dfrac{\Delta f(T)}{\Delta T}$

159

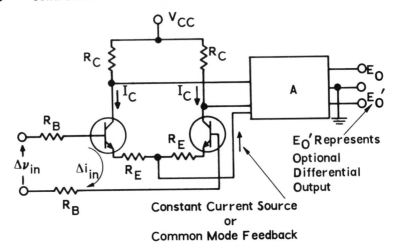

Figure 1

are related to the equivalent input voltage Δv_i and current drift Δi of the dual differential transistor by the following equations:

$$\Delta v_{in} = \Delta v + \Delta i (R_B + R_E)$$

$$\Delta i_{in} = \Delta i \qquad (1)$$

The equivalent input voltage drift Δv of the dual differential transistor is exactly equal to V_{BE} tracking or $\Delta V_{BE1} - \Delta V_{BE2}$. At this time there is no h_{FE} tracking specification in the industry which may be used to determine ΔI or $(\Delta I_{B1} - \Delta I_{B2})$. Therefore, there is no way to determine logically the exact drift performance of a

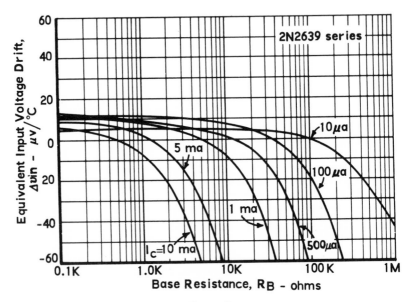

Figure 2

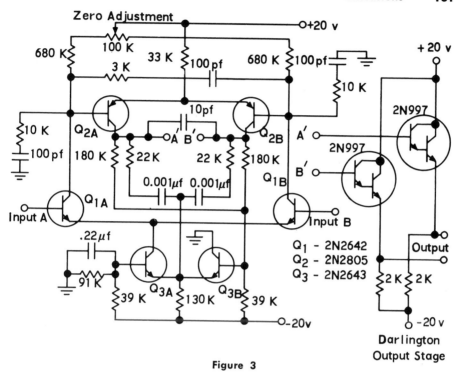

Figure 3

d-c amplifier from the guaranteed specifications, especially when there is a large base resistance. When there is no base or emitter resistance, the equivalent input voltage drift is represented by the equation:

$$\Delta v_{in} = \Delta v = \Delta V_{BE1} - \Delta V_{BE2} \tag{2}$$

This is an unusual case, and more often the d-c source resistance, or base resistance R_B, is from 10 K to 500 K. In Eq. (1) the predominant effect of ΔI or base current tracking is illustrated. It appears that the circuit engineer has no guaranteed specification to determine the drift. This is not true with the 2N2639 series transistors or any other high-beta transistor. Because the base current is so small for a high-beta low-current transistor, the difference base resistor voltage drop is still relatively small for large base resistance, as shown in Fig. 2. Careful examination of Fig. 2 shows that input voltage drift increases rapidly as collector current increases, even at lower base resistance. Also, note that the input voltage drift is equal to the V_{BE} tracking for very small base resistances.

APPLICATION: A HIGH-QUALITY DIRECT-COUPLED DIFFERENTIAL AMPLIFIER

The circuit in Fig. 3 has been designed for general use either as a complete amplifier with a Darlington output stage or as the first two stages of a low-drift high-gain amplifier without the output stage. The circuit provides both low and high common-mode rejection for either differential or single-ended outputs: high common-mode rejection is achieved by use of a common-mode feedback loop; low drift is achieved by using a dual transistor Q_3 as the first stage of the common-mode feedback loop. The functions of the loop and of the dual transistor Q_3 can be better understood by observing the amplifier circuit as shown in Fig. 4; here, transistors Q_1 and Q_2 act in parallel for common-mode signals. The average value of points A' and B' is compared with the ground or zero potential by Q_3 and its balanced resistive base divider network. By adjusting the ratio of either base divider with respect to the other, the average value of points A' and B' can be set precisely to the desired value. The dual transistor Q_1 acts as a common-base stage transferring with very little loss the amplified common-mode error signal, while it acts like a common-emitter stage with a very large emitter resistor (the output impedance of Q_3 operated at 20 μa) to the common-mode input source R_s and e_s, thus greatly attenuating it.

Low drift, large gain bandwidth, and low noise are obtained when duals with high gain, large bandwidth and tight matching are used throughout the circuit. Drift performance may be exchanged for economy if we know the effect of the matching parameters of each dual upon the performance. The matching of Q_1 is of utmost importance. If the amplifier is to perform well from a large d-c source (10 K to 1 M), Q_1 must be high in current gain. The input current tracking of Q_2 is the next most important characteristic for drift reduction, and the V_{BE} tracking of Q_2 is least important. The effect of high current gain in Q_3 is to improve common-mode rejection, and Q_3's ($V_{BE} - h_{FE}$) tracking affects the single-ended output common-mode rejection.

The drift and common-mode rejection performances are affected by the operating conditions of the transistors. The operating conditions of Q_1 are fixed at $I_c = 10$ μa and $V_{CE} = 15$ volts; the 10μa collector current helps reduce drift and

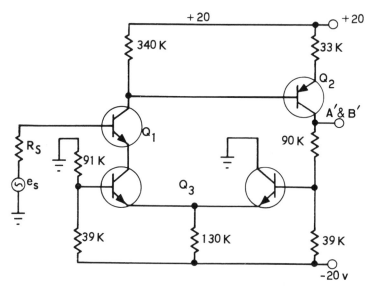

Figure 4

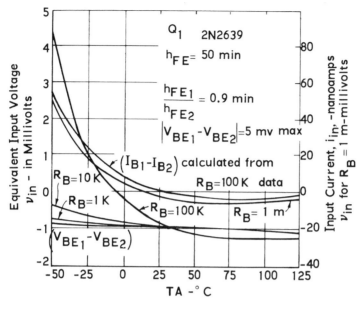

Figure 5

noise; the 15-volt collector-emitter voltage makes possible a positive 10-volt common-mode input voltage. The operating conditions of Q_2 are $I_c = 80$ μa and $V_{CE} = 15$ volts; these give a stable circuit current gain of 10 and a conservative positive 10-volt output swing, respectively. The collector-emitter voltage of Q_3 is set at -13 volts to accommodate a negative 10-volt common-mode input signal and to give maximum possible gain in the common-mode feedback loop. The output stage is operated at 10-ma collector current to give low output impedance.

PERFORMANCE CHARACTERISTICS

From the theory of amplifier drift as related to transistor matching, and from the foregoing circuit design, certain performance characteristics have been predicted and they should be evident in the following experimental results. The amplifier's equivalent input voltages v_{in} for zero output voltage vs temperature for four values of base resistance R_B are plotted in Fig. 5. The base-emitter difference ($V_{BE1} - V_{BE2}$) and base-current difference ($I_{B1} - I_{B2}$) vs temperature for a 2N2639 dual are also plotted in Fig. 5. A similar graph is given for a 2N2640 in Fig. 6, a 2N2642 in Fig. 7, and a 2N2643 in Fig. 8. In each case, the v_{in} for a small value of base resistance is almost identical to the V_{BE} difference voltage and for $R_B = 1$ M the input voltage is large and its variation with temperature approaches the shape of the base-current difference curve. The base-current difference was calculated from the $R_B = 100$ K data and the difference between the $R_B = 1$ M curve is approximately the V_{BE} difference showing that the experimental data are consistent with theory. The remaining results show that the input current is lower

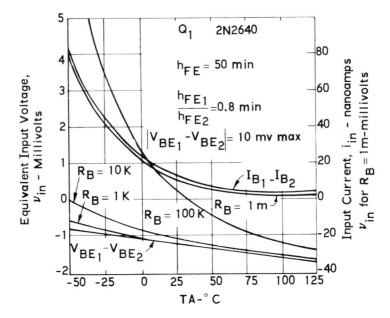

Figure 6

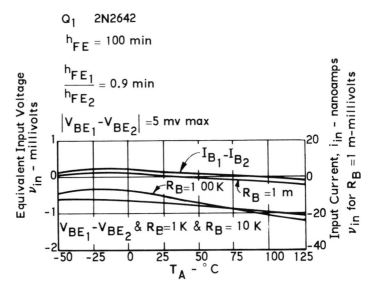

Figure 7

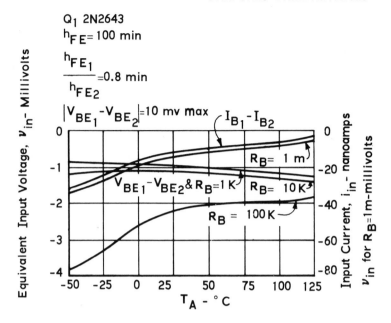

Figure 8

and more linear for duals with high current gain and tighter matched h_{FE}'s, e.g., 2N2642. Drift data as a function of the other transistor matchings were not taken, but data were taken on gain, frequency response, and common-mode rejection, since they are included in the design features.

Both the open-loop and the closed-loop single-ended voltage gains shown in Fig. 9 were made in the appropriate test circuits with one of the differential inputs grounded. Since the open-loop voltage-gain roll-off holds a constant -20 db per decade slope from its 850-cps break to beyond its 5-mc crossover, the amplifier is stable for output shorted to input (i.e., zero feedback resistance) and for operational integrator use.

Both open-loop and closed-loop common-mode rejection (CMR) data were taken in the appropriate test circuits with 20 volts peak-to-peak applied to both inputs. The very large CMR ratio even for a single-ended output is a result of the large amount of common-mode feedback and the close differential match of the first-stage parameters.

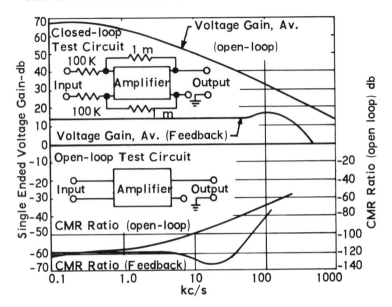

Figure 9

10

Low-level Operation of
the 2N929 and 2N930

The 2N929 and 2N930 represent a considerable aid to the designer of low-level and low-noise circuitry. By rigid exclusion of all contaminants from the crystal surface, room temperature leakage currents are held to near theoretical minimum values. Because the number of surface recombination centers is low, careful control of the diffusion processes results in h_{FE}'s that remain high even at very low current levels.

This paper presents circuit suggestions and typical parameter curves to permit the designer to predict the performance of these transistors in his circuit. Curves shown are typical of both the 2N929 and the 2N930 unless otherwise noted.

LOW-FREQUENCY LOW-NOISE APPLICATIONS

Two types of low-frequency low-noise applications will be considered. The first is an amplifier which must respond to only one frequency, or at most, to a narrow band of frequencies. An index of noise performance under these conditions is the amplifier's spot noise figure NF. Loosely speaking, a noise figure is a measure, in decibels, of the amount by which the signal-to-noise power ratio is degraded when the signal passes through the amplifier. From another viewpoint, it relates the noise power output of the actual amplifier, fed from a resistive source impedance, to the noise power output of a perfect (i.e., noiseless) amplifier having the same gain and fed from the same source. For spot noise figures, only the power contained in the noise signal frequencies within a very narrow passband (e.g., 1 cps) is considered.

The second type of low-frequency low-noise application concerns an amplifier that must respond to a wide band of frequencies. A typical example is the high-fidelity audio amplifier. To evaluate noise performance in this application, the so-called "broadband" noise figure is useful. In this paper, broadband noise figure will be denoted by NF, and it may be thought of as an averaged noise figure over a passband with 10 and 10,000 cps half-power frequencies.

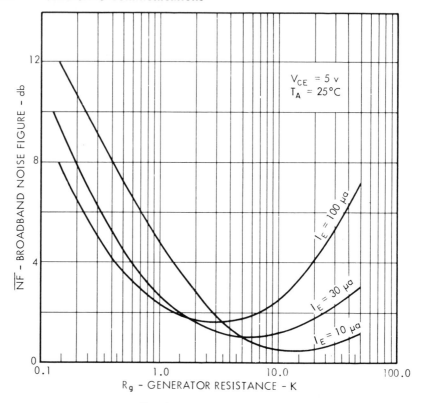

Fig. 1. Broadband noise figure vs. source impedance.

So long as the first-stage available power gain is greater than unity, the ultimate design objective is to minimize the noise figure. In theory, additional stages can always be added to provide any designed gain. Practically, however, good gain in the first stage simplifies the design problem by permitting RC coupling rather than transformer coupling and by reducing the effective noise contribution of the second stage.

The NF given by a particular transistor will vary with the emitter current, the signal source impedance and, to a lesser extent, the collector-emitter voltage. Typical NF's shown in Fig. 1 illustrate this. For this transistor series, optimum operating conditions for minimum NF will be about $I_E = 10$ μa, $R_g = 10$ K, and $V_{CE} = 5$ volts. However, it may sometimes be necessary to compromise the noise figure in order to accept a wider dynamic range of signals.

Typical NF's under these optimum conditions are displayed in Fig. 2.

High-frequency Low-noise Application. Over a frequency range of 2 kc to 1 mc, the NF's of the typical 2N929 and 2N930 remain 1 db or less. Above 1 mc, the NF rises, but the transistor remains useful to as high as 70 mc. Figure 3 illustrates this variation.

Figure 3 differs from the high-frequency spot noise curve shown on the transistor data sheet. This difference is due to a change in operating conditions. Data sheet curves were run at a constant emitter current of 1 ma, but this value is not optimum

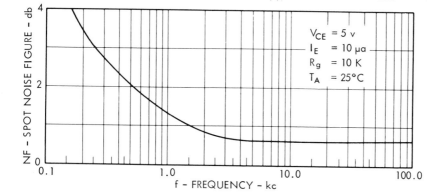

Fig. 2. Typical spot noise figure vs. frequency.

for the whole frequency range covered. To create the curve in Fig. 3, the source impedance and emitter current were varied with frequency as shown in Fig. 4.

To test the accuracy of Fig. 3, a 70-mc amplifier stage was constructed; details of this design are shown in Fig. 5. Averaged results for five units are given in Fig. 6. Optimum emitter currents and source impedances are well within the predicted range. NF is 0.6 db higher than predicted, probably due to differences in circuit losses or to measurement errors.

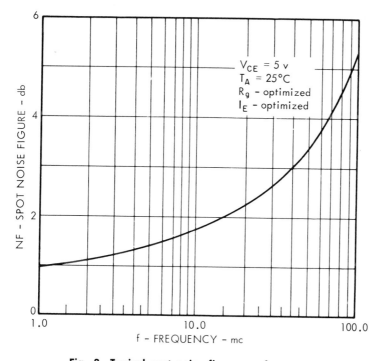

Fig. 3. Typical spot noise figure vs. frequency.

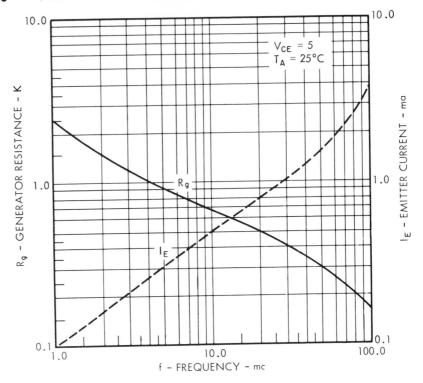

Fig. 4. Optimum source impedance and emitter current vs. frequency.

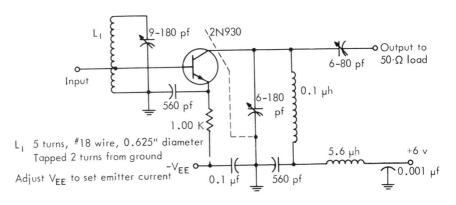

Fig. 5. 70-mc noise test amplifier.

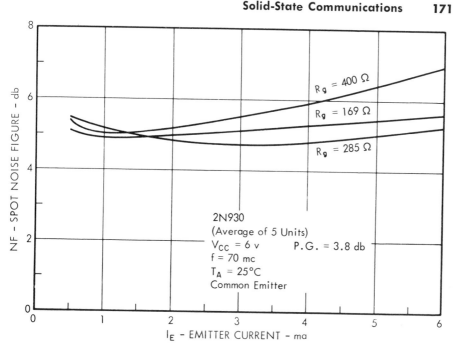

Fig. 6. Spot noise figure vs. I_E and R_g.

11

High Input Impedance Techniques

by Ralph Dean

INTRODUCTION

The bipolar transistor, being current controlled, is inherently a low input impedance device. Many transistor circuits perform very satisfactorily at input impedance
levels of a few kilohms or less. Other applications, however, require input impedances in the hundreds of megohms. The field-effect (unipolar) transistor, being a
voltage-controlled device, has an inherently high input resistance in the order of
10^{12} ohms. But the shunting effects of bias networks and junction capacitances
necessitate the use of special techniques in order to obtain high impedances over a
wide frequency range. Techniques presented here can yield hundreds of megohms
input impedance using either bipolar or unipolar transistors.

METHODS

All impedance multiplying techniques involve some form of feedback. Positive
feedback, negative feedback, or combinations of both can be used. There seems
to be no standard for describing feedback in general terms, so this subject will be
discussed briefly. In Figs. 1a through 1d, each basic amplifier and its associated
feedback network is represented by a four-terminal network. The manner in which
the networks are interconnected determines the effect of the feedback on gain, and
output impedance. In describing these configurations, the words "shunt" and "series"
will be used to describe the manner of interconnection. For example, the configuration of Fig. 1c would be described as "series-shunt." The first term describes the
interconnection at the input to the amplifier; the second term describes the interconnection at the output terminals. This configuration is also designated "h-type"
because the respective h-parameters of the networks are simply added to obtain the
composite h-parameters. The other configurations are called shunt-shunt, (y);
shunt-series, (g); and series-series, (z). In each case the parameter system is such
that composite parameters are obtained simply by the addition of corresponding
parameters.

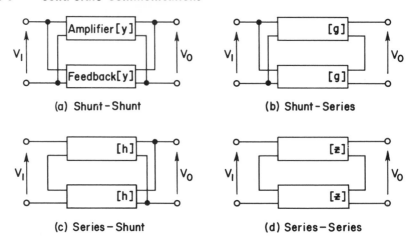

(a) Shunt–Shunt

(b) Shunt–Series

(c) Series–Shunt

(d) Series–Series

Fig. 1. Feedback configuration.

It is easily shown that series negative feedback at the input increases Z_{in} and reduces the voltage gain. It can also be shown that shunt negative feedback decreases Z_{in} and the current gain. Negative feedback taken in series from the output increases Z_o; if taken in shunt, it decreases Z_o. The opposite behavior is observed for positive feedback in all the above configurations.

When considering Z_{in}, the input terminals are of primary interest. Further references to feedback in this chapter will refer to the input terminals only, unless otherwise specified.

BASIC IMPEDANCE MULTIPLIERS

Perhaps the most common impedance multiplier is the negative series-shunt configuration shown in Fig. 2. The input impedance is $Z_{in} = Z_1 (1 + A\beta_f)$. If $A\beta_f$ is positive, the feedback is negative and causes the input impedance to increase.

The familiar emitter follower is illustrated in Fig. 3. The h-parameter matrix of the transistor is:

$$[h]_t = \begin{bmatrix} h_{ie} & -h_{re} \\ -h_{fe} & h_{oe} \end{bmatrix}$$

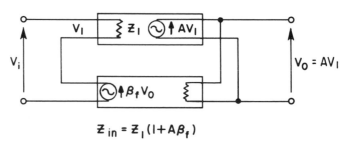

$$Z_{in} = Z_1 (1 + A\beta_f)$$

Fig. 2. Series-shunt connection.

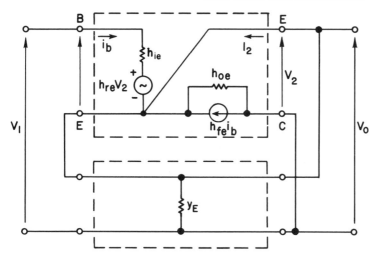

Fig. 3. h-parameter representation of emitter follower.

Negative signs are associated with h_{re} and h_{fe} because V_2 and I_2 are reversed from their normal sense. The h-matrix of the feedback network is

$$[h]_f = \begin{bmatrix} 0 & 1 \\ -1 & Y_E \end{bmatrix}$$

The composite matrix is

$$[h]_c = \begin{bmatrix} h_{ie} & (1-h_{re}) \\ -(h_{fe}+1) & (h_{oe}+Y_E) \end{bmatrix}$$

Substituting these parameters into the general input impedance equation,

$$Z_{in} = h_{11} - \frac{h_{12}h_{21}}{h_{22}+Y_L} \tag{1}$$

we obtain

$$Z_{in} = h_{ie} + \frac{(h_{fe}+1)(1-h_{re})}{h_{oe}+Y_E} \tag{2}$$

$$Z_{in} \cong h_{ie} + \frac{h_{fe}+1}{h_{oe}+Y_E} \tag{3}$$

Z_{in} is shown in this form to illustrate the ease of finding the composite h-parameters and hence the characteristic performance equations of such a composite network. For our present purposes however, it is more illustrative to write Eq. (2) in terms of the common-base T parameters

$$Z_{in} = r_b + \frac{(\beta+1)(R_E+r_e)r_c}{(\beta+1)(R_E+r_e)+r_c} \tag{4}$$

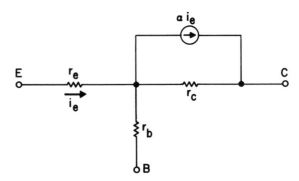

Fig. 4. Common-base T-equivalent circuit.

Equation (4) may be obtained by transformation from Eq. (2) or by direct derivation from the T-equivalent circuits of Figs. 4 and 5.

Note that the collector shunt resistance in the common-emitter configuration, Fig. 5, is less than the common-base value by the factor $(1-\alpha)$. The value of the common-emitter current gain is greater than the common-base gain by $1/(1-\alpha)$. The term $\beta = \alpha/(1-\alpha)$ should not be confused with β_f which was used previously for feedback factor. Typical values for the T parameters are:

$$\alpha = 0.9 \text{ to } 0.995$$
$$\beta = 10 \text{ to } 200$$
$$r_c = 1 \text{ to } 20 \text{ megohms}$$
$$r_b = 500 \text{ ohms}$$
$$r_e = 26/I_E \qquad \text{ohms/milliampere}$$

where I_E is the emitter bias current.

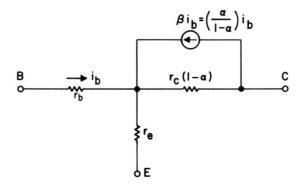

Fig. 5. Common-emitter T-equivalent circuit.

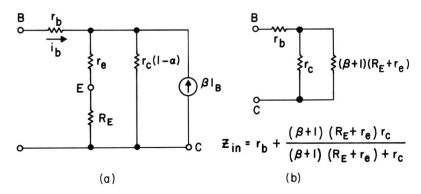

$$Z_{in} = r_b + \frac{(\beta+1)(R_E+r_e)r_c}{(\beta+1)(R_E+r_e)+r_c}$$

(a)   (b)

Fig. 6. Common-emitter T representation of emitter follower.

The term "current multiplication" has been applied to the type of impedance multiplier being discussed. This is illustrated in Fig. 6, where the common-emitter T equivalent is used with an emitter-follower amplifier. Here the input current is multiplied by the current gain β. Then the current which flows through the parallel combination of $r_e + R_E$ and $r_c(1-\alpha)$ is $(\beta+1) i_b$. This current passing through $(r_e + R_E)$ provides the negative series feedback which multiplies the feedback resistance by the current gain plus one. The input impedance is:

$$Z_{in} = r_b + \frac{(\beta + 1)(R_E + r_c)r_c}{(\beta+1)(R_E + r_e) + r_c} \tag{5}$$

Both the series emitter resistance and the collector shunt resistance are multiplied by $\beta + 1$, but since the collector shunt resistance is $r_c(1-\alpha)$, and $(1-\alpha)$ $(\beta+1) = 1$, this term reduces to r_c. The equivalent input network is shown in Fig. 6. The same result would have been obtained if the common-base equivalent had been used. This concept is illustrated in general terms in Fig. 7. In general,

$$Z_{in} = Z_1 + (A_I + 1)R_F \tag{6}$$

Several current amplifiers can be cascaded to obtain very large current multiplications. The Darlington configuration shown in Fig. 8 achieves a large current multiplication. However, the input impedance of the Darlington current multiplier is limited by the shunting effect of the collector resistance of Q_1. Circuits of this type can achieve input impedances in the order of a megohm. Techniques for reducing the effects of shunt resistance are discussed next.

$$Z_{in} = Z_1 + (A_i + 1) R_F$$

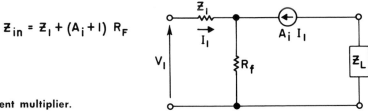

Fig. 7. Current multiplier.

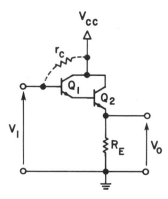

Fig. 8. Darlington emitter-follower configuration.

In Fig. 9, an idealized voltage amplifier is shown with shunt-shunt positive feedback. Although y-parameters would be used with a more complex system, for the simple amplifier shown it is more illustrative to use loop equations to obtain

$$Z_{in} = \frac{R_f Z_1}{R_f + (1-A)Z_1} = \frac{1}{\dfrac{1}{Z_1} + \dfrac{1-A}{R_F}} \tag{7}$$

Z_{in} approaches infinity as A approaches

$$\frac{R_f + Z_1}{Z_1}$$

Obviously, if A is made to approach this value, A and the circuit impedance must be carefully controlled to prevent negative impedances from occurring. If $A = 1$, Eq. (7) reduces to Z_1. That is, the R_f term vanishes. The use of shunt positive feedback to reduce the effect of a shunt impedance is known as bootstrapping. If the gain A is unity, the bootstrapping is complete. If A is less than unity, the bootstrapping is partial. In general, a shunt impedance such as R_f in Fig. 8 is magnified by the gain A such that

$$R_{equivalent} = \frac{R_f}{1-A} \tag{8}$$

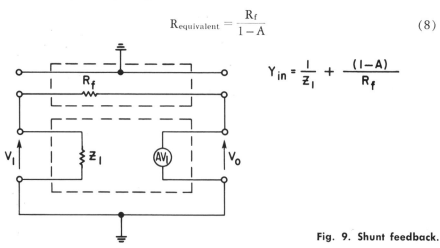

$$Y_{in} = \frac{1}{Z_1} + \frac{(1-A)}{R_f}$$

Fig. 9. Shunt feedback.

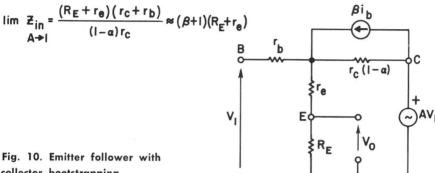

$$\lim_{A \to 1} \; \mathbb{Z}_{in} = \frac{(R_E + r_e)(r_c + r_b)}{(1-a)r_c} \approx (\beta+1)(R_E + r_e)$$

Fig. 10. Emitter follower with collector bootstrapping.

Now consider the bootstrapped emitter follower shown in Fig. 10. Since the collector of the transistor presents a fairly high impedance, it is easily driven from a low-impedance source. The exact manner in which this is done is not important at the moment. It is easily shown that

$$Z_{in} = \frac{(R_E + r_e)(r_c + r_b) + (1-A)r_c r_b}{(1-\alpha)r_c + (1-A)(R_E + r_e)} \tag{9}$$

if $A = 1$,
$$Z_{in} = r_b + \frac{R_E + r_e}{(1-\alpha)}\left(1 + \frac{r_b}{r_c}\right) \cong r_b + \frac{R_E + r_e}{1-\alpha} \tag{10}$$

The shunting effect of r_c has been virtually eliminated by bootstrapping.

To this point, nothing has been said about input capacitance. Normally, at low frequencies this is of no concern. However, as the resistive component of input impedance is increased the capacitive component quickly becomes significant. Fortunately the bootstrapping technique can be used to reduce the effective collector capacitance in the same manner as the shunt conductance can be reduced. Another way to view bootstrapping is to consider it as the reverse of Miller effect. For example, the common-emitter amplifier shown in Fig. 11 has a voltage gain A. The value of C_{in} then is $C_{OB}(1-A)$. Since A is negative in this case, C is effectively

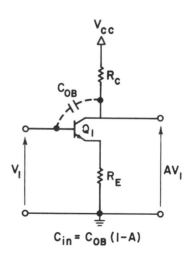

Fig. 11. Miller effect.

$$C_{in} = C_{OB}(1-A)$$

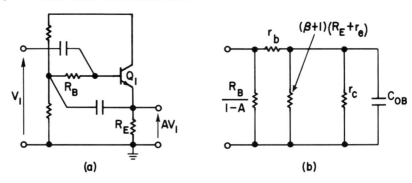

(a)   (b)

Fig. 12. Emitter follower with bias bootstrapping.

increased. If A is positive and unity, as in the case of perfect bootstrapping, the shunting effect of C_{OB} is eliminated.

The bootstrapping technique can also be applied to external impedances such as bias networks. Such an arrangement is shown in Fig. 12. In this case, the gain A is the gain of the emitter follower. Since $A < 1$, the effect of R_B cannot be completely eliminated. The series element r_b is usually a few hundred ohms, and may be neglected. The next shunt element $(\beta + 1)(R_E + r_e)$ is affected by the permissible values of R_E and current level. These in turn are related to the stability factor. The last shunt element r_c cannot be bootstrapped because a capacitor between the collector and emitter would short the collector generator. Input impedances of about a megohm can be obtained from this configuration.

In the circuit of Fig. 13, the second transistor increases the current multiplication, and allows the collector of Q_1 to be bootstrapped by isolating the output voltage from Q_1. An input impedance of several megohms can be obtained with this circuit.

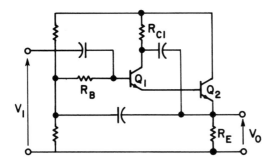

Fig. 13. Darlington emitter follower with collector and bias bootstrapping.

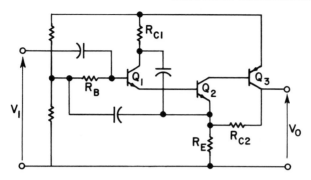

Fig. 14. Darlington complementary amplifier.

The circuit of Fig. 14 offers further current multiplication and higher gain for more effective bootstrapping. Frequency response is rather low in the circuits of Figs. 13 and 14 because the low-current level of Q_1 causes the frequency response of this transistor to be low.

Frequency response of these circuits can be improved by biasing Q_1 with a current generator in its emitter leg as shown in Fig. 15a. This raises I_E to a level where

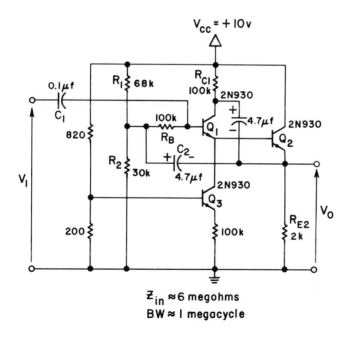

$Z_{in} \approx 6$ megohms
BW $\approx$ 1 megacycle

Fig. 15a. Cascaded emitter follower with current bias.

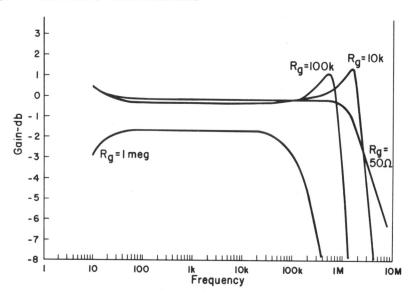

Fig. 15b. Frequency response curves of cascaded emitter follower.

the cutoff frequency of Q_1 is reasonably high, yet the external emitter impedance is maintained at a high level. An input impedance of 6 megohms was measured on this circuit. Frequency response curves are shown in Fig. 15b. The peak at high frequencies is caused by the normal phase shifts within the amplifier. The low-frequency peak is caused by resonance between the input capacitor C_1 and the effective inductance of R_B. This phenomenon is caused by phase shift within the bootstrap network, C_2, R_1, R_2. It can be shown that the resistor R_B appears to be inductive at low frequencies.

Increasing values of R_g lower the Q of the resonant circuit to a point where the peak is no longer seen.

In the circuit of Fig. 16a, a complementary transistor Q_4 has been added to increase current multiplication. This also increases the gain at the emitter of Q_2 by raising the effective value of R_{E2}. This higher gain makes the bootstrapping more effective. An input impedance of 25 megohms was obtained with this circuit. Response curves are shown in Fig. 16b. These curves are very similar to the curves of Fig. 15b.

In the circuit of Fig. 17a, positive shunt feedback is used to cancel the shunt impedance of the bias network and the transistor. Theoretical input impedances of ($h_{fe1}h_{fe2}R_{E1}$) can be obtained. In the illustration, R_{E1} is made small in order to obtain a gain of 10. As a result, Z_{in} is limited to about 1.5 megohms. Higher values can be obtained by increasing the ratio R_{E1}/R_{E2}. The feedback impedance R_f, and C_f could be further adjusted to cancel the impedance ($h_{fe1} h_{fe2} R_{E1}$), but since this term is by no means constant, instability would result. The major advantage of this circuit is that excellent bias stability is obtained. The three diodes, D_1, D_2, and D_3 compensate for variations in V_{BE1}, and the negative d-c feedback from R_{E2} further increases bias stability. Response curves for this circuit are shown in Fig. 17b. Voltage gain was observed to increase 1% over the temperature range -25 to $125°C$. The quiescent collector voltage of Q_2 decreased 6% over the same range.

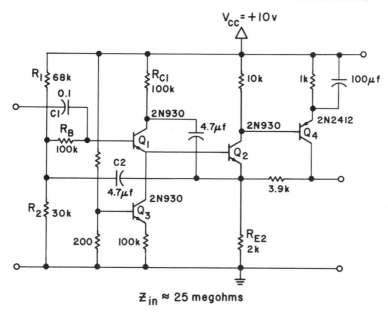

Fig. 16a. Complementary current multiplier.

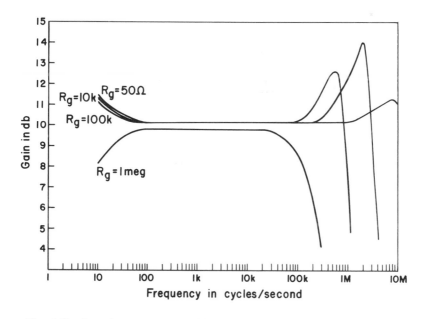

Fig. 16b. Complementary emitter-follower frequency response curves.

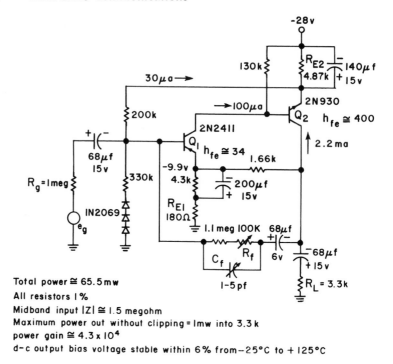

Total power ≅ 65.5 mw
All resistors 1%
Midband input |Z| ≅ 1.5 megohm
Maximum power out without clipping = 1mw into 3.3 k
power gain ≅ 4.3 x 10⁴
d-c output bias voltage stable within 6% from −25°C to +125°C

Figure 17a

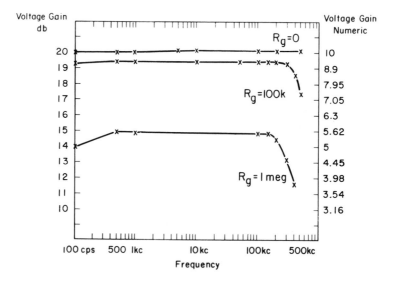

Fig. 17b. Voltage gain vs. frequency.

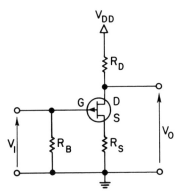

Fig. 18. Basic FET amplifier.

FIELD-EFFECT TRANSISTORS

The special techniques demonstrated thus far apply to increasing the input impedance of junction (bipolar) transistors. But the field-effect (unipolar) transistor exhibits an inherently high input resistance. Its behavior is very much like that of the vacuum pentode. Fig. 18 shows a very rudimentary FET amplifier. The G or gate terminal is the control electrode corresponding to the grid of a tube, the D or drain terminal corresponds to the plate, and the S or source terminal corresponds to the cathode. The FET illustrated is a P-channel device; the bias polarities are opposite those of the vacuum tube. The gate electrode is in this case one side of a P-N junction. In normal operation this junction is reverse biased, and it exhibits a finite junction capacitance.

The input impedance of the circuit shown is approximately 1000 megohms shunted by 9 pf. This capacitive component becomes significant at a rather low frequency, making it necessary to use bootstrapping to reduce the effective input capacitance. Consider now the source follower shown in Fig. 19. The gain is:

$$A_v = \frac{1}{1 + \dfrac{1}{g_m R_s}}$$

The transconductance g_m of the FET may be near 1000 micromhos at its maximum current. Then, to obtain $A_v = 0.98$, R_s must be greater than 50 kilohms. This conflicts with the requirement that the quiescent current should be large to obtain high g_m. This problem is alleviated in the circuit of Fig. 20 by obtaining the bias current from the current generator Q_2. The effective source resistance is now r_{c2} since Q_2 is effectively a common-base stage. This scheme is used in the circuit of Fig. 21. Q_1 is the FET and Q_2 is the current generator. Q_3 and Q_4 function as a complementary current multiplier. Bootstrapping for R_B is obtained directly from the emitter of Q_3. An adjustment R_{10} is provided in order to obtain greater than unity gain at the drain of Q_1. This allows the response to be peaked for high values of R_g. Voltage gain is 2 and input impedance is 200 megohms. Response curves are shown in Fig. 21a. The dashed curve ($R_g = 10$ megohms) was obtained using the peaking adjustment just described.

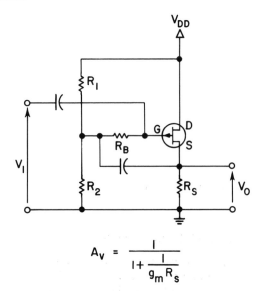

$$A_v = \frac{1}{1 + \dfrac{1}{g_m R_s}}$$

Fig. 19. Source follower.

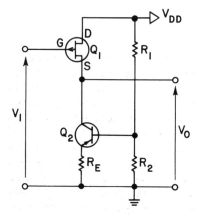

Fig. 20. Source follower with current-generator bias.

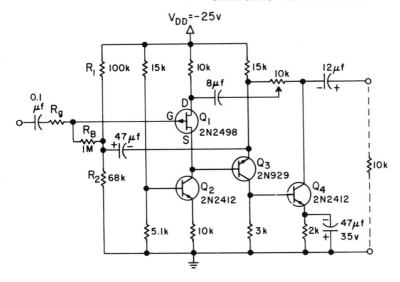

Fig. 21. 6-db high input Z FET amplifier.

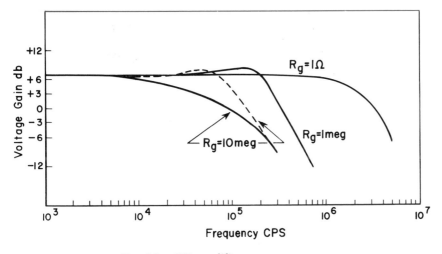

Fig. 21a. FET amplifier response curves.

CONCLUSIONS

The concepts of current multiplication and bootstrapping that have been defined and illustrated are those most widely used in high impedance circuits. The shunt positive feedback method, which has also been illustrated, has the advantage that very good stability factors can be obtained. Although the circuits presented exhibit relatively moderate input impedances, extension of the techniques involved can yield extremely high input impedances. Since all of these techniques involve feedback, it is well to do careful a-c and d-c stability analyses on any such circuit before adopting the design. In such analyses, the bias and temperature dependence of transistor parameters should be considered. A detailed treatment of such topics is too lengthy to include here; excellent treatments can be found in the literature. Some of these techniques can be extended to d-c amplifiers, but this subject is also a field in itself and will not be covered here.

BIBLIOGRAPHY

1. Montgomery, G. F.: "High Input Impedance Amplifier," *Electronic Design,* August 6, 1958.
2. Berstein-Bervey, S.: "Designing High Input Impedance Amplifiers," *Electronic Equipment Engineering,* August 1961, p. 61, September 1961, p. 59.
3. Middlebrook, R. D., and C. A. Mead, "Transistor AC and DC Amplifiers with High Input Impedance," *Semiconductor Products,* March 1959.
4. Willett, R. L.: "Positive and Negative Feedback Multiply Amplifier Impedance," *Electronics,* July 7, 1961, p. 52.
5. Hakim, S. S.: "Open and Closed Loop Response of Feedback Amplifiers," *Electronic Engineering,* October 1962, p. 682.
6. de Boer, E.: "Internal Resistance of Feedback Amplifiers," *Electronic Engineering,* September 1962, p. 600.
7. Nordling, K. I.: "Low-Frequency Instability in Cascaded Emitter Followers," *Electronic Design,* November 8, 1961, p. 36.
8. Beneteau, P. J.: "Stable Wideband Emitter Followers," *Solid State Design,* February 1962, p. 29.
9. Evans, A. D.: "High Input Impedance Amplifier Using Silicon Transistors," *Texas Instruments Application Report,* October 1958.
10. Dewitt, D., and A. L. Rossoff, *Transistor Electronics,* New York, McGraw-Hill, 1957, p. 219.

12

Noise Characterization

by Bob Crawford

INTRODUCTION

This chapter covers some of the general considerations involved in the design of low-noise linear amplifiers. The e_n, i_n method and the direct NF method of characterizing or presenting noise performance are covered. A method of noise characterization for the 1/f region is covered. The effect that correlation between generators has on NF is explained.

NOISE CHARACTERIZATION

e_n, i_n **Method.** For noise considerations, any linear two-port network or amplifier may be characterized by a series noise-voltage generator and by a parallel noise-current generator at the input. Figure 1 shows a noisy amplifier together with its representation by a noiseless amplifier with e_n and i_n brought out front. The term γ indicates the amount of correlation between the two generators. R_{in} is the input resistance of the amplifier.

Measurement of e_n and i_n is straightforward. For measurement of e_n, the input terminals of the network must be short circuited with a resistor value (R_{short}) that meets these two inequalities:

$$R_{short} \ll R_{in}$$

and
$$\frac{i_n R_{short}}{R_{in} + R_{short}} \ll \frac{e_n}{R_{in} + R_{short}}$$

The first condition assures that all of the generator voltage e_n will appear across the amplifier input. The second requirement limits the amount of signal current contributed by i_n. The output of the amplifier, as measured with a true-reading rms voltmeter, is divided by the gain of the amplifier to give the input series noise-voltage generator.

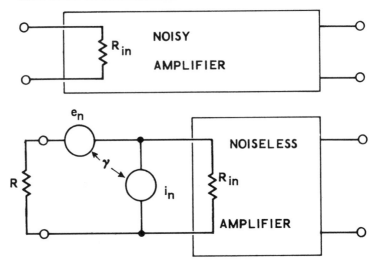

Figure 1

In the measurement of i_n, it is necessary to open-circuit the input of the amplifier with a resistor (R_{open}) so the two following inequalities are met:

$$R_{open} >> R_{in}$$

and

$$\frac{i_n R_{open}}{R_{in} + R_{open}} >> \frac{e_n}{R_{in} + R_{open}}$$

It is necessary that the gain of the amplifier be high so that any noise introduced in the following stages will be small compared to the input noise.

Now, assuming e_n and i_n are known, the noise factor of the amplifier can be calculated. Defining noise factor as

$$F = \frac{\text{Total noise power output}}{\text{Power out due to the thermal noise generated by } R_g} \qquad (1)$$

then by substituting e_n and i_n into Eq. (1), an expression for noise factor is derived:

$$F = 1 + \frac{1}{4kT\Delta F}\left(i_n^2 R_g + \frac{e_n^2}{R_g} + 2\gamma e_n i_n\right) \qquad (2)$$

where

k = Boltzmann's constant = 1.38×10^{-23} Joules/°K
T = temperature in degrees Kelvin = $273 + °C$
ΔF = noise power bandwidth
γ = correlation coefficient
$4kT$ = 1.66×10^{-20} watt-seconds at 25°C

Note that Eq. (2) is independent of R_{in} because it is a noiseless resistor. The input resistance for a common-emitter stage is approximately $h_{fe}r_e$. Because r_e is not a real resistance it generates no thermal noise. Any noise generator within the emitter junction has already been taken into account by the two noise generators.

Since F is a function of the generator resistance, R_g may be varied to find the minimum (or optimum) noise factor. This may be done in one of two ways:

(1) F may be differentiated with respect to R_g. The result is then set equal to zero. Solving for R_g will yield an optimum value of source resistance, $R_{(opt)}$. Substituting $R_{(opt)}$ into the general equation for noise factor yields the minimum noise factor (for a given bias level).

(2) The minimum noise factor occurs when each generator contributes equally to the total noise power. Looking at the first two terms within the parentheses of Eq. (2), it is noted these have the dimensions of power. Setting these two terms equal and solving for R_g yields the optimum generator resistance:

$$R_{(opt)} = \frac{e_n}{i_n} \qquad (3)$$

Substituting Eq. (3) into Eq. (2) yields the minimum or optimum noise factor obtainable, $F_{(opt)}$.

$$F_{(opt)} = 1 + (1 + \gamma)\frac{e_n i_n}{2kT\Delta F} \qquad (4)$$

Note that $F_{(opt)}$ depends upon the product of e_n and i_n, while $R_{(opt)}$ depends upon the ratio of e_n and i_n. The dependency of NF upon R_g can be seen in Fig. 2. Figure 2a is for a conventional transistor while Fig. 2b is for a field-effect transistor. Notice the lower current levels at which the 2N930 is run and the higher optimum source resistance for the 2N2500. Figure 2a also gives typical values for the e_n and i_n generators for the 2N930.

The quantities e_n and i_n are functions of I_E and therefore F is valid only at the bias condition at which e_n and i_n are measured. These two generators are fairly independent of collector voltage for voltages below six to ten volts.

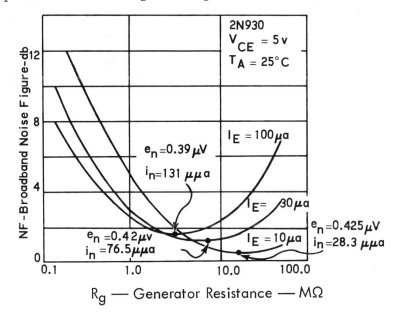

Figure 2a

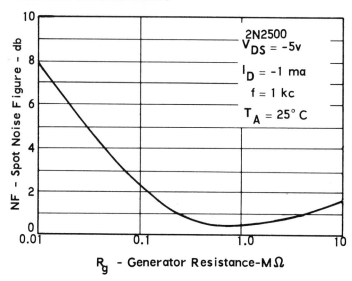

Figure 2b

Equation (4) states that, for a low noise factor, γ should be as small as possible. The significance of the correlation factor and its effect in a circuit can best be explained by an example where two generators are in series across a load (Fig. 3), each with an rms amplitude of a. The two extreme cases of γ will be examined. In the first case, let the two generators be of differing and randomly related frequencies, i.e., no correlation ($\gamma = 0$); while in the second case, $\gamma =$ unity, i.e., the generators have identical frequencies and phase. With $\gamma = 0$, the two voltage vectors add in quadrature, so that power into R is proportional to $a^2 + a^2 = 2a^2$. When $\gamma = 1$, the two generators are of the same frequency and exactly in phase. Their amplitudes can be added directly, that is, power into R is proportional to the quantity $(a + a)^2 = 4a^2$. Taking the ratio of the two cases where $\gamma = 1$ and 0, the power output in the first case is twice that of the second case.

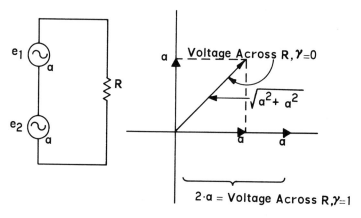

Figure 3

Considerations[1]* of γ. Since F depends upon γ, it will be interesting to investigate the dependency of the correlation coefficient upon transistor parameters. Noise factor as a function of γ, e_n and i_n has already been described in Eq. (2). Noise factor in terms of transistor parameters has been given in the literature by Nielson[2], and is presented below:

$$F = 1 + \frac{r'_b}{R_g} + \frac{r_e}{2R_g} + \frac{(r'_b + r_e + R_G)^2}{2\alpha_o^2 R_g r_e h_{FE}} \qquad (5)$$

Equating Eq. (5) to Eq. (2) and letting $R_g \to 0$, and $R_g \to \infty$, yields values for e_n and i_n, respectively. These values are given in the following two equations:

$$e_n^2 = 4kT\Delta f \left[r'_b + \frac{r_e}{2} + \frac{(r_e + r'_b)^2}{2\alpha_o^2 r_e h_{FE}} \right] \qquad (6)$$

$$i_n^2 = \frac{2kT\Delta f}{\alpha_o^2 r_e h_{FE}} \qquad (7)$$

Substituting these values into Eq. (2) and solving for γ:

$$\gamma = \frac{\dfrac{r'_b}{r_e} + 1}{\sqrt{\left(\dfrac{r'_b}{r_e} + \dfrac{1}{2}\right)\left(2\alpha_o^2 h_{FE}\right) + \left(\dfrac{r'_b}{r_e} + 1\right)^2}} \qquad (8)$$

In Fig. 4, γ is plotted as a function of h_{FE} with r'_b/r_e as a running parameter to describe a family of curves. At low emitter currents, $r_e \gg r'_b$, and γ reduces to:

$$\gamma \cong \frac{1}{\sqrt{h_{FE}}}$$

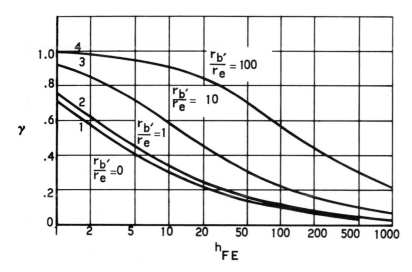

Figure 4

---

*Superscript numbers refer to bibliography entries at end of chapter.

Thus for large values of current gain, γ can be very small. Curves 1 and 2 of Fig. 4 would apply to most of the situations where a transistor is biased for low-noise operation. For current gain > 100, $\gamma < 0.1$. The following table will serve to illustrate the effect that γ has upon NF.

Table 1

	NF	F
$\gamma = 0$	1.5 db	1.41
$\gamma = 0.1$	1.62 db	1.45
$\gamma = 1.0$	2.64 db	1.82

It is obvious from the curve of Fig. 4 that a high current gain device is desirable for low-noise operation. Figure 5 shows the distribution of 1398 2N930's at three different current levels. Notice the very high h_{FE}, averaging around 200 (even at 10 μa).

NF Measurement. The following measurement in the audio range is one of the easiest noise measurements to make. It lends itself to the testing of large quantities of transistors. Once the measurement system has been set up, no calculations are necessary and NF is read directly.

The fundamental principle of this method lies with the basic definition of noise figure in Eq. (9):

$$NF = 10 \log_{10} \frac{\dfrac{S_{p\ in}}{N_{p\ in}}}{\dfrac{S_{p\ out}}{N_{p\ out}}} \qquad (9)$$

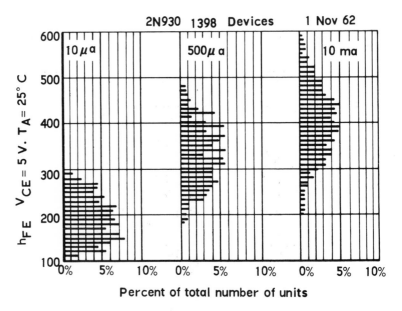

Figure 5

where
$$S_{p\ in} = \text{Signal power in}$$
$$N_{p\ in} = \text{Noise power in}$$
$$S_{p\ out} = \text{Signal power out}$$
$$N_{p\ out} = \text{Noise power out}$$

Since each signal and its associated noise work into the same load, the expression for NF can be written in terms of voltage rather than absolute power.

$$NF = 20 \log_{10} \frac{\dfrac{S_i}{N_i}}{\dfrac{S_o}{N_o}} \qquad (10)$$

where
$$S_i = \text{Signal voltage in}$$
$$N_i = \text{Noise voltage in}$$
$$S_o = \text{Signal voltage out}$$
$$N_o = \text{Noise voltage out}$$

Equation (10) can be written in the following form:

$$NF = 20 \log \frac{S_{in}}{N_{in}} - 20 \log \frac{S_o}{N_o} \qquad (11)$$

If the source resistance R_g is known, then the input noise to the amplifier can be calculated by the relationship $N_i = \sqrt{4kT\Delta fR_g}$. By setting the input signal 10 times greater than the input noise, the first term on the right side of the equation reduces to 20 db.

$$NF = 20 \text{ db} - 20 \log \frac{S_o}{N_o} \qquad (12)$$

With a noiseless amplifier, the second term would also be 20 db, indicating that the noise figure of the amplifier is zero. In an actual amplifier, the second term will be something less than 20 db — say, 19 db — making the amplifier NF = 1 db.

Figure 6 shows a test set-up for the described noise measurement. The audio oscillator at the input supplies a signal ten times greater than the input noise produced by R_g. Depending upon the amount of available power gain or the output signal level of the network *under test,* the low-noise amplifier may or may not be needed. The bandwidth is set by the filter. Potentiometer R_1 allows the VTVM to be adjusted to a convenient zero point (or varies the system gain). Output levels are observed with an oscilloscope to be sure that no clipping or stray 60-cycle pickup occurs within the circuit.

A step-by-step procedure for measuring noise figure is as follows:

1. Calculate input-noise voltage. $N_i = \sqrt{4kT\Delta fR_g}$.
2. Set signal level equal to ten times (20 db) the noise level.
3. Adjust R_1 so that the VTVM reads 10 db on some convenient scale.
4. Reduce the input signal to zero and note how many db the meter falls.
5. Subtract the meter drop (in db) from 20 db to obtain the NF of the amplifier.

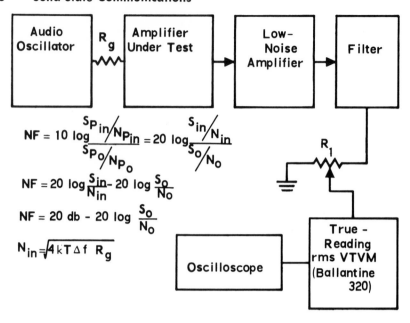

Figure 6

Referring to Eq. (12), steps number 1 and 2 set the 20-db term. Steps 3 and 4 determine the output signal-to-noise ratio $(20 \log S_o - 20 \log N_o)$. Step 5 subtracts the last term from the 20-db term, thus yielding NF.

In making noise measurements, a true-reading rms voltmeter (such as a Ballantine model 320) must be used. An average, or peak-reading, rms calibrated meter will give erroneous readings (unless suitable correction factors are used).

Some comment should be made on the accuracy of this method of measurement. This method is based upon the assumption that the output signal and noise can be measured separately (Eq. 12). This is not exactly true. The signal can be removed while reading the output noise; however, the noise cannot be turned off while measuring the output signal. In effect, the measured value of the output signal will also include the output noise. The last term in Eq. (12) is therefore changed to

$$20 \log \sqrt{S_o^2 + N_o^2} / N_o$$

(The numerator is written in this form because "The rms value of the total wave is the square root of the sum of the squares of the rms values of the components.") The error in this measurement may be figured by first calculating the measured noise figure (NF_m) and subtracting this from the true noise figure (NF_T).

$$\text{Error db} = NF_T - NF_m = 20 \log \sqrt{\left(\frac{S_o}{N_o}\right)^2 + 1} - 20 \log \frac{S_o}{N_o} \qquad (13)$$

To keep the error to a minimum, the signal-to-noise ratio should be as large as possible. The larger the S_o/N_o is, the less difference there is between the two terms in Eq. (13).

Equation (13) is plotted as a function of NF_m (Fig. 7). From this curve, the true noise figure may be obtained by adding the error (in db) to the measured noise figure. Two curves are shown in Fig. 7. The first curve is for the case where the input signal-to-noise ratio is selected to be 20 db while the second curve represents an input signal-to-noise ratio of 30 db. Each 10-db increase in the input signal-to-noise ratio transposes the curve 10 db to the right along the abscissa. For a 20-db input signal-to-noise ratio, transistor noise figures may be measured up to 10 db with less than 0.5-db error. This may be acceptable since the overall error of the equipment may be greater than 0.5 db anyway. Convenient levels for the input signal-to-noise ratio are 20 db and 40 db because they set the signal an even 10 times and 100 times greater than the noise.

The above method can be used for the broadband noise measurement (3 db down at 10 cps and 10 kc) or the spot noise measurement (narrow bandwidth). Because of the limited bandwidth in the spot noise method, the input signal and noise powers are greatly reduced as compared to the broadband measurement. Thus more gain will have to be supplied to increase the output to measurable levels. As bandwidths narrow, the time required to average the output readings increases. If the bandwidth is sufficiently small, an integrating circuit with a fairly long time constant may be required on the rms meter monitoring the output.

1/f Region. As operation in the audio range is pushed to lower frequencies the observed noise figure is seen to increase. The noise increase approaches a -3 db/octave slope asymptotically as frequency decreases. The 1/f noise curve in effect gives an indication of the relative amount of power that each noise generator at each frequency is capable of delivering. Thus, the noise power at 50 cps is twice the noise power at 100 cps (assuming these points are well within the 1/f region). The characteristic dependence of noise on frequency in this area labels this noise as 1/f noise. Since it is difficult to relate 1/f noise analytically to specific transistor parameters, empirical methods must be relied upon to furnish the desired information necessary to characterize this region.

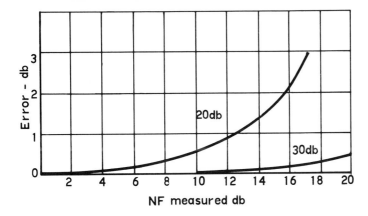

Figure 7

Of the various methods of noise characterization for the 1/f region, the most complete would be a spot noise check at a number of frequencies from well within the 1/f region to well within the plateau region. This method would plot out the actual NF curve and give detailed information at any frequency. This is not a practical method because of the time and cost involved in making a large number of noise measurements. (It is routinely done, however, on limited sample quantities for typical curves for the data sheet.)

Specifying the NF by the above method, but restricting the number of specified points to three yields a practical and very useful characterization. Of the three points selected:

1. One should be well within the 1/f region
2. One should lie on the "knee" of the curve
3. One should lie well within the plateau region

From these three points a fairly accurate picture of the low and middle frequency regions of the NF curve can be drawn. Figure 8 shows a typical curve drawn from three known points. A fourth point is actually also known. Considering the two asymptotes (1/f and plateau), the actual NF will be approximately 3 db higher than the cross point. Figure 9 shows a portion of the 2N2586 data sheet with the spot noise measurements. The three selected frequencies are 100 cps, 1 kc and 10 kc. A wideband NF is also given.

Specifying the noise corner frequency (the frequency where the NF is up 3 db from the plateau region) of transistors is not as useful a method as it might seem.

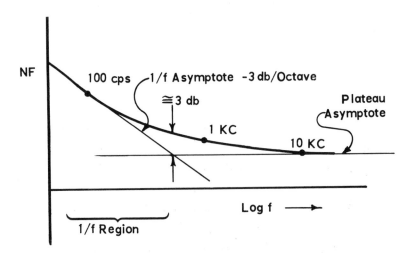

Figure 8

TENTATIVE DATA SHEET

TYPE 2N2586
N-P-N DOUBLE-DIFFUSED PLANAR SILICON TRANSISTOR

TYPE 2N2586
BULLETIN NO. DL-S 622987, AUGUST 1962

**FOR EXTREMELY-LOW-LEVEL,
LOW-NOISE, AMPLIFIER APPLICATIONS**

- Guaranteed Very-Low-Current h_{FE} — 80 min at $1\mu a$
- Guaranteed Low-Temperature h_{FE} — 40 min at $10\mu a$, – 55°C
- Complete Noise Characterization at $1\mu a$ and $10\mu a$
- Optional Package Available †

environmental tests

To ensure maximum integrity, stability, and long life, all finished transistors are subjected to sustained acceleration at a minimum of 35,000 G and verification of hermetic seal by the use of both helium leak and bubble testing.

mechanical data

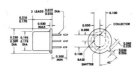

* THE COLLECTOR IS IN ELECTRICAL CONTACT WITH THE CASE.

* All JEDEC TO-18 dimensions and notes are applicable.

ALL DIMENSIONS ARE IN INCHES UNLESS OTHERWISE SPECIFIED.

*absolute maximum ratings at 25°C free-air temperature (unless otherwise noted)

Collector-Base Voltage	60 v
Collector-Emitter Voltage (See Note 1)	45 v
Emitter-Base Voltage	6 v
Collector Current	30 ma
Total Device Dissipation at (or below) 25°C Free-Air Temperature (See Note 2)	0.3 w
Total Device Dissipation at (or below) 25°C Case Temperature (See Note 3)	0.6 w
Operating Collector Junction Temperature	175°C
Storage Temperature Range	– 65°C to + 300°C

NOTES: 1. This value applies when the emitter-base diode is open circuited.
2. Derate linearly to 175°C free-air temperature at the rate of 2.0 mw/C°.
3. Derate linearly to 175°C case temperature at the rate of 4.0 mw/C°.
4. These parameters must be measured using pulse techniques. PW = 300 μsec, Duty Cycle ≤ 2%.

†Electrically identical transistors are also available upon request in TO-5 packages with the active elements insulated from the case.

*Indicates JEDEC registered data.

TEXAS INSTRUMENTS
I N C O R P O R A T E D
13500 N CENTRAL EXPRESSWAY
P. O. BOX 5012 • DALLAS 22, TEXAS

Figure 9

Two noise figure curves are shown in Fig. 10; one is for a high current gain device and the other is for a low current gain device. Both devices have the same 1/f characteristics and differ only in the plateau region. The figure shows that the higher current gain device will have a higher corner frequency (f_c) even though its noise performance is better than the low current gain device at all frequencies. The point where the −3 db/octave asymptote crosses the 0 db NF line is labeled f_n and is a function of only the 1/f noise. The point f_n would be independent of the plateau NF.

It should be noted that all of the curves in the 1/f noise region have assumed a constant bias point and R_g. This condition will not necessarily give optimum NF performance in the 1/f region. Consider for a moment a field-effect transistor. Since the 1/f noise comes from essentially one source, its representation can take the form of a single noise voltage generator in series with the input. This generator is considered in series with the e_n generator already mentioned. As operation is moved lower in frequency, the total voltage in series with the input increases. As e_u increases, the optimum source resistance will also increase to yield the optimum value for NF. (Alternatively, R_g may be held constant while bias current is decreased).

To illustrate this point, a curve (Fig. 11) of e_n and i_n as a function of frequency is given for the 2N2500 field-effect transistor. Notice the marked increase in e_n at low frequencies. Figure 12 illustrates the two cases where: first, 1/f curve was derived for a constant R_g, and second, R_g was selected for $R_{g(opt)}$ for each frequency.

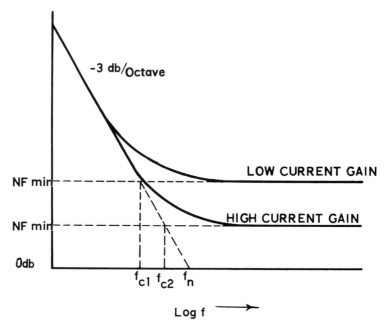

Figure 10

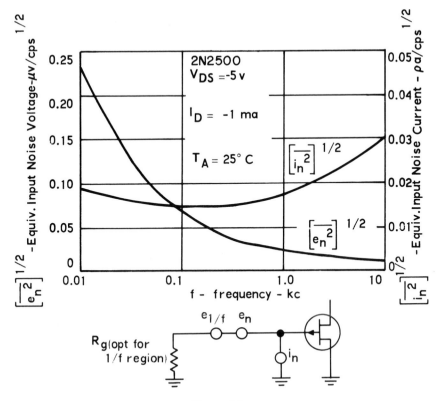

Figure 11

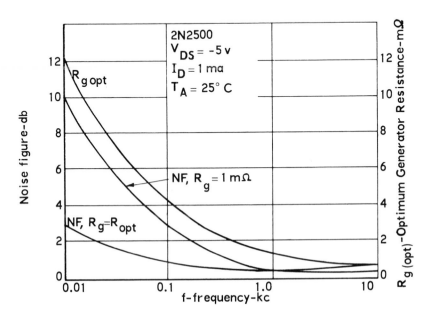

Figure 12

GENERAL CONSIDERATIONS IN LOW-NOISE DESIGN

Bias Point. Since NF is a function of I_E, care must be taken to bias the transistors for low-noise operation. In general, the bias current for best low-noise operation will lie somewhere between 10 μa and 200 μa. A specific bias point will call for a specific R_g to give minimum NF. As I_E decreases, this value of R_g usually increases.

In designing low-noise stages certain conditions are usually fixed so the designer does not have complete freedom in his design. If R_g is specified, the designer must select the device and bias current that will give the best low-noise results; however, the device and bias point may not be compatible with other circuit features such as stability and frequency response. When this occurs, compromises must be made. If the design calls for $I_E = 10$ μa for low-noise considerations, and the leakage current becomes 10 μa at elevated operating temperatures, it is obvious that a higher bias current must be used (sacrificing noise performance).

Devices. Figure 13 shows the noise figure of several TI devices as a function of frequency. The right device for any application will depend upon a compromise between circuit performance and cost.

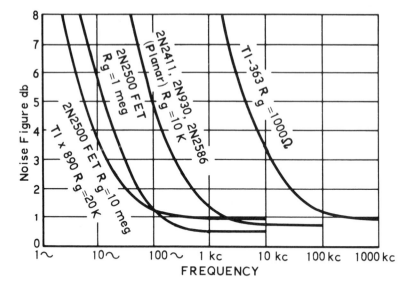

Figure 13

TERMS DEFINED

a	— constant
α_o	— low-frequency, common-base, a-c, current gain
Δf	— effective noise bandwidth
e_{Ln}	— thermal noise generator associated with the load resistor
e_n	— noise voltage generator
F	— noise factor
f_c	— corner frequency, NF curve has increased 3 db from the plateau region
f_n	— frequency at which the 1/f asymptote crosses the zero-db axis
F_{opt}	— optimum or minimum noise factor
e_{gn}	— thermal noise generator associated with the generator resistor
γ	— correlation factor
h_{fe}	— a-c current gain, common-emitter
h_{FE}	— d-c current gain, common-emitter
h_o	— output admittance of a transistor
i_n	— noise current generator
k	— Boltzmann's constant
NF	— noise figure, $NF = 10 \log F$
NF_m	— measured noise figure
NF_T	— true noise figure
N_i	— noise voltage in
N_o	— noise voltage out
$N_{p\ in}$	— noise power in
$N_{p\ out}$	— noise power out
R_g	— generator resistance
R_{in}	— input resistance
R_{open}	— resistance that simulates an open circuit
R_{opt}	— optimum generator resistance that gives minimum noise figure
R_{short}	— resistance that simulates a short circuit
r'_b	— ohmic base resistance in transistor equivalent circuit
r_e	— incremental emitter resistance in transistor equivalent circuit
S_i	— signal voltage in
S_o	— signal voltage out
$S_{p\ in}$	— signal power in
$S_{p\ out}$	— signal power out
T	— temperature in degrees Kelvin $T = 273 + \,^\circ C$

BIBLIOGRAPHY

"A Simplified Noise Theory and Its Application to the Design of Low-Noise Amplifiers," A. E. Sanderson and R. G. Fulks, IRE Transactions Audio, July-August, 1961, pp. 106–108.

1. "On the Two-Generator Method (e$_n$, i$_n$) of Noise Characterization," H. Cooke, Proc. IRE, Dec. 1962, pp. 2520–2521.
   "Optimum Noise Performance of Transistor Input Circuits," Middlebrook, Semiconductor Products, July/August 1958, pp. 14–20.
   "Noise Figure of Radio Receivers," Friis, Proc. IRE, Vol. 32, July, 1944, pp. 419–429.
   "Design Considerations for Low Noise Transistor Input Stages," W. A. Rheinfelder, Electronic Design, Sept. 13, 1961, pp. 48–52.
   "Interpreting Transistor Noise Performance," L. Calgano and R. E. Hobson, Electronic Industries, October, 1951, pp. 109–112.
   "Notes on Transistor Noise — What It Is and How It Is Measured," Norman H. Martens, Solid/State/Design, May, 1952, pp. 35–38.

2. "Behavior of Noise Figure in Junction Transistors," Nielson, Proc. IRE, July, 1957, pp. 957–963.
   Transistor Electronics, Dewitt and Rossoff, Chapter 16, McGraw-Hill Book Co., New York (1957).
   "Noise in Precision Film Resistors," Smith, Texas Instruments publication (August, 1961).
   Transistor Technology, Vol. 1, pp. 543–558, Bridgers, Schaff, Shive, D. Van Nostrand Co., Inc., New York.
   "Transistor AC and DC Amplifiers with High Input Impedance," Middlebrook and Mead, Semiconductor Products, March 1959, pp. 30–32.
   "A Recommended Standard Resistor, Noise Test System," Conrad, Newman, Stansbury, IRE Transactions on C. P., September 1960, pp. 71–88.
   "Noise Figure of the Darlington Compound Connection for Transistors," Bachmann, IRE Transactions on C. T., June 1958, pp. 145–147.
   Fluctuation Phenomena in Semiconductors, A. Van Der Ziel, Academic Press, Inc. (1959).
   "Noise Aspects of Low-Frequency Solid-State Circuits," A. Van Der Ziel, Solid/State/Design, March 1962, pp. 39–44.
   "Theory of Junction Diode and Junction Transistor Noise," A. Van Der Ziel, Proc. IRE., March 1958, pp. 589–594.
   "Noise in Junction Transistors," A. Van Der Ziel, Proc. IRE, June 1958, pp. 1019–1038.
   "Transistor Noise Figure," Harry F. Cooke, Texas Instruments Inc., Solid/State/Design, February 1963, pp. 37–42.
   "Transistor Noise Factor Tester," James J. Davidson, Semiconductor Products, February 1959, pp. 15–20.
   Transistor Circuit Analysis, Joyce and Clark, Chapter 7, Addison-Wesley Publishing Co., Reading, Mass. (1961).

"Representation of Noise in Linear Two-Ports," H. A. Haus, Proc. IRE, Jan. 1960, pp. 69–74.

"Optimum Noise Figure of Transistor Amplifiers," F. M. Gardner, IEEE Transistors on C. T., March 1963, pp. 45–48.

Acknowledgement. The author wishes to thank Harry Cooke for his helpful suggestions and valuable technical advice.

13

Transistor Gain Control

by Bill Tulloch

INTRODUCTION

Amplifiers are usually designed to meet predetermined gain, pass-band, and noise requirements. Additional requirements are created when these amplifiers are used as integral parts of a system. The requirement discussed here is the ability of a system to handle input signals that have wide dynamic ranges. A receiver that is capable of receiving input signals from several microvolts to several hundred millivolts without distorting the intelligence is an example of such a system.

To meet this requirement the designer provides a means of controlling the gain of the individual amplifier stages. This is accomplished by the use of feedback to automatically control the bias of the amplifier. The gain of a transistor amplifier can be controlled by three methods: external gain control, internal gain control, or a combination of external and internal control called hybrid gain control.

EXTERNAL GAIN CONTROL

External gain control is accomplished by reducing the signal available to either the input or the output of the amplifier. Three examples of external gain control are presented in Fig. 1. Figure 1a is of the input shunt type, in which the control element reduces the signal available to the input of the transistor, thereby reducing the effective gain of the stage. The output shunt type is shown in Fig. 1b; in this type, the gain is reduced by decreasing the collector a-c impedance. In Fig. 1c the control element is used to provide emitter degeneration to reduce the gain of the stage.

The major disadvantage of external gain control is the additional components needed for the separate biasing of the control elements. Since the characteristics of an external-gain-controlled amplifier are only slightly dependent on the characteristics of the transistor, the balance of this discussion deals with internal and hybrid gain control methods.

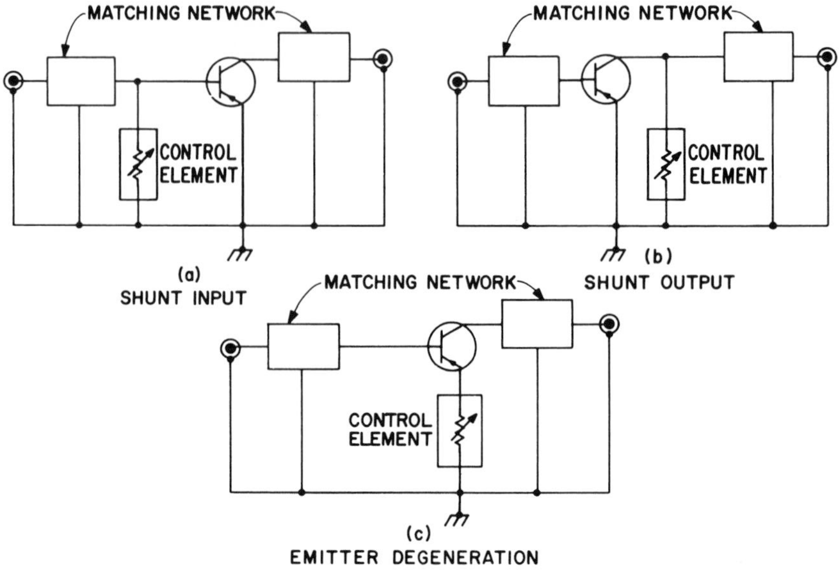

Fig. 1. Types of external gain control.

INTERNAL GAIN CONTROL

The internal gain control characteristics of a transistor amplifier may be predicted, given sufficient knowledge of the parameter variations versus bias. To obtain this information it is necessary to measure parameters of a number of transistors at various operating conditions for the frequencies of interest. The amplifier gain is then calculated at each bias point using conventional design techniques. It is enormously time-consuming to evaluate each amplifier to be designed for gain control.

Another method of evaluation is to design the amplifier for the desired gain, pass-band, and noise requirements using the manufacturer's recommended bias conditions. Once the amplifier has been constructed, the gain control characteristics may then be measured rapidly. This is the technique used in obtaining the curves presented later. There are three types of transistor internal gain control: forward, reverse, and tetrode.

Forward gain control is accomplished by varying the collector-base (or collector-emitter) voltage in accordance with the collector current. Figure 2 is a diagram of a forward-gain-controlled amplifier. The collector current increases as the AGC voltage is increased and V_{CB} is reduced due to the additional voltage developed across R_C. The output impedance of the transistor is considerably reduced at the high-current low-voltage conditions, so an increase in bandwidth is to be expected. The other transistor parameter variations are dependent on the type of transistor, frequency of operation, and circuit components. Forward gain control usually accepts larger input signals as the gain is reduced.

Figure 3 is a diagram of a reverse-gain-controlled amplifier. The gain of such an amplifier is reduced by decreasing the collector current with the collector voltage remaining relatively constant. There is no collector dropping resistor (R_C)

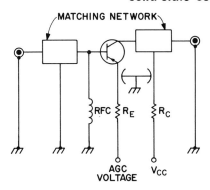

Fig. 2. Forward gain control.

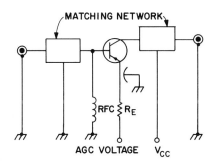

Fig. 3. Reverse gain control.

for this type of control. The bandwidth change is less with reverse gain control than with forward gain control; however, reverse gain control amplifiers have a decreasing input signal capability as the gain is reduced.

Figure 4 is an example of a tetrode-gain-controlled amplifier. Tetrode gain control is obtained by varying the base-2 current. The base-2 current for gain control ranges approximately from -100 to $+100\,\mu a$ depending on the frequency of operation and the desired gain range. A tetrode gain control amplifier uses less AGC power than the other two types and will handle increasingly larger input signals as the gain is reduced.

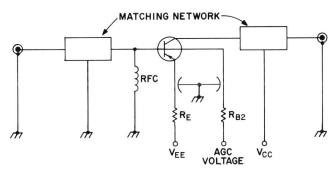

Fig. 4. Tetrode gain control.

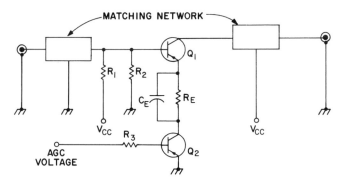

Fig. 5. Hybrid gain control.

HYBRID GAIN CONTROL

There are systems that demand the acceptance of maximum input signals of one to ten volts. None of the internal gain control types will perform this function. By using a transistor for the control element as shown in Fig. 5, it is possible to control the gain by two methods simultaneously. For maximum gain conditions, Q_2 is in saturation and Q_1 is biased for the desired gain and noise requirements. For gain control, the AGC voltage is changed so that Q_2 is brought out of saturation. The output impedance of Q_2 is increased as the collector current is decreased, providing emitter degeneration. At the same time, the collector current of Q_1 is also being reduced, giving reverse gain control action. This type of gain control has two advantages: a greater reduction in gain is possible in this type than with the reverse gain control only. Second, the capability of handling input signals of a large magnitude is available due to the increasing emitter impedance. The noise figure of this method of gain control usually is no more than 1 db greater than that of the basic amplifier at the same bias conditions.

GAIN-CONTROLLED AMPLIFIER STAGES

Six transistor amplifiers are presented to demonstrate the different methods of gain control. The gain, bandwidth, and center frequency characteristic curves are shown so that comparisons may be made. Maximum gain in the forward and reverse gain control curves are at the same bias point. The noise figures discussed are measured at this bias condition. Noise figure is of primary interest only at this point since at the reduced gain levels the signal-to-noise ratio is larger. Insertion gain is defined as the ratio of the output power to the generator power into the same load. Maximum input signal capability is defined as the RMS signal measured at the input of the amplifier that will result in a 0.75-db change in the output power with a 1-db input power change.

Figure 6 is a schematic of a 30-mc amplifier. This amplifier is used to evaluate both reverse and forward gain control characteristics. R_C is zero ohms for reverse gain control and 1000 ohms for forward gain control. The gain is 15 db with a typical noise figure of 5 db. Figure 7 shows that the reverse gain control range is 25 db from a collector current of 1.5 milliamps to 20 microamps. Figure 8 shows the pass-band characteristics with f_1 and f_2 being the lower- and upper-half power frequencies, respectively. Center frequency is indicated as f_0. Bandwidth change is less than 2:1 over the range shown.

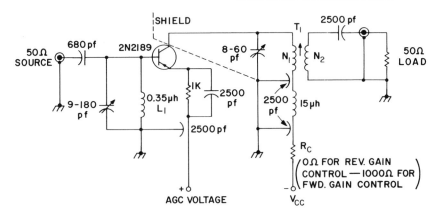

TYPICAL PERFORMANCE

$V_{CB} = -9v$; $I_C = -1.5ma$

GAIN = 15db
NF = 5db

T_1 – N_1 = 10t #30 WIRE
N_2 = 3t #30 WIRE
BIFILAR WOUND ON
CTC # PLS62C4L/20063D
COIL FORM

L_1 – 6t AIR DUX # 408

Fig. 6. 2N2189 30-mc amplifier.

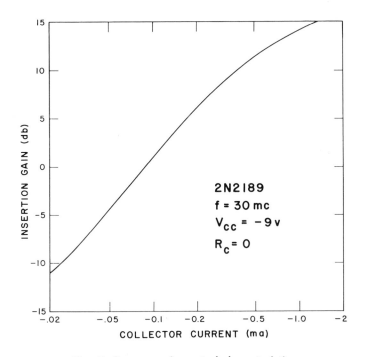

Fig. 7. Reverse gain control characteristics.

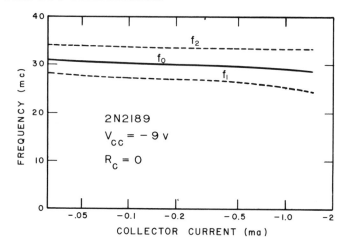

Fig. 8. Reverse gain control pass-band characteristics.

Figure 9 is the forward gain control characteristic. This circuit provides 20 db of forward gain control, but essentially all of the change is in the 8- to 10-milliamp region of collector current. The flatness of this curve can be used as a form of delayed AGC. Figure 10 presents the forward gain control pass-band characteristics. This curve is limited to 8 milliamps due to the large change in bandwidth and center frequency at higher currents. This change is caused by the transistor approaching saturation. Input signal capability is 35 millivolts at maximum gain, 3 millivolts at minimum reverse gain, and only 10 millivolts at minimum forward

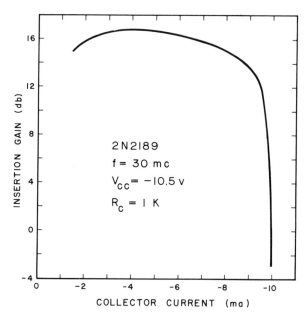

Fig. 9. Forward gain control characteristic.

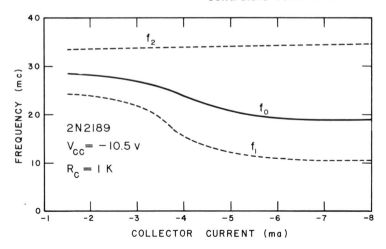

Fig. 10. Forward gain control pass-band characteristics.

gain. Lower signal capability at minimum forward gain is another indication that the transistor is almost in saturation.

Figure 11 is a 30-mc tetrode amplifier. Collector voltage and current are kept constant and the gain is changed in accordance with the base-2 current. The collector-base voltage is + 20 volts and the collector current is 1.3 milliamps. The gain is 21 db with a typical noise figure of 6 db at the base-2 current of − 100 microamps. Tetrode gain control characteristics also show a delay (Fig. 12). Figure 13 gives the pass-band characteristics. The increase in bandwidth is caused by a decrease in output impedance of the tetrode as the gain is reduced. The input signal capability of this circuit is 25 millivolts at − 100 microamps of base-2 current and 300 millivolts at + 20 microamps of base-2 current.

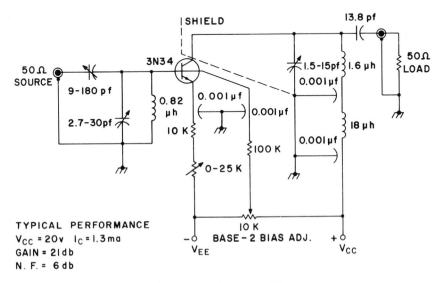

Fig. 11. 3N34 30-mc amplifier.

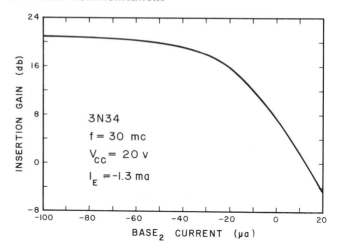

Fig. 12. Tetrode gain control characteristic.

Figure 14 is a 70-mc neutralized amplifier. At a collector voltage of −6 volts and a collector current of 2 milliamps, the gain is 27 db with a typical noise figure of less than 3 db. R_C for reverse gain control is 0 ohms and for forward gain control is 1000 ohms. Figure 15 shows a reverse control range of 35 db. The slope of this curve is approximately 20 db of gain for a decade of current change. Figure 16 presents the reverse gain control pass-band characteristics. The bandwidth is increasing at the lower current levels with this circuit. Figure 17 is the forward gain control characteristic. Forward gain control of 47 db is made available by increasing the collector current to approximately 7 ma. Again we notice a delay in the characteristic before the gain begins to fall. In Fig. 18 the bandwidth has greater than 4:1 change as the current is increased to 6 milliamps. The input signal capability is 40 millivolts at maximum gain, 5 millivolts at minimum reverse gain, and 200 millivolts at minimum forward gain.

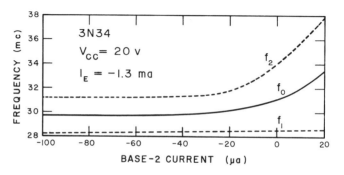

Fig. 13. Tetrode gain control pass-band characteristics.

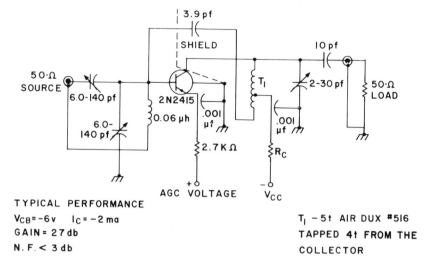

TYPICAL PERFORMANCE
$V_{CB} = -6v$ $I_C = -2 ma$
GAIN = 27 db
N. F. < 3 db

T_1 – 5 t AIR DUX #516
TAPPED 4 t FROM THE
COLLECTOR

Fig. 14. 2N2415 70-mc neutralized amplifier.

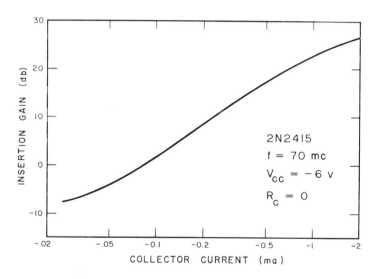

Fig. 15. Reverse gain control characteristic.

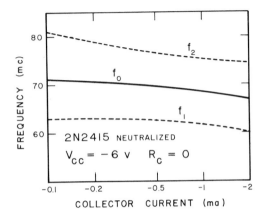

Fig. 16. Reverse gain control
pass-band characteristics.

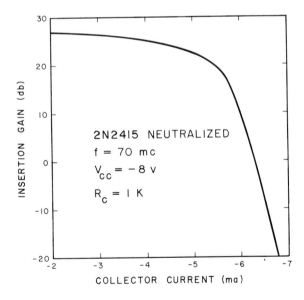

Fig. 17. Forward gain
control characteristic.

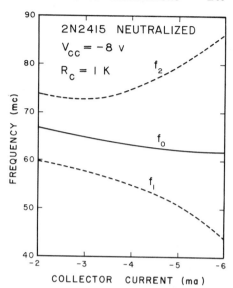

Fig. 18. Forward gain control pass-band characteristics.

Figure 19 is a 200-mc amplifier. At a collector voltage of -6 volts and a collector current of 1.5 milliamps, this circuit has a gain of 17 db with a typical noise figure of 3 db. Figure 20 presents the reverse gain control characteristic. There is a 32-db reduction in gain with a change in collector current from 1.5 milliamps to 20 microamps. This curve also has approximately 20-db change in gain per decade change of collector current. Figure 21 shows the reverse gain control pass-band characteristics. There is a 2:1 increase in bandwidth as the current is reduced, with a 24-mc change in the center frequency. Figure 22 indicates 24 db of forward gain control with the collector current increased to 9.5 milliamps. The top portion of this curve is not as flat as in some of the other amplifiers. Figure 23 is the forward gain control pass-band characteristic. This circuit has a 4:1 change in bandwidth with a 24-mc change in the center frequency as the gain is reduced for forward gain control. The input signal capability is approximately the same as for the 70-mc amplifier.

Figure 24 is a 450-mc amplifier that has a gain of 8 db with a typical noise figure of 4 db when biased with a collector voltage of -6 volts and a collector current of 2 milliamps. Figure 25 is the reverse gain control characteristic. Gain control of 21 db is available by decreasing the collector current to 20 microamps. The gain change is beginning to level off at 40 microamps of collector current for this amplifier. Figure 26 indicates only small changes in the pass-band characteristics for the full range of reverse gain control. This curve indicates that the pass-band characteristics for the 2N2415 at 450 mc are very stable with gain control. Figure 27 shows a 26-db range of forward gain control by increasing the collector current to 7 milliamps. Again we notice a delay region in the forward gain control characteristic before the gain begins to fall. Figure 28 indicates less than 1.5:1 increase in bandwidth with a collector current of 6.5 milliamps. There is practically no change in center frequency. The input signal capability is 50 mv at maximum gain, 20 mv at minimum reverse gain, and 500 mv at minimum forward gain. This indicates that the 2N2415 also performs very well as a forward-gain-controlled amplifier at 450 mc.

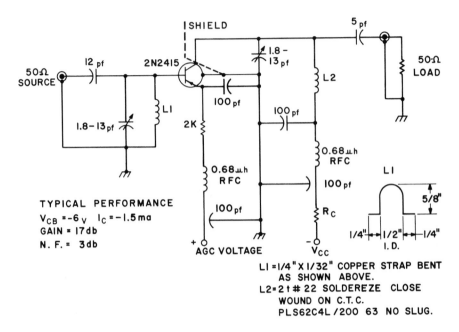

TYPICAL PERFORMANCE
$V_{CB} = -6$ v $I_C = -1.5$ ma
GAIN = 17 db
N. F. = 3 db

L1 = 1/4" X 1/32" COPPER STRAP BENT
AS SHOWN ABOVE.
L2 = 2 t # 22 SOLDEREZE CLOSE
WOUND ON C.T.C.
PLS62C4L /200 63 NO SLUG.

Fig. 19. 2N2415 200-mc amplifier.

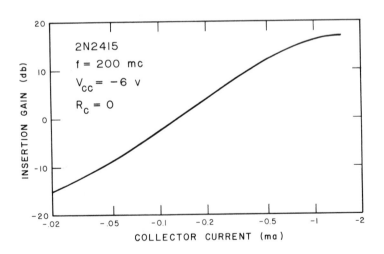

Fig. 20. Reverse gain control characteristic.

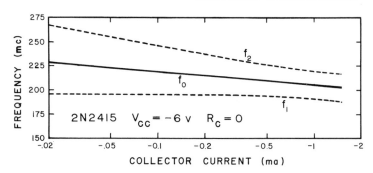

Fig. 21. Reverse gain control pass-band characteristics.

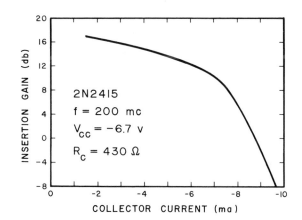

Fig. 22. Forward gain
control characteristic.

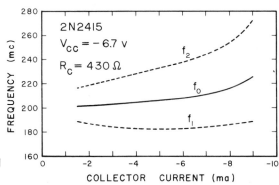

Fig. 23. Forward gain control
pass-band characteristics.

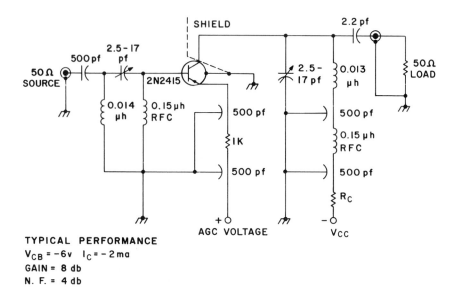

TYPICAL PERFORMANCE
V_{CB} = −6v I_C = −2 ma
GAIN = 8 db
N. F. = 4 db

Fig. 24. 2N2415 450-mc amplifier.

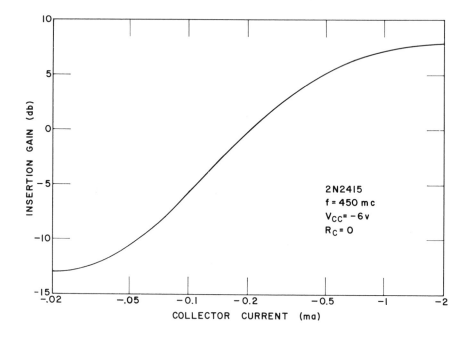

Fig. 25. Reverse gain control characteristic.

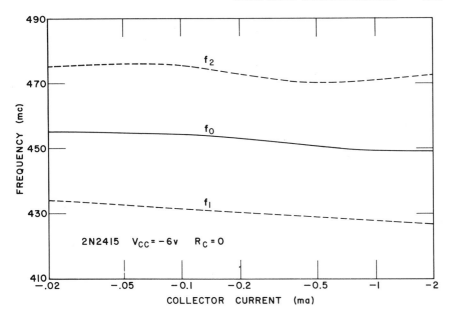

Fig. 26. Reverse gain control pass-band characteristics.

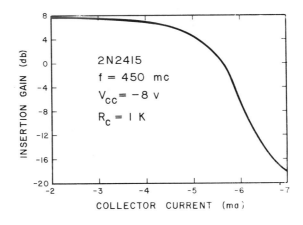

Fig. 27. Forward gain control characteristic.

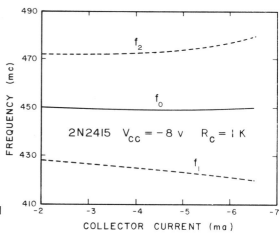

Fig. 28. Forward gain control pass-band characteristics.

Figure 29 is the 30-mc amplifier shown in Fig. 6, modified to demonstrate the hybrid gain control method. Q_2 acts as a variable impedance to give emitter degeneration, which is a form of external gain control. Q_2 also controls the collector current of Q_1 to give reverse gain control action, an internal gain control method. Figure 30 is the gain control characteristic for this circuit. The gain control range is 33 db (6 db more than for Fig. 6). There is a sharp change in gain as the collector current is reduced due to the increase in impedance of Q_2 as it is brought out of saturation. Figure 31 presents the pass-band characteristic of the hybrid circuit. There is a 2:1 change in bandwidth over the gain control range with most of the change from 1.0 to 1.5 ma of collector current. The center frequency shift is less than 1.5 mc. This circuit has a typical noise figure of 5.5 db (only 0.5 db more than that of Fig. 6). The input signal capability is 35 mv at maximum gain, but it is 11.5 volts at minimum gain. This is possible because of the high emitter impedance that Q_2 provides.

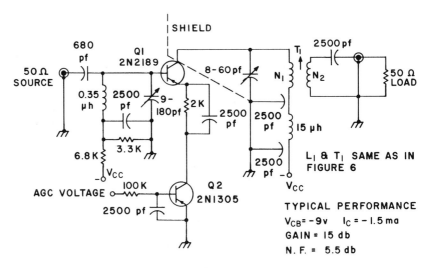

Fig. 29. 2N2189 30-mc amplifier (hybrid gain control).

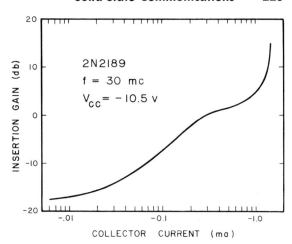

Fig. 30. Hybrid gain control characteristic.

COMMENTS

Comparisons of the different gain control methods may be made; however, the gain control characteristics of an amplifier depend not only on the transistor characteristics but are also influenced by the matching networks. Therefore, these comments are generalized only and may vary with individual circuits.

Reverse gain control circuits usually have a fairly predictable gain variation. The signal-handling capability decreases as the gain is reduced, and the changes in pass-band characteristics are reasonable. The AGC power required is relatively low.

Forward gain control characteristics vary more widely and depend upon the type of transistor, frequency, value of collector d-c resistance (R_C), and matching networks. Forward gain control will normally handle increasingly larger input signals as the gain is reduced unless transistor "saturation" is approached. The bandwidth will increase with reduced gain due to the decrease in transistor impedance with the increase in collector current. Higher AGC power is necessary to give the high collector currents for forward gain control.

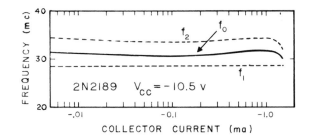

Fig. 31. Hybrid gain control pass-band characteristics.

Tetrode gain control requires the least amount of AGC power, and is able to accept increasing input signals as the gain is reduced. Receivers, using tetrodes, have been built that have greater than 100 db of linear gain control with close tolerances on the gain and phase characteristics.

The hybrid gain control circuit has the advantage of reverse gain control but also has the ability to handle input signals of much larger amplitudes with little degradation of available gain or noise figure. This method requires only an additional transistor, resistor, and capacitor.

BIBLIOGRAPHY

1. Shea, R. F.: *Transistor Circuit Engineering,* Wiley, N. Y., 1957.
2. Lo, et al: *Transistor Electronics,* Prentice-Hall, Englewood Cliffs, N. J., 1955.
3. Hunter, L. P.: *Handbook of Transistor Electronics,* McGraw-Hill, N. Y., 1956.
4. Terman, F. E.: *Radio Engineer's Handbook,* McGraw-Hill, N. Y., 1943.
5. Langford-Smith, F.: *Radiotron Designer's Handbook,* 4th ed., RCA Manufacturing Co., N. Y., 1954.
6. Texas Instruments Inc., *Transistor Circuit Design,* McGraw-Hill, N. Y., 1963.
7. Shirman, J.: "Designing a Stable Transistor AGC Amplifier," *Electronic Design,* May 11, 1960.
8. Weldon, L. A.: "Designing AGC for Transistorized Receivers," *Electronic Design,* Sept. 13 and Oct. 11, 1962.
9. Franke, Eugene: "AGC Design for Wide-Range Inputs," *Electronic Design,* Nov. 8, 1962.
10. Chow, W. F., and A. P. Stern: "Automatic Gain Control of Transistor Amplifiers," Proceedings of the IRE, Sept. 1955, pp. 1119–1127.

14

RF Harmonic Oscillators

by George Johnson

This chapter discusses some of the fundamentals of RF harmonic oscillator design. The characteristic equation for the various oscillator configurations is used to develop expressions for the natural frequency of oscillation and the necessary conditions for buildup of oscillation. Causes of frequency instability and methods of improving stability are discussed. The effects of changing load, changing passive parameters, and changing active parameters are analyzed. A brief treatment of crystal oscillators is presented along with a discussion of the crystal itself. Finally, a design procedure is proposed, and circuit examples are presented.

The general treatment of oscillators in this chapter is on a linear basis. However, the conditions of self-sustained oscillation must necessarily be nonlinear. Because of this linear analysis restriction, certain interesting topics such as limiting output voltage and current amplitude will be treated on a very approximate basis. To analyze these aspects more accurately would require limit-case solutions of the nonlinear differential equation describing the oscillator current or voltage in the phase plane, which are beyond the scope of this treatment.

OSCILLATOR CONFIGURATIONS

Necessary Conditions for Oscillation. The first necessary condition for self-sustained oscillation in a circuit is that the active device permit power gain at the frequency of oscillation. Furthermore, the device must have sufficient gain to overcome circuit losses and establish exactly unity gain around the feedback loop. The second necessary condition is that the phase shifts introduced by the active device and the feedback network result in exactly zero phase shift around the overall circuit.

These conditions will permit sustained oscillations, but they do not guarantee that oscillations will occur. In other words, it is not enough that unity loop gain can exist. There must be more than unity loop gain at first to cause buildup of oscillations. These, then, are the necessary and sufficient conditions for the buildup and maintenance of self-sustained oscillation in a circuit.

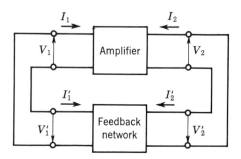

Fig. 1. Feedback oscillator configuration.

Basic Configurations. Most oscillator circuits can be regarded as having two basic components: the amplifier and the frequency-selective feedback circuit. This arrangement is known as a *feedback oscillator,* and is shown in Fig. 1. The frequency-selective circuit can be further reduced to the network arrangement shown in Fig. 2. This configuration allows a clear visualization of each of the basic oscillator types. If K_2 and K_1 are capacitors and K_3 is an inductor, the circuit is a Colpitts type. Figure 3 shows this configuration. If K_1 and K_2 are inductors and K_3 is a capacitor, the configuration is called a Hartley oscillator and is shown in Fig. 4. Figure 5 shows the Hartley configuration realized with a two-winding transformer. The choice between a two-winding transformer and a tapped coil depends partly on the frequency of operation, since the expressions for the natural frequency of oscillation are slightly different. Also, the tapped coil requires an extra d-c isolation capacitor, which is not necessary with the two-winding transformer. Because of the possibility of obtaining phase reversal with the two-winding transformer, the transistor can be changed from common base to common emitter.

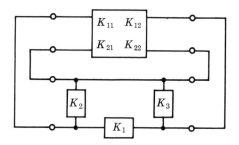

Fig. 2. π-type feedback oscillator.

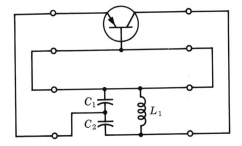

Fig. 3. The Colpitts type circuit.

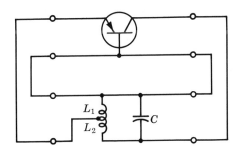

Fig. 4. The tapped Hartley circuit.

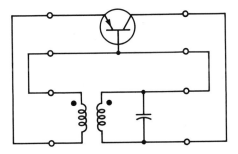

Fig. 5. Two-winding Hartley oscillator.

A modification to the Colpitts circuit results in the Clapp oscillator. In this circuit, the resonant frequency is determined primarily by the series combination of L and C. Figure 6 shows the arrangement. Where there is a requirement for high stability, crystals may be used for the frequency-determining element. A configuration using a crystal is shown in Fig. 7.

Some of the many possible modifications to the above basic configurations are shown in the circuit performance section. These arrangements of the active device and passive structure have been made so that it will be easy to combine the two-terminal pair parameters of each *black box* into one equation characterizing the composite network. The set of equations characterizing the active device in h parameters is shown in Eqs. (1) and (2).

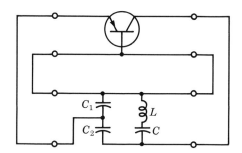

Fig. 6. The Clapp oscillator.

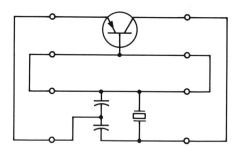

Fig. 7. Crystal oscillator.

$$V_1 = h_{ib}I_1 + h_{rb}V_2 \tag{1}$$

$$I_2 = h_{fb}I_1 + h_{ob}V_2 \tag{2}$$

Equations (3) and (4) characterize the passive structure.

$$V_1' = h_{11}I_1' + h_{12}V_2' \tag{3}$$

$$I_2' = h_{21}I_1' + h_{22}V_2' \tag{4}$$

The combination of these black boxes results in a set of equations which completely characterize the composite network. For the networks of the type shown in Fig. 2, the combination must be accomplished as indicated in Eqs. (5) and (6).*

$$V_1'' = (h_{ib} + h_{11})I_1'' + (h_{rb} - h_{12})V_2'' \tag{5}$$

$$I_2'' = (h_{fb} - h_{21})I_1'' + (h_{ob} + h_{22})V_2'' \tag{6}$$

Oscillator connections are special cases, however, since $V_1'' = 0$ and $I_2'' = 0$. These restrictions create the set of simultaneous homogeneous linear equations shown in Eqs. (7) and (8).

$$0 = (h_{ib} + h_{11})I_1'' + (h_{rb} - h_{12})V_2'' \tag{7}$$

$$0 = (h_{fb} - h_{21})I_1'' + (h_{ob} + h_{22})V_2'' \tag{8}$$

This set is, by definition, the characteristic equation of the combined network; and its solution for the imaginary part will yield the natural frequency of the system. This may be done by inserting actual circuit values into Eq. (9) and solving for the imaginary part equated to zero.

$$(h_{ib} + h_{11})(h_{ob} + h_{22}) - (h_{rb} - h_{12})(h_{fb} - h_{21}) = 0 \tag{9}$$

Evaluation of the real part of the expression is done in a similar way to yield the unity gain and, hence, starting conditions. Table 1 lists the natural frequencies and starting conditions for various configurations.

TANK CIRCUIT

Considerations for the Tank Circuit. Tuned LC circuits can be made to store energy. Used for this purpose, they have acquired the nickname of "tank" circuits. The frequency-determining LC circuit of an oscillator is such an example. The three essential parameters of the oscillator tank circuit are natural frequency of oscillation, selectivity, and characteristic impedance. The tank performs the following functions:

1. It determines the frequency of oscillation.
2. It is the feedback network.
3. It determines the stability of the oscillator.
4. It is a part of the coupling network to the load.
5. It affects the noise energy output of the oscillator.
6. It is a principal factor determining the circuit efficiency.

For a well-designed oscillator, the reactive components surrounding the tank are negligible in their effect on the resonant frequency set by the L and C of the tank.

---

*See Ref. 3, p. 553, for further discussion.

It is easily seen in Figs. 1 to 3 that the tank can be treated as a feedback network connected across the active device. Even in the Clapp connection of Fig. 6 this is still true, but now the feedback is primarily determined by divider action of C_1 and C_2, and the frequency is determined by L and C in series.

Frequency stability is primarily determined by the Q_L of the tank. The reason for this is that the frequency deviation required to develop a given phase correction to establish exactly 360° phase shift around the feedback loop is inversely proportional to the loaded Q. Frequency stability is usually the most difficult specification to meet, and meeting it will usually more than satisfy the other requirements of constant Q and constant characteristic impedance. In other words, the environment of the tank tends to change not only for f_o, but also Q and Z_o: * By satisfying the requirement for stability of f_o, one usually satisfies the requirements of stability of Q and Z_o also.

The load on a transistor oscillator is usually magnetically or capacitively coupled into the tank circuit. The load determines both the power drawn from the oscillator and the loaded Q of the tank circuit. The ratio of loaded Q to unloaded Q for the tank circuit should be low for good circuit efficiency.

Components of the Tank. *Capacitors.* One of the most desirable types of capacitors for use in RF oscillators is the silvered-mica type. Since the silver plates are applied on the mica by vacuum evaporation, the silvered-mica capacitor is much more stable than ordinary mica capacitors with plates of foil pressed against the mica insulation. Mica has high secular† stability, a low temperature coefficient of capacity, and a low power factor. Typical values are $+ 20$ ppm/°C temperature coefficient and 0.015% power factor at 1 mc, over a range of -60°C to $+ 80$°C. Dielectric constants of 6 are typical. Very low parasitic inductance and d-c leakage (the leakage is principally over the surface of the plastic jacket) are features of the silvered-mica capacitor.

Ceramic capacitors offer two interesting advantages. Ceramic has, when mixed with titanium, negative temperature coefficients as high as 750 ppm/°C and about 10 times greater dielectric constant than mica. These advantages lead to the following possibilities: First, owing to the negative temperature coefficient, some compensation can be made for the positive coefficient of most inductance coils. Second, since such high dielectrics are available, it is possible to obtain large capacitance in small noninductive structures. Secular stability is very good, and power factors range from 0.02 to 0.05% at 1 mc to 0.04 to 0.1% at 100 mc. The temperature coefficient with frequency is about constant between 1 and 100 mc.

Inductance. Normally, the capacitors used in LC tank circuits of RF oscillators have very low losses compared to the losses in the coil. For this reason, the unloaded Q of a resonator depends almost entirely on the Q of the coil. The exact design of a coil is quite complicated because of the many factors which must be considered. The coil must have the correct inductance and be stable with time and temperature. It must have low parasitic capacitance and a high, reasonably stable unloaded Q.

The form of inductance coil most frequently used in RF circuitry is the single-layer solenoid, although powdered iron cores are sometimes used for better Q or for a variable inductance. The inductance is determined by the number of turns

---

*Z_o is the antiresonant tank resistance.

†Secular stability is the property of a material which enables it to retrace its path when one of its parameters is cycled with respect to temperature.

and the geometry of the coil. The self-inductance and the resistivity will vary with the frequency because of proximity and skin effects. Since the resistivity of a conductor varies rapidly with temperature changes, the inductance of a coil may be very sensitive to temperature changes, even though no appreciable change occurs in its dimensions. The problem, therefore, is to design the coil so that its dimensions are independent of time, temperature, and atmospheric conditions. The current distribution through the wire cross section must also be independent of temperature over the range specified.

If severe vibration is not expected, a coil may be self-supported at one end and connected at the other end by flexible braid. This results in reasonably stable coils having low losses. If both ends are rigidly attached, temperature-expansion coefficients may become a problem.

As stated before, the self-inductance of a coil is a function of skin effect. Skin effect is, in turn, a function of conductivity. At high frequencies the penetration of current into the conductor is very shallow, while at low frequencies it may cover the entire cross section. The inductance is a function of both frequency and resistivity. Since this resistivity increases rapidly with temperature, the inductance also increases. The temperature coefficient of copper is about 4,000 ppm/°C, and the inductance coefficient due to this effect alone may be as high as 100 ppm/°C. At higher frequencies, where small inductance values are needed, sheet-copper strap is used to form the coil. This provides a large surface area and reduces skin effect for a given inductance.

Because it is expensive as well as difficult to build coils with low positive temperature coefficients of inductance, negative-temperature-coefficient capacitors are often used for compensation. This method is sometimes impractical, however, since the elements must track each other and must be reproducible in large-scale production.

Typically, a poorly built LC resonator may be affected by temperature so that its self-resonant frequency drifts by about 40 ppm/°C. The drift of a GT cut crystal will usually be 1/10,000 as great.

Crystal Discussion. When extreme frequency stability is required of an oscillator, a crystal is usually used as a substitute for the tank circuit or in the feedback loop to stabilize the frequency. The tolerance on most commercial crystals is about 0.002% from −55 to +90°C. An example of a Colpitts-Pierce crystal-oscillator configuration is shown in Fig. 7. Here the crystal is operated at a frequency just slightly below its parallel resonant frequency so that it will appear as an inductance.

The equivalent circuit for a crystal is shown in Fig. 8.

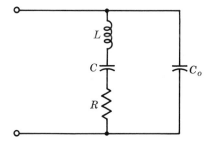

Fig. 8. Equivalent circuit of

a quartz crystal.

The L is analogous to the mass of the crystal structure, C is analogous to the crystal elasticity, and R is analogous to mechanical friction, accounting for energy lost as heat in the crystal. C_o is the total effective shunt capacitance contributed by the distributed capacitance of the leads and terminals of the mounting structure, the nonvibrating electrostatic capacitance across the quartz-crystal faces with the quartz serving as the dielectric, and any capacitance added by the crystal holder.

Crystals may also be operated at certain overtones of the fundamental, but even though the overtone Q is approximately the same as the fundamental Q, the activity or piezoelectric effect will be progressively smaller, the higher the overtone. Also, since in the parallel mode the activity is inversely proportional to the square of the terminal capacitance, care should be taken to minimize external capacitance so as to preserve crystal activity.

In RF circuits, the dissipation must often be held to a few milliwatts. Temperature coefficients are normally specified in the form of Eq. (10):

$$\text{Drift} = \frac{\Delta f/f_o}{\Delta T} \qquad (10)$$

In other words, the specification is in parts per million per degree or in per cent per degree. This coefficient can be positive, negative, or zero over small temperature ranges, depending on the crystal cut. Crystal-oscillator design will not be elaborated here, in view of the wide range of crystal types and possible circuits.

ACTIVE DEVICE

Requirements.   The primary function of the active device is to develop enough output power at the frequency of operation to supply the required load power, the tank losses, and the drive power for itself. It should also generate as little noise voltage as possible. The active device should have a maximum frequency of oscillation well above the design frequency. Because these requirements are rather loose, many transistor types will function properly as oscillators. However, certain types of manufacturing processes result in device parameters which yield better oscillator performance. Paramount among these is the epitaxial mesa technique which allows a relatively lower value of effective collector bulk resistance, permitting higher operating efficiency.

Parameter Variation.   At low frequencies the transistor parameters in the characteristic equation do not have large imaginary components, but at RF frequencies these parameters must be inserted in the characteristic equation in complex form. Solution of the real and imaginary parts, therefore, will include the effects of input, output, and transfer immittances. The sensitivity of frequency and starting conditions to changes in any of these immittances with the temperature, age, or bias point can be evaluated. Examination of Table 1 and the design example shows the form of these equations and the specific parameters involved.

FREQUENCY STABILITY

Causes of Frequency Instability.   Oscillator frequency stability is a measure of the amount of drift in frequency away from the design center value. There are two causes of drift. First, the active parameters may change. The equations for ω^2 in Table 1 indicate the particular active parameters involved. Inserting actual

Table 1.

Circuit	Natural frequency (ω^2)	Starting condition
Colpitts	$= \dfrac{1}{LC} + \dfrac{r}{L}\dfrac{1}{C_1 h_{ie}} + \dfrac{\Delta h_e^*}{C_1 h_{ie}} + \dfrac{h_{oe}}{C_1 C_2 h_{ie}}$ $\cong \dfrac{1}{LC}\left(1 + \dfrac{LCh_{oe}}{C_1 C_2 h_{ie}}\right)$ where $C = \dfrac{C_1 C_2}{C_1 + C_2}$ and r = a-c series resistance of coil L	$h_{fe} > \dfrac{r(C_1 + C_2)h_{ie}}{L} + \dfrac{C_2}{C_1} + \dfrac{C_1}{C_2}\,\Delta h_e \cong \dfrac{C_2}{C_1}$
Colpitts	$= \dfrac{1}{LC} + \dfrac{h_{ob}}{h_{ib}C_1 C_2} \cong \dfrac{1}{LC}$	$h_{fb} > \dfrac{-C_2}{C_1 + C_2}$
Hartley (tapped)	$= \dfrac{h_{ie}}{C(Lh_{ie}) + (L_1 r_2 + L_2 r_1)h_{fe} + (L_1 L_2 - M^2)h_{oe}}$ $\cong \dfrac{1}{LC + (L_1 L_2 - M^2)\dfrac{h_{oe}}{h_{ie}}}$ where $L = L_1 + L_2 + 2M$ r_1 = a-c series resistance of coil L_1 r_2 = a-c series resistance of coil L_2	$h_{fe} > \dfrac{rLCh_{ie} + (M + L_1)^2 + (L_1 r_2 + L_2 r_1)\dfrac{\Delta h_e^*}{h_{ie}}}{(L_1 + M)(L_2 + M)}$ $\cong \dfrac{L_1 + M}{L_2 + M} \cong \dfrac{1 + KN}{1/N^2 + KN}$ where $K = \dfrac{M}{\sqrt{L_1 L_2}}$ $N = \sqrt{\dfrac{L_2}{L_1}}$
Hartley (tapped)	$= \dfrac{1}{LC + (h_{ob}/h_{ib})(L_2 L_1 - M^2)} \cong \dfrac{1}{LC}$ where $L = L_1 + L_2 + 2M$	$h_{fb} > \dfrac{L_1 + M}{L_1 + L_2 + 2M} \cong -\dfrac{N_1}{N_2}$ where N_1 = number of turns of L_1 N_2 = number of turns of L_2
Clapp	$\cong \dfrac{1}{LC} + \dfrac{1}{L}\dfrac{C_1 + C_2}{C_1 C_2}$ where C = series capacity with L	$h_{fb} > -\dfrac{C_2}{C_1 + C_2}\,h_{fe} > \dfrac{C_2}{C_1}$

*Δh_e = common-emitter determinant = $h_{ie}h_{oe} - h_{re}h_{fe}$.

values gives an indication of their influence. Second, the passive parameters may change. Both active and passive parameters generally change for two reasons: temperature and age.

Specification of Frequency Stability. An explicit expression for frequency variation with temperature is given in Eq. (11).

$$\text{Drift} = \frac{\Delta f / f_o}{\Delta T / T_o} \tag{11}$$

This expression gives the sensitivity of center frequency, f_o, to temperature change at a particular center frequency and operating temperature. Another expression that can be used is given in Eq. (12),

$$\text{Drift} = \frac{\Delta f / f_o}{\Delta T} \tag{12}$$

usually expressed as parts per million per centigrade degree.

Techniques for Improving Frequency Stability. As mentioned earlier, minimization of active device influence will improve stability. For the Colpitts connection, this is satisfied by the following inequality:

$$\frac{h_{ob}}{h_{ib} C_1 C_2} < \frac{C_1 + C_2}{L C_1 C_2} \tag{13}$$

Similar inequalities for other oscillator connections may be found from Table 1. Selection of an active device which satisfies this inequality is therefore the first technique.

The second technique is to *swamp out* part of the particular active parameter which enters the frequency expression by putting appropriately sized resistances in series with h_{ib} and in parallel with h_{ob}. The characteristic equation below shows the effect of this approach.

$$(h_{ib} + R_1 + h_{11p})(h_{ob} + \frac{1}{R_2} + h_{22p}) - (h_{rb} - h_{12p})(h_{fb} - h_{21p}) = 0 \tag{14}$$

Now if $h_{ib} < R_1$ and $h_{ob} < 1/R_2$, the equation becomes

$$(R_1 + h_{11p})(G_2 + h_{22p}) - (h_{rb} - h_{12p})(h_{fb} - h_{21p}) = 0 \tag{15}$$

The resonant frequency is solved for in the same way, except that now R_1 and G_2 are the terms in the expression instead of h_{ob} and h_{ib}.

The effect of load change on frequency may be shown by inserting Y_L into the characteristic equation. This is shown in Eq. (16).

$$(h_{ib} + h_{11p})(h_{ob} + h_{22p} + Y_L) - (h_{rb} - h_{12p})(h_{fb} - h_{21p}) = 0 \tag{16}$$

If $Y_L < (h_{ob} + h_{22p})$, its change will be minimized in the expression for frequency. This condition is generally established by a buffer stage. On the other hand, the solution of Eq. (16) for Y_L will yield the maximum load conductance which will still satisfy the conditions for oscillation. This load is important if the oscillator is intended as a power source rather than as a frequency source.

OSCILLATOR DESIGN PROCEDURE

Discussion. The design procedure for transistor oscillators is usually treated on a linear basis even though self-sustained oscillation indicates nonlinear operation. Therefore, the preliminary design calculations provide only approximate values for components, and these components must be adjusted experimentally in the final design.

Since a design procedure must be tailored to the individual oscillator specification no exact procedure can be given other than the general steps involved. The following is a listing of these design steps:

Design Steps

1. Select a transistor capable of providing sufficient gain and desired power output at the operating frequency, based on data sheet specifications.
2. Select the oscillator configuration to be used, based on the application. For example, the oscillator will probably be used either as a frequency-determining element or as a source of power at a given frequency.
3. Design the d-c bias network to establish the bias point and provide the necessary stability.
4. Design the tank or frequency-determining network using the formulas for operating frequency and starting conditions given in "Oscillator Configurations" and in Table 1. The table gives natural frequency (ω^2) and starting conditions in terms of h parameters.
5. Make necessary adjustments in the feedback and bias networks to optimize efficiency. Be sure not to sacrifice ease of starting when adjusting the bias network for possible class B or C operation.
6. Use a trimming capacitor to make final adjustments, if necessary, to oscillator frequency.

DESIGN EXAMPLE

Specifications for the low-power oscillator design example are as follows:

$$f_o = 90 \text{ mc}$$
$$V_o = 2V_{(rms)} \text{ across a 1,000-ohm load}$$
$$V_{CC} = 10 \text{ volts}$$

The design procedure is as follows:

1. Select the 2N743 to provide this specified output power and voltage. It has an f_t which is, at the normal bias point of 5 volts and 5 ma, about three times f_o.
2. The Colpitts connection is selected for this frequency range because it yields values of tank inductance and capacitance which should be fairly insensitive to transistor parameter variation. The circuit configuration is shown in Fig. 9.
3. The d-c values for the network are as follows:
   Let the drop across R_3 be 2.5 volts.

$$R_3 = \frac{2.5 \text{ volts}}{5 \text{ ma}} = 500 \text{ ohms}$$

Let the current through R_1 and R_2 be 5 ma, so that the value of R_2 will be

$$R_2 = \frac{3.1 \text{ volts}}{5 \text{ ma}} = 620 \text{ ohms}$$

This leaves $V_{R1} = 10 - 3.1 = 6.9$ volts; if I_B is about 0.4 ma,

$$R_1 = \frac{6.9 \text{ volts}}{5.4 \text{ ma}} = 1.3 \text{ kilohms}$$

R_4 will have about 2.5 volts across it; therefore,

$$R_4 = \frac{2.5 \text{ volts}}{4.5 \text{ ma}} = 550 \text{ ohms}$$

4. The a-c circuit design is carried out as follows: Since R_2 is 620 ohms, adequate bypass is about 5 ohms. This gives $C_1 = 300$ pf; to avoid a self-resonant frequency at or around 90 mc, C_1 must have a total lead length less than 0.4 ma. C_4 and C_5 are 500-pf feed-through capacitors.

At 5 volts, 5 ma, and about 90 mc, the h_b parameters for the 2N743 are:

$$h_{ib} = 21.3 \; \underline{/\;45.6°} = (15.2 + j15) \text{ ohms} \tag{17}$$

$$h_{rb} = 0.069 \; \underline{/\;77°} = 0.0672 + j0.0154 \tag{18}$$

$$h_{fb} = 0.97 \; \underline{/\;182.3°} = -0.969 - j0.039 \tag{19}$$

$$h_{ob} = 2.76 \times 10^{-3} \; \underline{/\;15.3°} = (2.66 + j0.73) \times 10^{-3} \text{ mho} \tag{20}$$

The expression for ω^2 is

$$\omega^2 = \left(\frac{h_{ib}}{L} + \frac{h_{ob}}{C_1 + C_2} \right) \frac{C_1 + C_2}{C_1 C_2} \frac{1}{h_{ib}}$$

$$= \frac{1}{L} \frac{C_1 + C_2}{C_1 C_2} + \frac{h_{ob}}{h_{ib}(C_1 C_2)}$$

$$= \frac{1}{L\, C_1 C_2/C_1 + C_2} + \frac{1}{h_{ibr}/h_{obr}(C_1 C_2)} \tag{21}$$

By experimentally adjusting the capacitance ratio of the tank, we found that the following ratio gave the desired signal across the 1-kilohm load:

$$\frac{C_2}{C_3} = \frac{43}{91} = 0.47 \qquad \frac{C_2 C_3}{C_2 + C_3} = \frac{(43)(91)}{134} = 29 \text{ pf}$$

The inductance is 0.11 μh ($\cong$ 2 turns no. 18 wire on $\frac{1}{2}$ in. diameter.) $V_o = 2$ volts across the 1-kilohm load.

In order to determine the effect of the transistor parameters on the frequency of oscillation, we will compare the values obtained from the following expressions. Frequency determined by considering only the tank:

$$\omega^2 = \frac{1}{L[C_1C_2/(C_1 + C_2)]}$$

$$\omega_0{}^2 = \frac{1}{(0.11 \times 10^{-6})(29 \times 10^{-12})}$$

$$f_0 = \frac{1}{(6.28)(3.2 \times 10^{-18})^{1/2}} = \frac{1}{(6.28)(1.79)10^{-9}} = 90 \text{ mc}$$

Using h_{ibr} and h_{obr} equal to 15.2 ohms and 2.66×10^{-3} mho, respectively,

$$\omega_0{}^2 = \frac{1}{L[C_1C_2/(C_1 + C_2)]} + \frac{1}{(h_{ibr}/h_{obr})(C_1C_2)}$$

$$= \frac{1}{(0.11 \times 10^{-6})(29 \times 10^{-12})} + \frac{1}{(15.2/2.66)\,3.94 \times 10^{-18}}$$

$$= 0.313 \times 10^{18} + 0.044 \times 10^{18}$$

$$\omega_0{}^2 = 0.359 \times 10^{18} \qquad f_0 = 95.4 \text{ mc}$$

Evaluation of the operating frequency, using the full set of complex values for the h parameters, indicates that the frequency is still almost completely determined by the tank components. Experimental measurements of frequency agreed very well with the predicted value. Figure 9 shows the circuit.

ADDITIONAL CIRCUITS AND PERFORMANCE

23-mc Oscillator. The 23-mc push-pull oscillator of Fig. 10 was designed to deliver 75 mw to a 50-ohm load. A π-matching network is used to optimize the output to a 50-ohm load with a noncritical design for the output transformer. Transistor type used is the Dalmesa 2N2188.

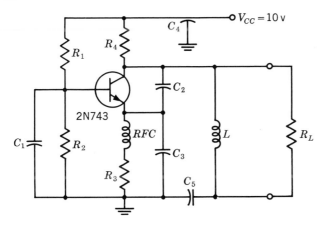

Fig. 9. 95-mc oscillator. Circuit uses a silicon epitaxial mesa to deliver about 2 volts (rms) across a 1-kilohm load at 95 mc. Typical circuit efficiency $\cong$ 3%.

24-mc Oscillator. Figure 11 shows a 24-mc Clapp oscillator designed to deliver 300 mw into a 50-ohm load. Typical collector efficiency is 35%. The transistor type used is the 2N696.

30-mc Oscillator. Figure 12 shows a 30-mc oscillator designed to operate over a temperature range of −40 to +60°C. Typical power out is 23 mw at −40°C and 20 mw at +60°C. Typical collector efficiency is 30%. Transistor type used is the Dalmesa 2N2188.

60-mc Oscillator. The common-base circuit in Fig. 13 is a 60-mc oscillator designed to deliver approximately 10 mw to a 50-ohm load at 25°C. Collector efficiency is typically 8 to 10%. Transistor type used is the Dalmesa 2N2188.

BIBLIOGRAPHY

1. Linvill, J. C., and J. F. Gibbons: "Transistors and Active Circuits," McGraw-Hill Book Company, Inc., New York, 1961.
2. Cote, A. J., Jr., and J. B. Oakes: "Linear Vacuum Tube and Transistor Circuits," McGraw-Hill Book Company, Inc., New York, 1961.
3. Gartner, W. W.: "Transistors: Principles, Design, and Applications," D. Van Nostrand Company, Inc., Princeton, N. J., 1960.
4. Reich, H. J.: "Functional Circuits and Oscillators," D. Van Nostrand Company, Inc., Princeton, N. J., 1961.
5. Pullen, K. A.: "Handbook of Transistor Circuit Design," Prentice-Hall, Inc., Englewood Cliffs, N. J., 1961.

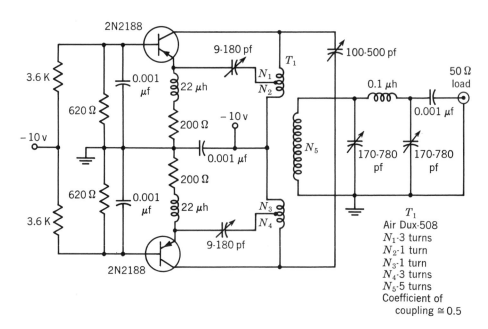

Fig. 10. 23-mc push-pull oscillator.

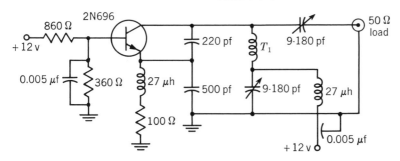

Fig. 11. 24-mc oscillator.

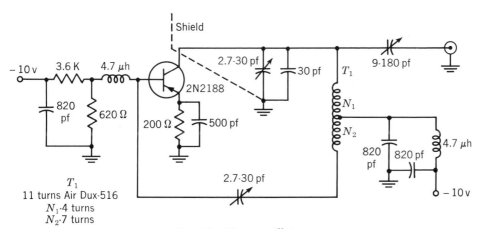

Fig. 12. 30-mc oscillator.

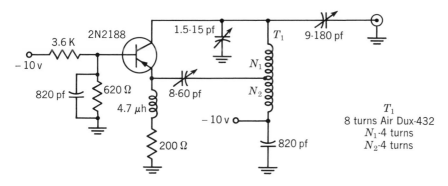

Fig. 13. 60-mc oscillator.

6. Edson, W. A.: "Vacuum Tube Oscillators," John Wiley & Sons, Inc., New York, 1953.

7. Guillemin, E. A.: "Communication Networks," 2 vols., John Wiley & Sons, Inc., New York, 1931, 1935.

8. Buchanan, J. P.: Handbook of Piezoelectric Crystals for Radio Equipment Designers, *WADC Tech. Rep.* 56–156, ASTIA Document AD 110448, October, 1956.

15

Transistors in Wide-band Low-distortion Amplifiers

by Roger Webster

INTRODUCTION

Line amplifiers used for repeaters or multicouplers are characterized by:
1. Wide bandwidths
2. Very low distortion and intermodulation products
3. Modest output power level
4. Modest power gain
5. Wide dynamic range

The frequency spectrum of the amplifiers to be discussed extends from a few hundred Kc to 30 Mc or higher. Intermodulation products should be down 60 db or more at maximum signal levels. The output power level is in the order of 10 to 50 mw and the gain is in the order of 10 to 15 db.

The dynamic range is a function of the difference between system noise and the maximum signal handling capability. For a given maximum signal level, dynamic range will be maximum for a system with lowest noise figure.

GENERAL CONSIDERATIONS

Type of Transistor. Linear operation over a wide range of frequencies is a prime consideration. Operating the transistor at fairly high currents and voltages serves to restrict current and voltage swings to a small percentage of the operating point, and generally enhances linearity. For these and other reasons to be discussed later, the desirable transistor characteristics may be summarized as follows:
1. Fairly substantial dissipation capability
2. Fairly high current and voltage rating
3. High cutoff frequency relative to operating frequency
4. Fairly low capacitance
5. The following parameters should be as independent of operating point (i.e., current and voltage) as possible:

a. current gain
b. base resistance
c. cutoff frequency
d. capacitance
e. emitter and collector body (parasitic) resistance.
6. Low collector-base leakage current
7. High d-c current gain
8. Low base resistance

Although either silicon or germanium might be used, requirements 1 and 2 can more easily be met with silicon in a small-area, low-capacitance device. Low capacitance is important because of the requirement that the device operate at reasonably high frequencies. Characteristics 6, 7, and 8 are included because transistor applications require low-noise devices.

Configuration. The common-base connection is clearly superior for greatest linearity and smallest gain variation with frequency. A comparison of the common-emitter and common-base transfer characteristics will demonstrate the inherent advantage of common-base operation. Figure 1 shows such a comparison.

Fortunately, gain requirements are usually modest and, thus, common-base operation is satisfactory. A further advantage of common-base operation is that gain is primarily determined by an impedance transformation ratio, which is determined by the external circuit rather than the device. A still further advantage is that the output impedance of the common-base stage is both much higher and more independent of operating point than is the common-emitter output impedance.

DISTORTION ANALYSIS

Generation of Harmonics and Intermodulation Products.

Harmonics, cross modulation and intermodulation products are produced by non-linearity in the input-output characteristics. The three principle effects ordinarily considered are:[1]

First order: Output is strictly proportional to input. No intermodulation or cross modulation products exists.

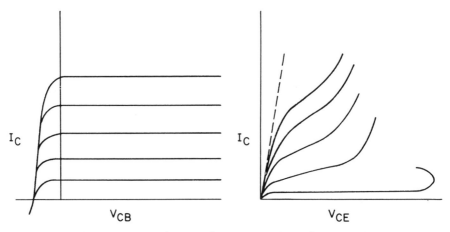

Fig. 1. Common-base and common-emitter characteristics.

Second order: Output is proportional to the square of the input signal, and to curvature of the transfer characteristics. It generates a d-c component, second harmonics, and sum and difference frequencies if two input signals are present.

Third order: Output is proportional to the cube of the input signal, and to rate of change of curvature of the transfer characteristics. It generates third harmonics and odd-order combination frequencies if two input signals are present (e.g., $2\omega_a \pm \omega_b$ or $2\omega_b \pm \omega_a$).

Since there is a fundamental component proportional to the cube of the input signal, the total output at the fundamental is not proportional to the input. Moreover, when two signals are present, the amplitude of the first is dependent upon the amplitude of the second, giving rise to cross-modulation.

Higher-order components cause similar effects. Even orders generate even harmonics, d-c components, and even-order combination frequencies, while odd orders generate odd harmonics, odd-order combination frequencies, lack of proportionality between input and output, and cross-modulation.

As a practical matter, second-order and all higher even-order effects may be substantially reduced by a balanced push-pull circuit. Thus the third-order effect is ordinarily the dominant effect in the class of amplifiers described here.

Sources of Distortion in Transistors.

1. Nonlinear input characteristics:

  a. Emitter-base diode characteristics:

    The emitter-base diode has the usual semiconductor diode exponential current-voltage relationship. Ideally, this relationship is:

$$I = I_o \left(e^{\frac{qV}{kT}} - 1 \right) \tag{1}$$

A series expansion of this relationship shows that all harmonics are present in the current flow for a sinusoidal applied voltage. The relative magnitude of the harmonics is proportional to the applied voltage. When two sinusoidal voltages are applied, intermodulation and cross modulation products are also generated.

When $e^{\frac{qV}{kT}} \gg 1$, the rate of change of current in the ideal diode is:

$$\frac{dI}{I} = \frac{q}{kT} \, dv \tag{2}$$

Thus, in the ideal diode, the curvature of the diode characteristic for a given change in voltage is independent of the current. As a result, the relative magnitudes of the distortion components are functions only of the applied signal voltages, and are independent of the operating current.

  In any practical structure, the foregoing statements must be modified considerably. This will be discussed further in a following section on the influence of the operating point.

b. Non-constant base resistance:

Any variation in base resistance will cause a corresponding variation in the input impedance. Variations in base resistance result primarily from (1) modulation of resistivity by heavy injection of minority carriers, and (2) base-width modulation. There are at least two different causes of base-width modulation. A variation in base width results because the collector-base junction depletion layer width is dependent on applied voltage. As voltage changes, the location of the edges of the junction depletion layer moves. This is known as the "Early" effect[2] and is shown in Fig. 2. Base-width modulation is also caused by the inability of the collector depletion region or the collector body, or both, to support more than some finite current density without radical changes in internal parameters. The depletion layer contracts and tends to move into the collector body, thus in effect widening the base.[3]

2. *Non-constant transfer characteristics:*

Not all of the emitter current is injected into the base, nor does all of the injected current reach the collector, nor is the collector current all injected current. This may be expressed as follows:

$$\alpha = \alpha^* \beta \gamma \qquad (3)$$

where α = emitter-collector current gain
  α^* = collector multiplication factor
  β = base transport efficiency
  γ = emitter injection efficiency

The fact that none of these factors is unity is not a problem in itself. However, these factors are not constant and depend on terminal currents and voltages. This results in non-constant transfer characteristics and nonlinear distortion. Some of the factors influencing each of these will be discussed in the following paragraphs.

Variation of emitter injection efficiency results from a variation in the total number of base impurities as seen by the emitter. This is caused by base-width

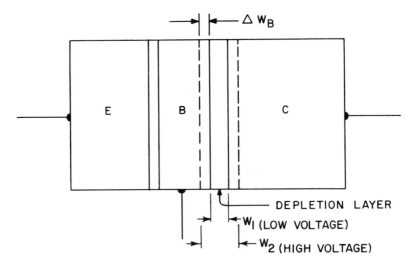

Fig. 2. Early effect — base width modulation.

modulation and base-conductivity modulation. Both of these were discussed in the previous section.

The variation of base transport efficiency also results in a corresponding change in current gain and, thus, a nonlinear transfer characteristic. This variation is primarily caused by base-width modulation. Since high-frequency current gain (common emitter) is inversely proportional[2] to base width, current gain may vary considerably. In common base, this may be manifested largely as a phase-angle modulation.

Collector multiplication may result from a number of factors. The most significant of these in modern transistors is collector junction avalanche multiplication. Collector avalanche multiplication occurs in the collector-base junction; thus it is out of the input-signal path. The multiplication factor is voltage dependent. For these two reasons, avalanche multiplication generates unwanted distortion components.

3. *Non-constant output characteristics:*

It may be shown analytically and experimentally that many of the previous variations will also influence the output impedance. This, in turn, introduces distortion components into the signal.

Influence of the Operating Point.

1. *Reduction of distortion components:*

Earlier, in discussing nonlinear input characteristics, it was shown that in the ideal diode the relative magnitudes of the distortion components are independent of the operating point. This is not true of practical structures because series impedances in the structure (notably base resistance) considerably modify the terminal characteristics. Consider the simple equivalent transistor input circuit shown in Fig. 3.[4]

$$I = I_0(\exp \frac{qV}{kT} - 1)$$

$$\text{WHEN} \quad V \gg \frac{q}{kT}$$

$$\frac{dI}{I} = \frac{q}{kT} dV$$

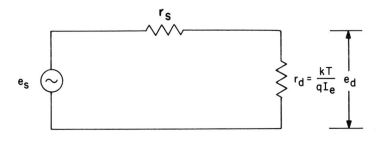

Fig. 3. Simple transistor input equivalent circuit.

In Fig. 3, e_s is an applied signal voltage, r_s is an equivalent series resistance, r_d is the emitter diode impedance, and e_d is the signal voltage appearing across the diode.

At large emitter currents, $r_d << r_s$, and in the simple voltage divider circuit shown:

$$e_d \propto \frac{1}{I_e} \tag{4}$$

Therefore, operation at high emitter current reduces distortion by virtue of the fact that the applied signal voltage across the diode proper is reduced. Two factors oppose increasing operating current indefinitely. Shot noise generated in the emitter-base and collector-base diodes is directly proportional to current, so that noise figure is degraded by increasing the operating current. Moreover, nonlinearities eventually appear in the transfer characteristics as current is increased. This leads to increased distortion components.

2. Cancellation or reduction of certain distortion products:

D. R. Fewer was the first to show that the second-order distortion products may be reduced substantially by proper selection of source impedance and emitter current.[5] However, the exact point at which this occurs is dependent on the individual transistor. Moreover, the third-order components do not show such a minimum, but in general tend to decrease as emitter current is increased. It therefore appears more practical to use balanced push-pull pairs to cancel second-order products, and to operate the transistors in a region of low third-order distortion.

CIRCUIT ARRANGEMENTS FOR DISTORTION REDUCTION

Boxall described a method for distortion reduction in which the base current of a common-base output stage is fed back into the input.[6] The base current is an exact measure of how far the collector current departs from the input current. If the input current represents exactly what is to be reproduced, then reinserting the base current at the input will give an output current which is an exact reproduction of the input current. Figure 4 shows how the reinsertion may be accomplished. The d-c circuitry is omitted for clarity.

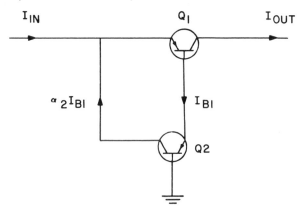

Fig. 4. Base current feedback.

If the current gain of Q_2 is close to unity, the desired effects are accomplished. The results of such a feedback arrangement are to:

1. make the effective overall current gain close to unity. If α_T is the overall current gain, then:

$$\alpha_T = \frac{\alpha_1}{1 - \alpha_2(1 - \alpha_1)} \qquad (5)$$

2. raise the effective output impedance:

$$Z_T = Z_1 \; \frac{1 - \alpha_2(1 - \alpha_1)}{1 - \alpha_2} \cong Z_1 \; \frac{\alpha_1}{1 - \alpha_2} \qquad (6)$$

where Z_1 is the open-circuit output impedance of Q_1 without feedback.

3. lower the distortion current flowing in the output:

$$D_T \cong (1 - \alpha_2) D_1 \qquad (7)$$

where D_1 is the per-unit distortion current flowing in the output without feedback.

Aldridge has shown a variation of this arrangement which he calls a "cascade" circuit.[7] Distortion reduction of 15 db of third-harmonic components at high frequencies is realized.

BIBLIOGRAPHY

1. Terman, F. E.: "Radio Engineers Handbook," McGraw-Hill Book Company, pp. 462–466, First Edition.
2. Early, J. M.: Effects of Space Charge Layer Widening in Junction Transistors, *Proc. IRE,* p. 1401, November, 1952.
3. Kirk, C. T., Jr.: A Theory of Transistor Cutoff Frequency (f_T) Fall Off at High Current Densities, *IRE Trans. on Electron Devices,* vol. ED-9, no. 2, p. 164, March, 1962.
4. Jones, B. L.: Cross Modulation in Transistor Amplifiers, *Solid State Design,* p. 31, November, 1962.
5. Fewer, D. R.: Transistor Nonlinearity — Dependence on Emitter Bias Current in PNP Alloy Junction Transistors, *IRE Trans. on Audio,* vol. AV-6, p. 41, 1959.
6. Boxall, F. S.: Base Current Feedback and Feedback Compound Transistor, *Semiconductor Products,* vol. 1, no. 5, pp. 17–24, September-October, 1958.
7. Aldridge, E. E.: Engineering Treatment of Transistor Distortion, *IRE Trans. on Circuit Theory,* vol. CT-9, p. 183, June, 1962.

16

VHF and UHF Amplifiers and Oscillators Using Silicon Transistors

by Harry F. Cooke

INTRODUCTION

The amplifiers, oscillators, and signal sources to be discussed in this chapter cover a variety of applications at frequencies from 500 Mc through X band. These include wide-band, low-noise amplifiers, oscillators delivering 50 mw at 2 Gc, harmonic power up to 25 mw at 4 Gc and (with a varactor multiplier) up to 25 mw at 9.2 Gc.

The transistors used in these applications are a new generation of UHF silicon devices.

THE TI 3016A AND 2N3570

The TI3016A and 2N3570 are identical electrically, but are supplied in different packages (TI-line* and TO-18, respectively). These devices are planar-epitaxial silicon transistors that feature very small dimensions made possible by advanced photomasking techniques. Interdigitated base and emitter contacts result in very low base resistance. Figure 1 is a photograph of the completed silicon chip. Four base fingers and three emitter fingers are clearly seen, as well as the expanded areas for making external contacts. The total area of the base diffusion window is 7.2 sq mils.

The outstanding performance of this unit results from the following high-frequency parameters:

1. very high cutoff frequency: $f_T \cong 1.8$ Gc
2. very low base resistance: $r_b' \cong 10$ to 20 ohms
3. low capacitance: $C_c \cong 0.5$ pf

These parameters are the result of the very narrow base (base width is in the order of 0.01 mils) and the other very small dimensions. The electrical charac-

*Trademark of Texas Instruments

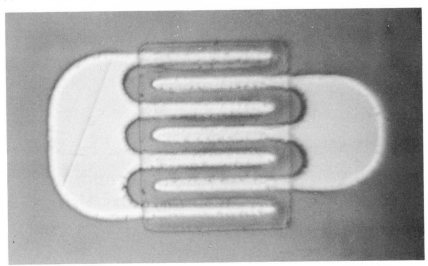

Fig. 1. 2N3570, TI3016A geometry showing the four base fingers and three emitter fingers.

teristics of this unit are summarized in Table 1.

Some of the design considerations involved in the TI3016A are of interest:

1. *High cutoff frequency:* Several structure-determined time constants are involved in cutoff frequency. The most important of these is the base width. An important phase of the development of this transistor was the development of suitable base and emitter diffusions so that a base width of about 0.01 mil could be consistently realized.

Table 1. Characteristics of 2N3570 and TI3016A

	2N3570 (TO-18 package) (Useful to 1.5 Gc and then package limited)			TI3016A (TI-line package)		
	Min.	Typical	Max.	Min.	Typical	Max.
BV_{CBO}	30 v ($10 \mu a$)			30 v ($10 \mu a$)		
h_{FE} (6 v, 5 ma)	20		200	20		200
$r_b'C_c$ (6 v, 5 ma)		5 psec	8 psec		5 psec	
f_T (6 v, 5 ma)	1.5 Gc	1.7 Gc			1.7 Gc	
NF 1 Gc (6 v, 2 ma)		6.0 db	7.0 db		6.0 db	
F_{max}		4 Gc			4 Gc	
P_o (1 Gc, 20 v, 15 ma)		60 mw		30 mw (2 Gc)		

2. *Low base resistance:* For convenience, the base resistance may be separated into two components: that part underneath the emitter and that part between the emitter and base contacts. The first part may be minimized by using very narrow emitters. The emitter width is about 0.1 mil in the TI3016A. The second part is minimized by close spacing between emitter and base contacts and by paralleling many paths. The spacing between emitter and base contacts is 0.2 mils in these units, and the interdigitated geometry provides six parallel paths.

Base resistance may also be lowered by proper diffusion profile, although other factors must be considered. The TI3016A has a very heavy concentration of impurities in the base and a very shallow diffusion front. These lower the resistivity of the base, particularly under the emitter where an appreciable portion of the base resistance usually exists.

By combining an optimum diffusion profile with interdigitated geometry, a small-signal silicon transistor with r_b' in the order of 15 ohms has been realized.

3. *Low capacitance:* Low capacitance is a desirable feature in any high-frequency device. The most effective way to reduce capacitance is to reduce the junction areas. The junctions of the TI3106A and 2N3570 are quite small; the actual areas are:

$$\text{Collector-base junction area} \cong 7.2 \text{ sq mil}$$
$$\text{Emitter-base junction area} \cong 0.9 \text{ sq mil}$$

It is possible to reduce collector capacitance by raising collector resistivity, or by increasing the collector-base voltage. There are practical limits to these changes, however, and other factors must be considered. Among these are collector series resistance, and behavior of the device at various voltages and currents (which is influenced by the width resistivity of the collector epitaxial region).

LARGE-SIGNAL BEHAVIOR OF TI3016A

These devices work well as large-signal oscillators and amplifiers. The factors that influence large-signal behavior are discussed here, along with some modifications to the basic structure which will permit even higher outputs.

Variation of Parameters. Under large-signal conditions, the a-c signal is of sufficient magnitude to influence the d-c operating point of the amplifier or oscillator. It is important, therefore, that the parameters be as nearly independent of current and voltage as possible. For example, the high-frequency current gain is always current and voltage dependent to some degree, but proper use of epitaxial techniques will tend to minimize this dependence.

At large-signal levels and high emitter currents, the input impedance of a transistor is essentially r_b'. Since this is a loss resistance, it is important to keep r_b' low — even more important than in the small-signal case. The collector capacitance C_C is voltage dependent and may vary considerably as the collector voltage swings with large signals. This effect is generally secondary compared to other effects, but may be useful to enhance harmonic generation.

Dissipation. Although the TI3016A and 2N3570 are relatively efficient devices and will deliver appreciable power at microwave frequencies, it is of interest to consider methods for increasing power handling capability.

Obviously, the package must provide adequate thermal properties, as well as the proper high-frequency characteristics.

A unique problem is associated with the silicon chip itself. The active area of the transistor is so small that it acts as a point source of heat. When the wafer or chip is mounted on an adequate header, the bulk of the thermal impedance is in the silicon wafer. Under these conditions, increasing the size of the active transistor area is an inefficient way to increase dissipation. It is more efficient thermally to provide two or more small units dispersed over the chip. If these units are separated by at least the thickness of the wafer, the thermal impedance is nearly inversely proportional to the number of units. The actual spacing between such multiple devices on a single chip is a compromise between dissipation and the parasitic inductance and capacitance added by interconnecting leads. Paralleling devices with evaporated lead patterns can significantly alter performance because of the additional capacitance of the leads.

Such multiple-unit-chip devices as the TIXS12 (four TI3016's in parallel) can offer greatly increased power capability. The TIXS12 produces a minimum of 0.25 watts at 1.5 Gc.

APPLICATION OF THE TI3016A AND 2N3570

A description of these devices, with some of their performance characteristics, has been presented earlier. This section provides more specific information on performance and circuit design using these devices.

Admittance Parameters. The admittance parameters provide probably the most useful source of information on gain, matching, and stability.* A complete set of the common-emitter admittance parameters is given in Figs. 2 through 5.

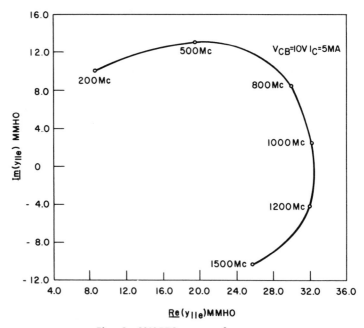

Fig. 2. 2N3570 y_{11e} vs. frequency.

*One of the more helpful considerations of admittance parameters is presented in Rollett, J. M.: Stability and Power Gain Invariants of Linear Twoports, *IRE Trans.*, vol. CT-9, no. 1, pp. 29–32, March, 1962.

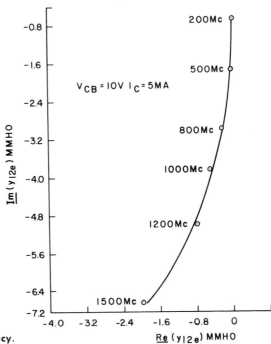

Fig. 3. 2N3570 y_{12e} vs. frequency.

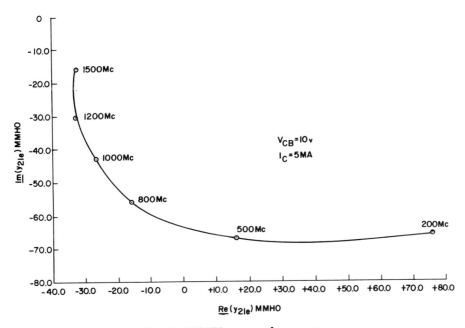

Fig. 4. 2N3570 y_{21e} vs. frequency.

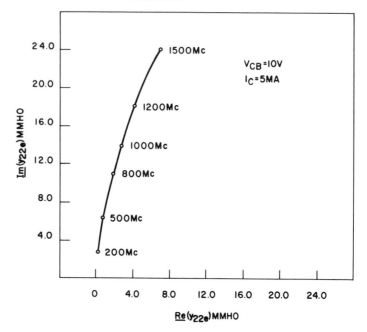

Fig. 5. 2N3570 y_{22e} vs. frequency.

These are plotted with frequency as a parameter from 200 to 1500 Mc, the upper limit of the General Radio 1607A Transfer Function and Immittance Bridge. These parameters are also plotted vs current at 500 Mc in Figs. 6 through 9.

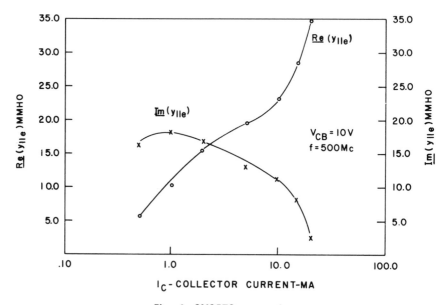

Fig. 6. 2N3570 y_{11e} vs. I_C.

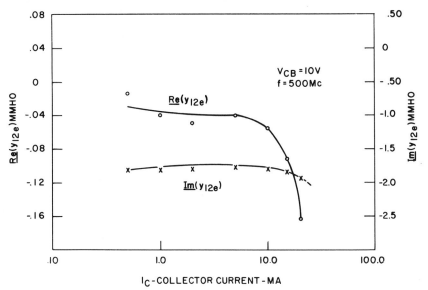

Fig. 7. 2N3570 y_{12e} vs. I_C.

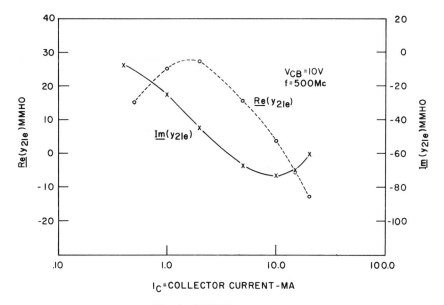

Fig. 8. 2N3570 y_{21e} vs. I_C.

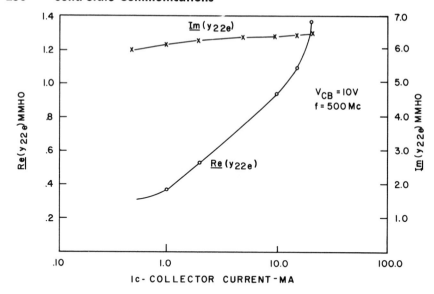

Fig. 9. 2N3570 y_{22e} vs. I_C.

Noise Figure. Plots of noise figure vs frequency for an average 2N3570 are shown in Figs. 10 and 11. Two currents and source impedances are indicated.

Selecting Operating Points. The primary requirements of an amplifier are usually a minimum acceptable gain and a maximum acceptable noise figure. Other requirements, such as bandwidth, linearity, or stability in an environment, may be nearly as important, and in some cases may force a compromise in other characteristics. For the present, however, let gain and noise figure be the primary considerations.

If gain were the only criterion, selection of an operating point would be straightforward. The operating point giving maximum (or near maximum) gain is selected. When noise figure also must be considered, selecting the operating point may not be so simple, since the noise figure of the amplifier may be a function of both gain and noise figure of the devices in the first two (or possibly three) stages.

Power gain usually increases with increasing emitter current and then becomes flat for an appreciable range of current. Gain will also increase slowly with increasing collector voltage up to breakdown. The power gain of the TI 2N3570 is essentially constant with emitter current from 3 to 15 ma, and collector voltage from 4 to 20 volts.

Noise figure, on the other hand, is relatively independent of collector voltage, although there may be a broad minimum. Noise figure is at a minimum at a fairly well-defined emitter current. The noise figure of the 2N3570 tends to a minimum value at emitter currents between 1 and 3 ma, and collector voltages between 3 and 10 volts. The minimum noise figure tends to occur at higher currents as frequency is increased.

500-Mc Amplifier. The first design example to be considered is a 500-Mc linear amplifier using the 2N3570. Assume that the requirement is for an amplifier with a noise figure of 4 db or better and an average gain of about 16 db. From

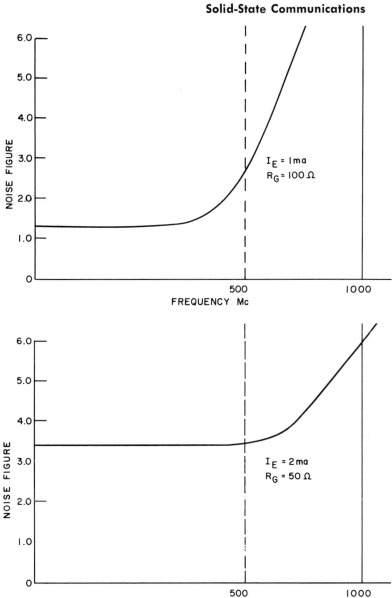

Figs. 10 and 11. Effect of R_G and operating point on noise figure.

Fig. 11, the average noise figure is 3 db for a transistor operated at 5 ma and with an R_g of 50 ohms. The amplifier could be operated at a lower current to obtain a better noise figure, but at lower gain.

The next step is to obtain the 500-Mc y-parameters from Figs. 6 through 9. These are listed in Table 2. The calculated unilateral gain is only slightly greater than 16 db, the design objective. Therefore, the amplifier must be neutralized. Neglecting the effects of the neutralizing network, the input resistance of the transistor is 1/0.0195 or 51 ohms; the output resistance is 1/0.00076 or 1300

Table 2. Typical Common-emitter y Parameters of the 2N3570 at 500 mc

$$y_{11} = + 19.5 + j13.5 \text{ millimhos}$$
$$y_{21} = + 15.7 - j66.8 \text{ millimhos}$$
$$y_{22} = + 0.76 + j 6.36 \text{ millimhos}$$
$$y_{12} = - 0.04 - j 1.76 \text{ millimhos}$$

Unilateral Gain, $U = 18.6$ db, from y parameters

ohms, in parallel with 1.8 pf. The input can be connected directly to the 50-ohm source with a negligible mismatch loss. The output will be matched by a modified pi network.

Figure 12 shows the pi network with an additional series capacitor to increase the flexibility of the system. A piece of $\frac{1}{4}''$ silverplated brass rod serves as the inductor. The design of the pi network will not be covered here as it has been thoroughly described in the literature.[1,2]

Figure 13 shows the complete schematic of a one-stage amplifier. The input network contains an additional element C_3 so that the source can be connected alternately at point A. This would be desirable, for example, when minimum noise figure is desired. Neutralizing voltage is obtained from a coupling loop L_3 which is a silverplated strip of beryllium copper running parallel to L_2. Figure 14 is a photograph of the complete amplifier. The placement of L_3 can be critical.

Table 3 shows a comparison of measured and calculated gains made on this amplifier. The agreement is fairly good, the difference in measured gain being attributable to circuit losses.

If the prime requirement had been for minimum noise figure, the design procedure would have varied somewhat. The best combination of emitter current and source resistance can be found by using an automatic noise figure meter in combination with a stub tuner and a suitable test fixture.* At high frequencies, the correlation factor between input and output noise of a transistor has the dimensions of capacitance. As a result, the optimum noise source is slightly inductive. In general, the optimum noise source resistance decreases with increasing frequency. The

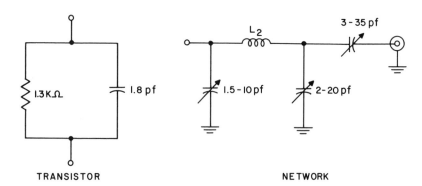

TRANSISTOR   NETWORK

Fig. 12. Output network for 500-mc amplifier.

---

*A suitable fixture is described in a later chapter, "Noise Figure Measurement."

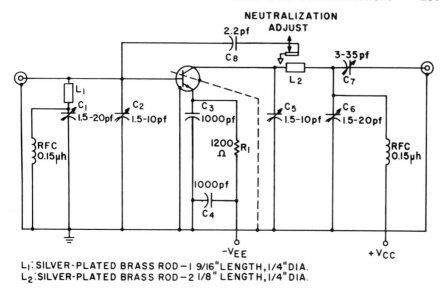

L₁: SILVER-PLATED BRASS ROD–1 9/16"LENGTH,1/4"DIA.
L₂: SILVER-PLATED BRASS ROD–2 1/8" LENGTH,1/4"DIA.

Fig. 13. 500-mc small-signal common-emitter amplifier.

optimum emitter current, however, increases with increasing frequency, reaching a maximum near the upper useful frequency. The maximum value of I_e is approximately the value at which f_α peaks. Figure 11 shows this effect; the 1-ma, 100-ohm curve is about optimum for 500 Mc, and the 5-ma, 50-ohm curve is best for 1 Gc.

Fig. 14. 500-mc amplifier.

Table 3. Comparison of Calculated and Measured Gains of 2N3570 at 500 mc

	Calculated		Measured	Test fixture loss (approx.)
	From f_T & $r_b'C_c$	From y parameters		
1.	18.5 db	18.7 db	16.2 db	2 db
2.	18.9 db	18.9 db	16.5 db	2 db
3.	18.5 db	19.7 db	16.7 db	2 db
4.	18.5 db	19.9 db	17.0 db	2 db

If linearity had been a factor in the design, this would have complicated the selection of an operating point still further. When low distortion is important, it is desirable to operate at a higher emitter current.

500-Mc Power Amplifier-oscillator. Power amplifiers or oscillators cannot be designed as simply as linear amplifiers because most of the transistor parameters vary widely with signal level. Thus, this design will be started with a few simple calculations, and then will proceed to a description of the hardware. Assume that a power of 200 mw is desired. Approximate values for the maximum collector voltage and load impedance may be calculated as follows:

$$V_{CB} \cong \frac{BV_{CBO}}{2}$$

$$= \frac{40}{2} = 20 \text{ volts}$$

$$R_L \cong \frac{(V_{CB})^2}{2P_o} = \frac{20^2}{2(0.2)} = 1000 \text{ ohms}$$

Since R_L is greater than 50 ohms, a simple capacitance probe can be used for matching. R_L is, however, high enough that care should be exercised to see that element Q's are high. A tunable cavity will assure this and will give the additional flexibility of wide-range tuning.

The design shown in Fig. 15 will accommodate either TO-5 or TO-18 transistors, if the collector is tied to the case internally. If the collector is isolated, a connection must be made between collector lead and cavity. Alternately, the collector lead may be soldered to the case. The center conductor of the cavity is a copper rod, and the transistor is inserted into the end to make electrical connection. The copper rod is a very efficient heat sink.

The top of the cavity is made of two plates, the upper one being insulated from the body of the cavity by 0.001-inch Mylar*. The upper plate is the base connection, and is at RF ground, but is isolated for biasing. Lastly, the emitter is connected to a modified N-type receptacle. An outside d-c block gives the necessary isolation to the emitter line for biasing the emitter. The movable piston makes contact with the cavity walls and the center rod, through beryllium-copper helical springs set into 0.05-inch lands in the piston.

When used as an oscillator, a sliding short is connected to the emitter via the outside d-c block. By adjusting the sliding short, the optimum susceptance for oscillation can be presented to the emitter. Frequency is adjusted by sliding the

---

*Reg. Trademark, E. I. DuPont.

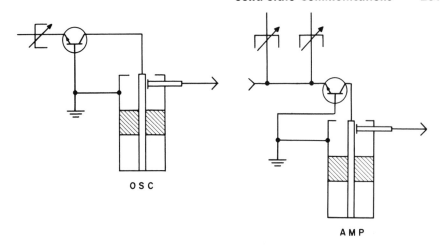

OSC

AMP

Fig. 15. Tunable high-power fixture for TO-5 and TO-18 transistors.

piston to the appropriate length. The 2N3570 will tune from about 400 to 1000 Mc in this cavity.

The cavity also can be used as a common-base power amplifier by simply replacing the sliding short with a stub tuner to match the input to a generator.

Wideband Amplifier, 0.5 to 1.45 Gc. Wideband amplification with transistors at L band was first described by Hamasaki[3] in a design using germanium mesa transistors. The amplifier described here uses TI3016A silicon transistors in a somewhat different circuit configuration. The interstage coupling in this design is a simple LC combination with peaking designed to compensate for the high-frequency gain falloff of the transistor. A single stage of the amplifier is shown in Fig. 16.

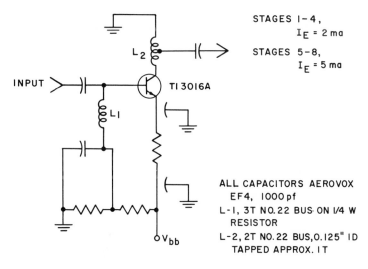

STAGES 1–4,
I_E = 2 ma

STAGES 5–8,
I_E = 5 ma

INPUT

L_2

TI 3016A

L_1

V_{bb}

ALL CAPACITORS AEROVOX
EF4, 1000 pf
L-1, 3T NO. 22 BUS ON 1/4 W
RESISTOR
L-2, 2T NO. 22 BUS, 0.125" ID
TAPPED APPROX. 1 T

Fig. 16. L-band amplifier single stage.

An unneutralized common-emitter stage was chosen because, of several connections, this gives the greatest bandwidth and is unconditionally stable. However, the stage gain is low, averaging less than 4 db per stage. The low stage gain means that the overall noise figure is strongly influenced by the noise in the second and third stages, as well as the first. A new design using a common-base first stage has been built. It also may be possible to alternate common-base and common-emitter stages to obtain better gain and lower noise figure in fewer stages, while still maintaining the absolute stability of the present design.

The operating current for optimum noise is a compromise necessitated by the low stage gain and large bandwidth of the amplifier. Since the intrinsic transistor noise figure is rising rapidly at the upper end of the amplifier response, it is best to make a design that favors the higher frequencies.

In selecting the stage current, the early stages need to have a minimum noise measure, i.e., both gain and noise must be considered in the overall noise figure. The later stages are biased for maximum gain. For this amplifier, a 2-ma operating point is used in the first stage, increasing to 5 ma in the last four stages. A photo of the complete amplifier is shown in Fig. 17. Figure 18 shows the performance of the amplifier in graphic form. The gain is flat within ± 1 db across the specified passband. The noise figure is good but not as low as that of a similar amplifier that was built using the 2N2999 germanium mesa transistor. Phase response is also very good, although this was not a design criterion.

General-purpose Fixed Tuned Oscillator Amplifier. A transistor mounted in a TO-18 package can be used to about 1.5 Gc before losses become excessive, although package resonances in some units may set a lower limit. In the fixture described next, the 2N3570 will give 50 to 100 mw as a self-excited oscillator at 1 Gc. The design is similar to the 500-Mc cavity except that frequency is trimmed with a capacitive probe. Figure 19 is a drawing of the fixture.

One of the unique features of this cavity is the method of introducing the collector bias. A discoidal capacitor is soldered to the top of the tubular center conductor of the cavity. The bias lead enters the cavity through the bottom and terminates in the discoidal capacitor which, in turn, is connected to the collector of the transistor.

Note that the transistor socket is mounted horizontally and that the transistor is plugged into the open end of the socket. This arrangement allows a minimum of lead length for all elements. The base grounds directly to the cavity cover, while the emitter is connected to the N-type receptacle. An outside d-c block connects

Fig. 17. Wide-band amplifier.

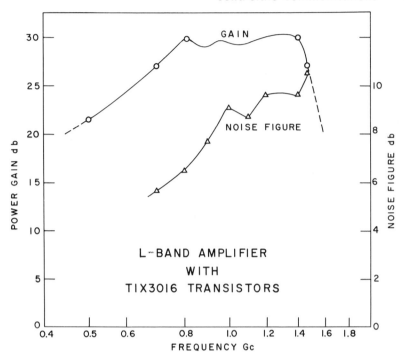

Fig. 18. L-band amplifier with TI3016A transistors.

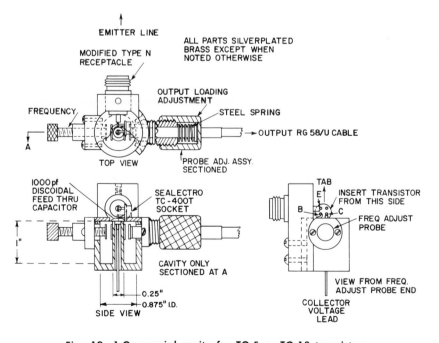

Fig. 19. 1-Gc coaxial cavity for TO-5 or TO-18 transistors.

to the receptacle and thus makes it possible to bias the emitter via the line joined to the d-c block.

Another way to bias the emitter is to feed bias through a shunt choke or resistor. This method results in a much more compact system and can be used where either the absolute maximum output power is not needed, or the transistor is being operated so far below f_{max} that emitter immittance is not critical.

Since the cavity does not have the case connected to a heat sink, it is limited to modest input power — e.g., less than 1 watt. For most measurements, the can is left floating, although it can be grounded when testing transistors such as the 2N3570 with an isolated collector. At 1 Gc it is not necessary to add additional feedback capacitance external to the transistor if the can is left floating.

It also appears that transistors in some types of encapsulation require external capacitance to maintain oscillation. A capacitive "gimmick" which will do this can be made by sliding a piece of Teflon*-insulated wire inside a small eyelet and soldering these between the collector and emitter. Moving the wire in and out of the eyelet will usually give sufficient range of adjustment. This cavity, like the one described previously, can also be used as an amplifier by connecting a stub tuner to the input.

2-Gc Oscillator. The TI-line†-packaged TI3016A can be used as a 2-Gc power source with an average output of 50 mw. Efficiency is about 16 per cent. The base is the common terminal in the TI-line package. The oscillator circuit is shown in Fig. 20. Note that a double-stub tuner in the collector line acts both as a tuning and a matching element. As in the other oscillators previously discussed, the internal capacitance of the transistor is the feedback element.

Both the double-stub tuner and the tunable emitter cavity are isolated from the V-shaped center piece by 0.001-inch Mylar* film for biasing purposes. The capacitance across these connections is greater than 100 pf, which is adequate for the range of frequencies covered by the fixture. The emitter cavity is tuned by a movable piston using beryllium-copper springs for contacts. The latter are wound from 0.005-inch wire with an outside diameter of 0.05 inch, and are inserted into 0.045-inch lands in the piston. This type of contact appears to be very efficient and lends itself better to small assemblies than bigger stock.

An interesting characteristic of the TI3016A in this kind of oscillator is its second harmonic efficiency. If, for example, a 3-Gc high-pass filter is inserted in the

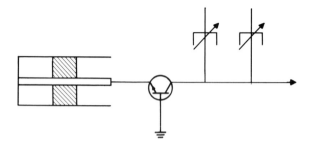

Fig. 20. 2-Gc transistor test cavity.

---

*Reg. Trademark, E. I. DuPont
†Trademark of Texas Instruments

output, and the output is retuned slightly, the harmonic power will be only 3 to 6 db below the fundamental, and up to 25 mw may be obtained at 4 Gc. Possibly one of the reasons for the good harmonic efficiency of the TI3016A is that, with proper tuning, the collector capacitance operates as a varactor multiplier.

This oscillator has been used to drive a single 4X gallium varactor frequency multiplier to obtain 25 mw at 9.2 Gc. Another design uses a TIXS13 with two varactor triplers to obtain 30 mw at 16.5 Gc. The simplicity of such systems makes them attractive for applications requiring wideband tuning.

BIBLIOGRAPHY

1. Roach, W. E.: Designing High Power Transistor Oscillators, *Electronics,* January 8, 1960.
2. Rheinfelder, W. A.: Three Coupling Networks for Transistor Output Stages, *Electronic Design,* October 25, 1962.
3. Hamasaki, J.: A Wideband High Gain Transistor Amplifier at L Band, Digest of Papers, International Solid State Circuits Conference, p. 46, February, 1963.

17

Causes of Noise

by Harry F. Cooke

INTRODUCTION

The process of low-noise amplification is now almost exclusively dominated by solid-state devices. Recently, we have seen many refinements in the technology of device fabrication, rather than the discovery of new types of devices using new principles. These refinements are in large part responsible for the rather spectacular noise performance of today's semiconductors.

Throughout this chapter we shall use the term "noise figure" to describe noisiness of a device. It is the most common term in use today and means simply the degradation in signal-to-noise ratio caused by an amplifier, expressed as a ratio or in db. As an example of device improvement, we may cite Shockley's early audio transistor noise figure of 70 db, compared with 0.2 db obtainable today. One of the reasons our technology has been so successful in improving semiconductor devices is that our understanding of the noise mechanism in semiconductors is now fairly complete. Even those types of noise which are not completely understood can be controlled to a degree.

In Fig. 1, the noise characteristics of a number of types of semiconductor amplifiers from sub-audio to microwave frequencies are shown. Note that the parametric amplifier provides the lowest noise figure at both ends of the spectrum. The great complexity of the parametric amplifier, however, makes it uneconomical to use where other devices are available. Silicon FET's or planar devices are most used at low frequencies, while both mesa and planar devices are useful in the microwave region.

TYPES OF NOISE

We will now describe briefly some of the types of noise found in semiconductor amplifiers. For some of the types of noise there are simple circuit equivalents, which are shown.

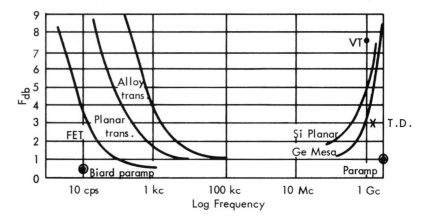

Figure 1

Thermal Noise. Thermal noise power is generated by all solids not at absolute zero; it arises from the fact that the thermal agitation of carriers gives rise to electrical energy. The thermal power generated depends only on the temperature (and the bandwidth over which it is measured). This agitation is so completely random that when we attach terminals to the medium, we find that the voltage at the terminals covers all frequencies. In fact, the mean-squared value of the voltage is proportional only to resistance, temperature, bandwidth, and a constant called "Boltzmann's Constant." Figure 2 shows how we can represent this voltage from a circuit point of view.

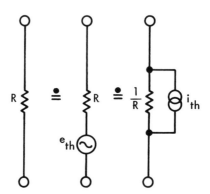

$$G = \frac{1}{R}$$

where

$$\overline{i^2_{th}} = 4kT\Delta fG$$

$$\overline{e^2_{th}} = 4kT\Delta fR$$

k = Boltzmann's constant = 1.38×10^{-23} joules/°K

T = temperature in degrees Kelvin = 300° at room temperature

Δf = bandwidth in cps

R = resistance in ohms

Figure 2

Here we equate a noisy resistor with a noiseless resistor plus a voltage generator. In semiconductors, thermal noise voltage is found wherever there is an appreciable bulk resistance, as in the base resistance of a transistor. Note that the noise power is proportional to bandwidth, but not frequency; the voltage is the same regardless of where we take our slice of bandwidth in the frequency spectrum.

Shot Noise. The second type of noise with which we will be concerned is shot noise. Shot noise occurs whenever a current flows, as from the influence of a field in vacuum tubes, or a concentration gradient in transistors and diodes. Although there is some degree of organization in the motion of carriers (their average motion is in one direction), their final arrival is completely random. This randomness gives rise to a uniform frequency spectrum of noise, as in the thermal case. The mean-squared noise current is proportional to the charge on an electron, the d-c current flowing, and the bandwidth.

Figure 3 gives the circuit representation of shot noise in a diode.

The noisy diode is here equated with a resistance equal to the dynamic resistance

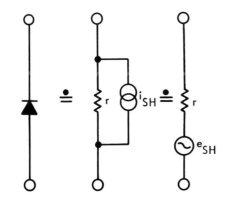

$$\overline{i_{SH}^2} = 2q I_{dc} \Delta f$$

$$r = \frac{nkT}{q I_{dc}} \cong \frac{25}{I_{dc}} \text{ ohms}$$

$$\overline{e_{SH}^2} = \overline{i_{SH}^2} \, r^2$$

$$= 2 q I_{dc} \Delta f \left(\frac{nkT}{q I_{dc}}\right)^2$$

$$= 2 k T \Delta f r$$

q = charge of an electron = 1.59×10^{-19} coulombs

n = a constant $\cong 1$ for transistor

Δf = bandwidth in cps

Figure 3

of the diode in parallel with a noise-current generator. The dynamic resistance of a diode at average carrier injection levels has been shown to be equal to nkT/qI_{dc}, where the symbols have the meaning shown in Fig. 3. In many circuits it is more convenient to have a voltage generator than a current generator. Since the dynamic resistance of the diode has been defined in terms similar to the noise current, we find that a simple arithmetical manipulation transforms the shot-noise current generator into a resistance in series with a voltage generator as shown. Note that the form of the shot-noise voltage generator is almost identical to the thermal-noise generator, but is $\sqrt{2}/2$ times as large. At very high frequencies, where the transit time of carriers across the diode becomes appreciable, the diode resistance decreases. In other words, the diode behaves as if we had paralleled another resistor with it. It has been found that this resistance shows full thermal noise.

Other Types of Noise. The two types of noise just mentioned are the only kinds that affect high-frequency transistors and other RF devices to any degree. The remaining types of noise which we will now discuss do not affect semiconductor operation except under special conditions.

The first and most important of these is $1/f$ noise, sometimes called flicker, or scintillation noise. It is called $1/f$ noise because the noise power per unit bandwidth increases inversely with frequency. It usually occurs only at the lower audio frequency, but can manifest itself up into the UHF region. The exact causes of $1/f$ noise are not known at present, although many theories have been set forth in explanation of the phenomenon. It is even difficult mathematically to write a simple expression for $1/f$ noise. Most $1/f$ noise in transistors has been localized to what are called slow states within the emitter depletion layer. These slow states, or traps, capture and release carriers at different rates, but with energy levels varying inversely with frequency.

Figure 4 shows a plot of the low-frequency noise figure of a transistor vs. log frequency. The noise figure increases at a 3 db per octave rate for frequencies

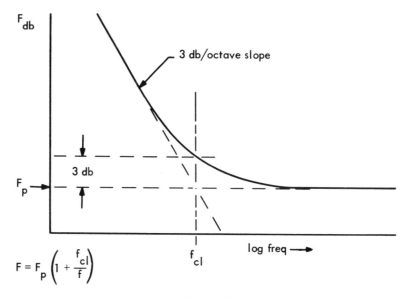

$$F = F_p \left(1 + \frac{f_{cl}}{f}\right)$$

Figure 4

below the point called the corner frequency f_{CL}. The corner frequency is defined as that frequency at which the $1/f$ noise power equals the mid-frequency noise power. At this frequency the noise figure has increased 3 db over the mid-frequency figure. Once the corner frequency has been determined, we may write the noise factor in the $1/f$ region as:

$$F = F_p \left(1 + \frac{f_c}{f}\right)$$

Admittedly, we have used a mathematical convenience to define a type of noise that we cannot designate by other means. However, once we have found the corner frequency for a given type of transistor, this frequency will remain fairly constant for a given set of operating conditions with other transistors of this type. Excessive $1/f$ noise may be an indication of defects in transistor fabrication. In general, planar and FET transistors have lower $1/f$ corner frequencies than other types.

Another type of noise commonly found in transistors is generation-recombination noise. G-R noise is basically a thermal effect. The noise is generated when carriers recombine or separate after crossing a junction causing a net change in charge. G-R noise is generally negligible in good transistors. It appears most often in transistors having very low current gain, and falls off rapidly at high frequencies.

Avalanche noise is present in Zener diodes and transistors operated in the breakdown region. Its presence is due to the fact that carriers under the influence of very large fields may collide with and release other carriers within the crystal lattice. This multiplication of carriers during breakdown can produce very large noise voltages. Fortunately, the effect occurs in a region where transistors are normally never operated for other reasons, and is of no importance in amplifying devices. It has been used as a noise source for test purposes.

NOISE SOURCES AND EQUIVALENT CIRCUITS

We will next show how noise sources fit into the equivalent circuits for four types of semiconductor amplifiers. See Fig. 5.

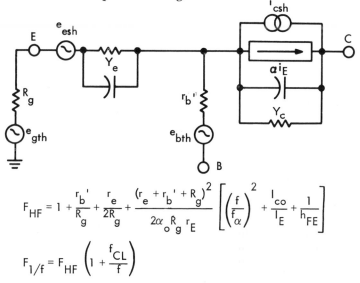

$$F_{HF} = 1 + \frac{r_b{}'}{R_g} + \frac{r_e}{2R_g} + \frac{(r_e + r_b{}' + R_g)^2}{2\alpha_o R_g r_E}\left[\left(\frac{f}{f_\alpha}\right)^2 + \frac{I_{co}}{I_E} + \frac{1}{h_{FE}}\right]$$

$$F_{1/f} = F_{HF}\left(1 + \frac{f_{CL}}{f}\right)$$

Figure 5

The transistor, except in the 1/f region, has two types of noise sources; thermal and shot. The thermal noise comes from the base spreading resistance, or more simply r'_b. The emitter-base diode develops full shot noise as does the collector-base diode. When we calculate the noise figure of the transistor, we must recognize that the shot noise in the two diodes comes about from almost exactly the same carriers. Therefore, we must subtract from one diode that noise which we have already accounted for in the other. If we sum the noise voltages in the output of the transistor, only the uncorrelated part of the collector noise is added. In the simplest case, the collector and emitter shot-noise generators are correlated by the alpha of the transistor. The noise figure expressions for the common-base and common-emitter connections are the same. The three terms shown in the noise figure equation represent the contributions of the base resistance, emitter, and un-correlated collector noise, respectively. If we examine the noise figure equation, we can immediately make some observations as to the most desirable features of a low-noise transistor. First of all, the base resistance should be low. Next, f_α and h_{FE} should be high. I_{co} should be as low as possible. The term α_o approaches 1 when h_{FE} is high. At low frequencies the frequency-dependent part f/f_α vanishes, and the last term of the noise figure depends primarily on the common-emitter current gain h_{FE}. At low frequencies and high source impedances, the entire equation degenerates to:

$$F = 1 + \frac{R_g}{2r_e h_{FE}} \tag{1}$$

$$R_{g(opt)} = \left[(r_e + r'_b)^2 + \frac{\alpha_o r_e (2r'_b + r_e)}{\dfrac{1}{h_{FE}} + \left(\dfrac{f}{f_\alpha}\right)^2 + \dfrac{I_{co}}{I_E}} \right]^{1/2} \tag{2}$$

$$= r_e \sqrt{h_{FE}} \qquad \text{if } r_b << r_e, \text{ at low frequencies}$$

$$= r_e + r'_b \qquad \text{at very high frequencies}$$

The next most obvious question is "What R_g will give the best noise figure?" This is found by differentiating the noise equation with respect to R_g. The result is then set equal to 0, and R_g is solved for. The result is shown in Eqs. (1) and (2). At high frequencies $R_{g(opt)}$ simplifies to $r'_b + r_e$. This value of $R_{g(opt)}$ may be substituted in the original noise figure equation to get the expression for the minimum noise figure F_{min}.

Noise in Other Solid-state Amplifying Devices. *The field-effect transistor (FET)* in the present state of the art is used most at low frequencies, but it is becoming a UHF device. It is subject to the same types of noise that are found in a conventional transistor, including 1/f noise. Most FET's are planar in design, and the 1/f noise does not become significant until a very low frequency is reached.

The noise mechanisms in the FET are quite similar to those in the diffusion transistor except for the part which capacitance plays. Gate-to-source capacitance can couple output noise back to the input since input impedance is high. Since this capacitance is distributed in nature, not all the capacitance acts as a feedback element. To properly divide the channel resistance, Bechtel* has suggested a constant, λ. The significance of λ is shown in Fig. 6. A more conventional schematic of an FET and the equation for noise figure are shown in Fig. 7.

*Bechtel, N. G.: A Circuit and Noise Model of the Field-effect Transistor, Proc. of the International Solid State Circuits Conf., February, 1963.

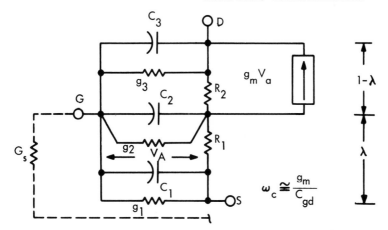

Figure 6

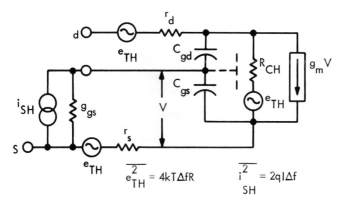

$$\overline{e_{TH}^2} = 4kT\Delta fR \qquad \overline{i_{SH}^2} = 2q|\Delta f$$

For all frequencies except l/f region:

$$F = 1 + \frac{2\lambda\omega}{g_m}(C_{gs} + C_{gd}) + \frac{\lambda}{g_m}\left[\frac{G_s - \omega(C_{gs} + C_{gd})}{G_s}\right]^2$$

For <u>low</u> frequencies except l/f region:

$$F_{low} = 1 + \frac{\lambda G}{g_m}$$

$$G_{opt} \cong \omega(C_{gs} + C_{gd})$$

where

G_s = source conductance

g_m = low-frequency transconductance

ω = frequency of operation

Figure 7

The main sources of noise in a field-effect transistor are: thermal noise in the channel, shot noise in the gate-to-channel leakage, thermal noise in the bulk resistances, and capacitance-coupled thermal noise at the input. Note that the low-frequency noise figure depends on λ, which is about 0.5. For the vacuum tube, λ = 2.5. Thus, for the same g_m, the FET is less noisy than the vacuum tube.

The tunnel diode is a relative newcomer to the field of low-noise amplification. It is a very-low-noise device, but since it has only two terminals, its application differs radically from the transistors discussed previously. As with all two-terminal amplifiers, its performance is affected by the noise in the load as well as the source.

See Fig. 8; the noise figure of the tunnel diode is: (3)

$$F = 1 + \frac{R_g}{R_L}\frac{R_g}{R - r_s}\frac{1 + \omega^2 R^2 C^2}{\left(\dfrac{\omega}{\omega_c}\right)^2 + \omega_c^2 R^2 C^2} + \frac{q(I_{eq})R}{2kT}\frac{R_g}{r_s}\frac{R}{R - r_s}\frac{1}{\left(\dfrac{\omega}{\omega_c}\right)^2 + \omega_c^2 R^2 C^2}$$

The first term in the noise expression is the thermal noise in the load resistance r_L. The second term is the thermal noise from r_s. The third term is the equivalent shot noise term. This last term needs some explanation since it actually accounts for two separate currents. In some regions of operation, both of these currents show full shot noise. Since these currents flow in opposition, the net terminal d-c current may be much less than either one of the two internal currents that make it up. Thus we use the term, "equivalent current" which can be larger than the actual external d-c current flowing at the point of operation. The term ω_c, the angular cutoff frequency, is the highest frequency at which the device terminals still show negative resistance. A good noise figure of merit for a tunnel diode is the reciprocal of the negative resistance times the equivalent shot-noise current at the point where this is maximum. It is beyond the scope of this work to discuss the many circuit variations that are possible with a tunnel diode.

The varactor, or variable capacitance diode, is the active element in most so-called parametric amplifiers. The capacitance of a reverse-biased diode varies with voltage and according to the law of $C = \dfrac{k}{V - \frac{1}{n}}$, where n usually lies between 2 and

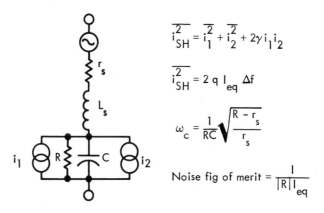

$$\overline{i_{SH}^2} = \overline{i_1^2} + \overline{i_2^2} + 2\gamma i_1 i_2$$

$$\overline{i_{SH}^2} = 2 q I_{eq} \Delta f$$

$$\omega_c = \frac{1}{RC}\sqrt{\frac{R - r_s}{r_s}}$$

$$\text{Noise fig of merit} = \frac{1}{|R| I_{eq}}$$

Figure 8

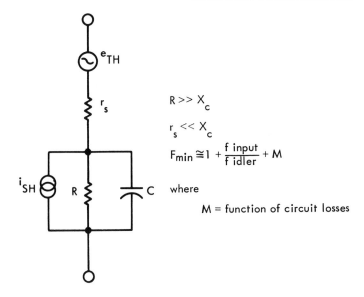

$$R \gg X_c$$

$$r_s \ll X_c$$

$$F_{min} \cong 1 + \frac{f\ input}{f\ idler} + M$$

where

$\quad$ M = function of circuit losses

Figure 9

3. The parametric amplifier utilizes the variable capacitance effect to obtain power gain by translating (pumping) energy at one frequency to a higher frequency. See Fig. 9.

The sources of noise in the parametric amplifier are thermal noise in the series resistance, shot noise from the leakage current, and thermal noise, in the load, idler, and input circuits respectively. The first two are characteristics of the diode alone, the last terms are functions of the circuit. Both of the noise sources in the diode can be made negligible by proper fabrication and design. With careful attention to circuit details, overall noise figures of less than 1 db are attainable. Note that we have talked about only one type of parametric amplifier. Readers interested in the details of other types are referred to the many papers that have been written on the subject.

Design Precautions. The following discussion will illustrate some of the precautions to be used in designing a low-noise transistor amplifier. Consider the circuit shown in Fig. 10 and the noise equivalent. The following points are to be noted:

1. Bias resistors when they appear across an input circuit always attenuate the desired signal to some extent. At higher frequencies their value may be much less than that indicated by d-c measurements. It is always best to bias through the ground end of the input tank circuit if at all possible.

2. The unloaded Q of the input tank should be as high as possible or the loaded Q should be as low as possible, or both. This ensures that input losses from the tuning circuits will be low. It usually also implies that input selectivity will be quite broad.

3. Since R_g is seldom the same as $R_{g(opt)}$, some transformation is usually necessary. This can be done with tapped transformers (as shown), LC networks, baluns, or distributed type transformers. The losses in these networks should also be low.

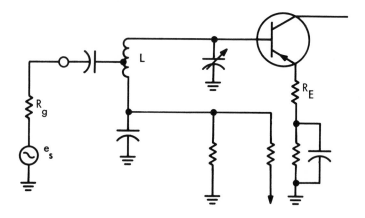

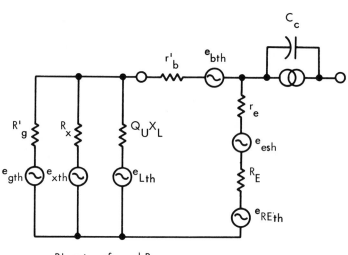

R'_g = transformed R_g

R_x = equivalent loss resistance, miscellaneous losses

$Q_U X_L$ = coil loss resistance

Figure 10

4. In the UHF and microwave range all component losses can be important, e.g., those from socket leads and coupling capacitors.

One final word of caution. Under certain circumstances it is possible that a transistor, when operated to give best noise figure in the input stage, will not give the minimum overall noise figure which includes the second and following stages.

The overall noise figure for several stages is shown in Fig. 11. If the point of operation chosen to minimize F_1 is such that G_1 is low or F_2 is high, or both, then the overall noise figure may be improved by choosing a value for R_g which increases the gain. This will deteriorate the noise figure of the first stage, but the overall noise figure will be lower.

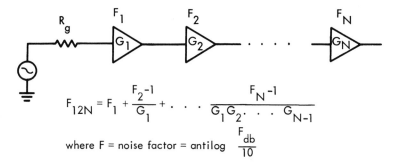

$$F_{12N} = F_1 + \frac{F_2 - 1}{G_1} + \ \cdots \ \frac{F_N - 1}{G_1 G_2 \cdots G_{N-1}}$$

where F = noise factor = antilog $\dfrac{F_{db}}{10}$

Figure 11

18

Transistor Noise Figure

by Harry F. Cooke

INTRODUCTION

The noise figure of junction transistors has been treated by several authors (particularly Nielsen[1], van der Ziel[2-4], and Strutt[5]) in great detail and with mathematical rigor. However, a development of the noise-figure expression using a somewhat simplified approach is useful to many engineers, particularly those engaged in circuit design. A great deal of noise theory is statistical in nature and quite complex. The actual derivation of the thermal and shot-noise generators is avoided in this chapter for this reason. The development of the noise-figure expression and following remarks attempt to use circuit concepts more familiar to the average engineer.

There are three broad classifications of noise sources usually found in a transistor — flicker (or 1/f) noise, thermal noise, and shot noise. Flicker noise begins to influence noise figure at some relatively low frequency (f_{CL}, the low-frequency noise corner, Fig. 1) and increases as frequency decreases at a 3 db/octave rate. As yet, flicker noise is not completely mathematically predictable. Fortunately, the

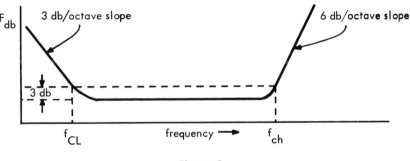

Figure 1

flicker noise corner can be lowered to some extent by transistor fabrication techniques, and usually is not important to high-frequency operation.

Neither thermal noise nor shot noise is frequency dependent, and both exhibit uniform noise output through the entire useful frequency range of the transistor. The internal gain of the transistor does vary with frequency, however, and falls off as frequency increases. The noise figure begins to rise when the loss in gain becomes appreciable. The frequency at which this occurs is called f_{CH}, the upper- or high-frequency noise corner. Since the power gain falls inversely as frequency squared, the noise figure rises as frequency squared, or 6 db per octave. This is shown graphically in Fig. 1.

THERMAL NOISE

Thermal noise is due to the disorganized nature of the motion of charges within a device. This motion gives rise to an electrical power that is proportional to the absolute temperature and the bandwidth. The noise voltage across the terminals of a device is a function of the power and the resistance of the device. The mean-squared noise voltage, $\overline{e_{nth}^2}$, which appears at the terminals is:

$$\overline{e_{nth}^2} = 4kTR\Delta f, (\text{volts})^2, \tag{1}$$

$$\text{or } e_{nth} = 126\,\sqrt{R\Delta f} \times 10^{-12} \text{ volts at } 290°K$$

where
$$k = \text{Boltzmann's constant} = 1.38 \times 10^{-23} \text{ joules/K}°$$
$$T = \text{temperature in degrees Kelvin}$$
$$R = \text{resistance of the device in ohms at its terminals}$$
$$f = \text{bandwidth in cycles/sec.}$$

Because of the random character of the motion of the charges, the thermal noise spectrum is uniform throughout the useful range of present transistors as long as R is a pure resistance.

From a circuit viewpoint, thermal noise may be represented as a voltage generator in series with a noiseless resistor, as shown in Fig. 2.

SHOT NOISE

Shot noise occurs under certain conditions when a current flows. The current flow may be caused by a field as in vacuum tubes or by a concentration gradient (i.e., diffusion) as in transistors. In both cases, it is caused by the random nature of the arrival of the charges. If the charges arrived uniformly, a single frequency would be generated which would be about 10^{16} cycles/ma of d-c current. However, the process is completely random and, like thermal noise, the shot noise spectrum is uniform.

$$e_n = \sqrt{4\,kT\Delta fR}$$

R

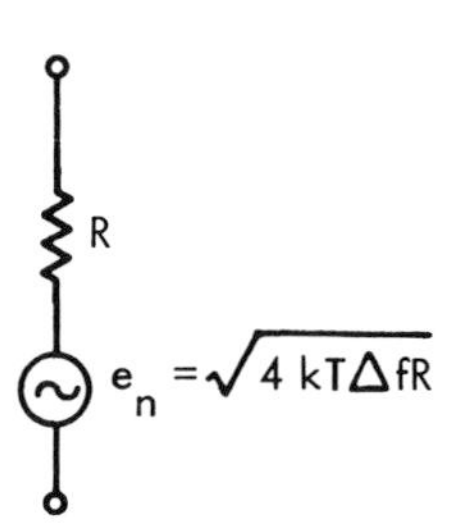

Figure 2

The shot-noise energy associated with a stream of carriers (or charges) — i.e., a d-c current — is proportional to the charge of an electron, the d-c current flowing, and the bandwidth. This can be represented by a constant-current generator, i_n^2, where:

$$\overline{i_n^2} = 2qI_{dc}\Delta f \tag{2}$$

where

q = charge of an electron = 1.6×10^{-19} coulombs
I_{dc} = d-c current flow in amperes
Δf = bandwidth in cps

The equivalent circuit is that of a current generator in parallel with a noiseless conductance, g_0, where g_0 is the effective conductance of the region through which the current stream flows (Fig. 3).

For transistors and semiconductor diodes at low carrier injection levels, the conductance g_0 is the incremental conductance of the P-N junction and is given by the following expression:

$$g_0 = \frac{qI_{dc}}{kT} \tag{3}$$

$$= \frac{I_{dc}\,ma}{25}\ mhos \tag{3a}$$

where q, I_{dc}, k, and T have the same meaning as used previously.

Since we now have an expression for the conductance of the diode, it is possible to convert the mean-squared shot-noise current generator to an equivalent voltage generator.

$$\overline{e_n^2} = \frac{\overline{i_n^2}}{g_0^2}$$

$$= \frac{2qI_{dc}\Delta f}{qI_{dc}} kT \frac{1}{g_0}$$

$$= \frac{2kT\Delta f}{g_0}$$

$$= 2kTr_0\Delta f \tag{4}$$

where

$$r_0 = \frac{1}{g_0}$$

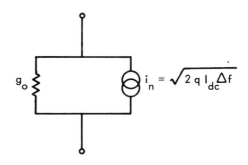

Figure 3

Note that the shot-noise voltage is exactly the same in form as the thermal-noise voltage, but is $\sqrt{2}/2$ times as large. The alternate equivalent circuit is then as shown in Fig. 4. The equivalent circuit again is that of a voltage generator in series with a noiseless resistance.

At very high frequencies, usually beyond the useful range of present transistors, the transit time of the carriers across the diode becomes appreciable. This introduces a conductance in addition to g_0 shunting the diode which will show full thermal noise. The total shot-noise current under these conditions will be:

$$\overline{i_n^2} = 2qI_{dc}\Delta f + 4kT(g - g_0)\Delta f \tag{5}$$

where g is the high-frequency diode conductance.

This additional noise in transistors is attributed by van der Ziel to carriers that cross the emitter-base junction to the base but return and recombine in the emitter region where they originated.

TRANSISTOR NOISE-FIGURE EQUATION, HIGH FREQUENCY

The development that follows is based on the common-base configuration, but Nielsen[1] has shown it to be valid for both common-base and common-emitter. The common-collector stage, because of its larger noise figure, is usually of little interest in high-frequency applications.

The transistor itself has three main internal noise generators:
1. shot noise in the emitter-base junction,
2. thermal noise in the base resistance, and
3. shot noise in the collector-base junction.

These noise sources can best be shown in the high-frequency T-equivalent circuit of Fig. 5.

In Fig. 5: e_{esh} = emitter shot noise equivalent voltage generator = $\sqrt{2kTr_e\Delta f}$

$\quad i_{esh}$ = emitter shot noise equivalent current generator = $\sqrt{2qI_E\Delta f}$
$\quad i_{csh}$ = collector shot noise current generator (includes noise from I_{CO})
$\quad e_{gth}$ = thermal noise from the generator resistance
$\quad i_c$ = collector current at frequency of test
$\quad I_E$ = d-c emitter current
$\quad I_C$ = d-c collector current due to d-c emitter current (does not include I_{CO})
$\quad I_{CO}$ = d-c collector cutoff current
$\quad e_{bth}$ = thermal noise from the base resistance, r_b'
$\quad \alpha$ = common-base current gain at frequency of test

$\quad z_e$ = emitter diode impedance $= \dfrac{1}{y_e} = \dfrac{1}{g_e + j\omega C_e}$

$\quad r_e = 25/I_E$ma ohms, the real part of the emitter impedance at low frequencies

$\quad R_g$ = source resistance

Both the emitter and collector junctions have shot-noise generators, but some of the noise is due to the flow of the same charges and is, therefore, the same noise.

$$r_o = \frac{1}{g_o}$$

$$e_n = \sqrt{2\,kT\Delta f r_o}$$

Figure 4

In other words, these two generators are strongly correlated. When we add the total noise in the output we must make an allowance for this by *subtracting* from the collector noise that part of the noise which came directly from the emitter. If the emitter shot-noise current generator is i_{esh}, the part of the noise that reaches the collector is αi_{esh}. The total shot noise at the collector junction is then:

$$i_{csh(total)} = i_{esh} - \alpha i_{esh}.$$

To get the mean-squared value, both sides are squared and the correlation factor is taken according to van der Ziel.[6] The result is:

$$\overline{i_{csh(total)}^2} = 2q\Delta f \left(I_C + I_{CO} + |\alpha|^2 I_E - 2|\alpha|^2 I_E \frac{\alpha_{dc}}{\alpha_o} \right) \qquad (6)$$

Before we proceed with the noise-figure deriviation from Fig. 5, two assumptions will be made:

1. All of the noise and signal transfer from the input of the transistor to the output will be made through transistor action via the collector current generator, $|\alpha| i_e$. The signal transfer through r_c' and z_c is negligible, provided $r_c'\omega C_e << 1$ or $r_b' << |z_c|$.

2. The emitter impedance z_e can be approximated by its real part r_e. Again, this is true for most regions of usefulness of the transistor.

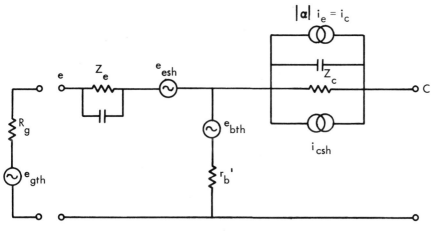

Figure 5

NOISE FIGURE CALCULATION

A conventional definition of noise figure is:

$$F = \frac{\text{Total mean-squared open-circuit noise voltage at transistor output}}{\begin{array}{c}\text{Total mean-squared open-circuit noise voltage at transistor output}\\ \text{from } R_g \text{ alone}\end{array}} \quad (7)$$

The total noise current flowing in the emitter, i_{en}, can be found by adding the input loop noise voltages and dividing by the loop impedance.

$$i_{en} = \frac{e_{gth} + e_{esh} + e_{bth}}{(R_g + r_e + r_b')}$$

This current will appear in the output as $|\alpha| i_{en}$, or as an open-circuit noise voltage, $|\alpha| i_{en} z_c$. The three noise voltages are squared separately since they are uncorrelated. Hence, the mean-squared open-circuit noise voltage is:

$$|\alpha|^2 \overline{i_{en}^2} z_c^2 = \frac{|\alpha|^2 |z_c|^2 (\overline{e_{gth}^2} + \overline{e_{esh}^2} + \overline{e_{bth}^2})}{(R_g + r_e + r_b')^2} \quad (8)$$

The mean-squared open-circuit noise voltage from the collector is:

$$\overline{e_{oc}^2} = \overline{i_{csh}^2} |z_c|^2 \quad (9)$$

Equations (8) and (9) may now be combined to yield the numerator of Eq. (7). The denominator

$$\frac{|\alpha|^2 |z_c|^2 \overline{e_{gth}^2}}{(R_g + r_e + r_b')^2}$$

is the thermal noise from the source as it appears in the output. Hence, from Eq. (7)

$$F = \frac{\dfrac{|\alpha|^2 z_c^2 (\overline{e_{gth}^2} + \overline{e_{esh}^2} + \overline{e_{bth}^2})}{(R_g + r_e + r_b')^2} + \overline{i_{csh}^2} |z_c|^2}{\dfrac{|\alpha|^2 |z_c|^2 \overline{e_{gth}^2}}{(R_g + r_e + r_b')^2}}$$

Rearranging terms:

$$F = 1 + \frac{\overline{e_{esh}^2}}{\overline{e_{gth}^2}} + \frac{\overline{e_{bth}^2}}{\overline{e_{gth}^2}} + \frac{\overline{i_{csh}^2}}{\overline{e_{gth}^2}} \frac{(R_g + r_e + r_b')^2}{|\alpha|^2}$$

The voltage and current generator now are replaced by their equivalents from Eqs. (1), (4), and (6).

$$F = 1 + \frac{r_e}{2R_g} + \frac{r_b'}{R_g} + \frac{q}{kT}\left(\frac{I_{co} + I_c}{|\alpha|^2} + I_E - 2I_E \frac{\alpha_{dc}}{\alpha_o}\right)\frac{(R_g + r_e + r_b')^2}{2R_g} \quad (10)$$

This is not yet in a very useful form and, therefore, several more substitutions will be made. The amplitude of alpha of a transistor frequency can be assumed to behave like an RC network, thus:

$$\alpha = \frac{\alpha_o}{1 + j\dfrac{f}{f_\alpha}} \quad (11)$$

where α_o is the low-frequency alpha (*not* the d-c α), f is the frequency of measurement, and f_α is the frequency at which alpha has decreased to $\dfrac{\sqrt{2}}{2} \alpha_o$ (i.e., $0.707\, \alpha_o$).

From Eq. (11) we obtain:

$$|\alpha|^2 = \frac{\alpha_o^2}{1 + \left(\dfrac{f}{f_\alpha}\right)^2} \tag{12}$$

From Eq. (3):

$$\frac{q}{kT} = \frac{g_e}{I_E} = \frac{1}{r_e I_E} \tag{3a}$$

Also, we know that:

$$I_C = \alpha_{dc} I_E \tag{13}$$

Combining Eqs. (10), (12), (3a), and (13):

$$F = 1 + \frac{r_e}{2R_g} + \frac{r_b'}{R_g} + \frac{(R_g + r_e + r_b')^2}{2R_g r_e}$$
$$\left\{ \left(\frac{I_{co}}{I_E} + \alpha_{dc}\right) \left[1 + \left(\frac{f}{f_\alpha}\right)^2\right] \frac{1}{\alpha_o^2} + 1 - \frac{2\alpha_{dc}}{\alpha_o} \right\} \tag{14}$$

Making the following assumptions:

$$(a)\ \alpha_{dc} + \frac{I_{co}}{I_E} \cong 1 + \frac{I_{co}}{I_E}$$

$$(b)\ \alpha_{dc} \cong \alpha_o$$

$$(c)\ \frac{I_{co}}{I_E} \ll 1$$

$$(d)\ \frac{\alpha_{dc}^2}{h_{FE}} \cong \frac{1}{h_{FE}}$$

Eq. (14) can be manipulated to give:

$$F = 1 + \frac{r_e}{2R_g} + \frac{r_b'}{R_g} + \frac{(R_g + r_e + r_b')^2}{2\alpha_o R_g r_e} \left[\frac{1}{h_{FE}} + \frac{I_{co}}{I_E} + \left(\frac{f}{f_\alpha}\right)^2\right] \tag{14a}$$

where h_{FE} is the common-emitter d-c current gain.

The noise-figure expression of Eq. (14a) can be used for frequencies above the low-frequency corner in the plateau region and in the 6 db/octave region of Fig. 1. The accuracy with which F can be predicted from other measured parameters is approximately 0.5 db at higher frequencies due principally to difficulties in measuring f_α. Parasitics such as lead inductance, header capacitance, etc., can cause large errors in measurement of f_α above 500 mc. The noise figure itself may be the most accurate index of f_α. At low frequencies, generator-recombination noise may cause errors in noise measurement when $h_{FE} < 10$. Figure 6 shows a normalized noise figure plot with the contributions of the various noise sources.

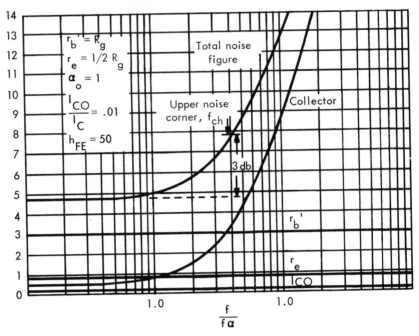

Fig. 6. Normalized transistor noise figure vs. frequency.

OPTIMUM NOISE SOURCE

If Eq. (14a) is examined, it will be noted that the collector term contains R_g in both the numerator and denominator, while R_g appears in the denominator only in the base and emitter terms. From this we conclude that by proper selection of R_g the noise figure can be minimized. To determine this value, we differentiate Eq. (14a), set the result equal to zero, and solve for R_g. The result $R_{g(opt)}$ is:

$$R_{g(opt)} = \left[(r_e + r_b')^2 + \frac{\alpha_o r_e (2r_b' + r_e)}{\dfrac{1}{h_{FE}} + \left(\dfrac{f}{f_\alpha}\right)^2 + \dfrac{I_{co}}{I_E}} \right]^{1/2} \tag{15}$$

As the frequency f approaches f_α, the second term becomes small and the optimum source approaches $(r_b' + r_e)$. At low frequencies where $(f/f_\alpha)^2$ is small, a transistor having a high d-c current gain will require a high source resistance R_g for best noise performance.

The optimum noise source in the 1/f region cannot be determined from the type of calculation described above.

TRANSISTOR NOISE FIGURE, MEDIUM AND LOW FREQUENCIES

In the low-frequency region, near and below the low-frequency noise corner, the 1/f noise begins to dominate the noise figure. Unfortunately, there is no accurate way to predict noise in this region from known accessible parameters, and we must rely on empirical means for deriving a noise-figure expression. If the noise figure is measured carefully from the plateau region where it begins to increase, and well into the 1/f region, a curve like Fig. 7 will result.

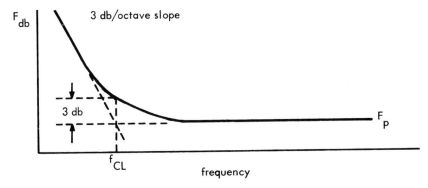

Figure 7

A tangent drawn to the low-frequency part of the curve will intersect the extension of the plateau noise figure at a point 3 db below the actual curve. The frequency at this point is called the low-frequency noise corner f_{CL}. The noise figure now can be defined for this region, using F_p, the plateau noise figure, and f_{CL}.

$$F_{\text{low freq}} = F_p \left(1 + \frac{f_{CL}}{f} \right) \tag{16}$$

The plateau noise figure F_p is the same as Eq. (14a) except that the $(f/f_\alpha)^2$ term is so small that it can be dropped. The low-frequency noise figure is then:

$$F_{\text{low freq}} = \left(1 + \frac{f_{CL}}{f} \right) \left[1 + \frac{r_b'}{R_g} + \frac{r_e}{2R_g} + \frac{(R_g + r_e + r_b')^2}{2\alpha_0 R_g r_e} \left(\frac{1}{h_{FE}} + \frac{I_{CO}}{I_E} \right) \right] \tag{17}$$

Equation (17) is not as useful as Eq. (14a) since f_{CL} must be obtained by experiment. However, once the value for f_{CL} is obtained, it is usually fairly constant for a given value of transistor when operated with a given generator resistance and emitter current. Exceptions to this rule, interestingly enough, are sometimes excessive noise figures from defective transistors. The defects may not be apparent from any other measurement, but may show up after many hours of operation.

BIBLIOGRAPHY

1. Nielsen, E. G.: "Behavior of Noise Figures in Junction Transistors," *Proc. IRE,* vol. *45,* no. 7, p. 957, June, 1957.
2. van der Ziel, A.: "Shot Noise in Junction Transistors and Diodes," *Proc. IRE,* vol. *43,* p. 1639, November, 1955.
3. van der Ziel, A., and A. G. T. Becking, "Theory of Junction Diode and Junction Transistor Noise," *Proc. IRE,* vol. *46,* p. 589, March, 1959.
4. van der Ziel, A.: "Noise in Junction Transistors," *Proc. IRE,* vol. *46,* p. 1019, June, 1958.
5. Guggenbuehl, W., and M. J. O. Strutt, "Theory and Experiments on Shot Noise in Semiconductor Junction Diodes and Transistors," *Proc. IRE,* vol. *45,* p. 839, June, 1957.
6. van der Ziel, A.: "Shot Noise in Transistors," *Proc. IRE,* vol. *48,* p. 114, January, 1960.
7. Bess, L.: "A Possible Mechanism of 1/f Noise Generation in Semiconductor Filaments, *Phys. Rev.,* 91–1569, 1953.

19

Communications
Circuit Applications

This chapter offers forty tested circuit designs, categorized in the following order:

Low-level Low-frequency Amplifiers
RF Amplifiers
Oscillators, Mixers, and Converters
IF Amplifiers
Power Amplifiers
Transmitters

Although sufficient circuit information is presented to enable an experienced engineer to reproduce the circuits, these designs are presented to stimulate creative engineering, and not to serve as construction exercises.

LOW-LEVEL LOW-FREQUENCY AMPLIFIERS

High-impedance Low-noise Wideband Amplifier. This broadband amplifier (Fig. 1) offers input impedances greater than 30 megohms with a noise figure of less than 3 db over a wide range of generator resistances. Bootstrapping of the input stage enhances the high input impedance of the TI 2N2498 field-effect transistor. Miller capacitance effects are reduced, permitting an extremely wide bandwidth with the use of a TI 2N930 in a grounded-base configuration following the input stage. This amplifier will operate at very low frequencies without the need for large-dimension capacitors.

Characteristics:

High input impedance > 30 megohms

Low noise figure < 3 db, 50 kilohms $\leqq R_g \leqq 5$ megohms

Wide frequency response = average 1 db BW, 1 cps to 500 kc at $R_g = 100$ kilohms

Stable voltage gain = 40 ± 0.5 db from -55 to $+125°C$

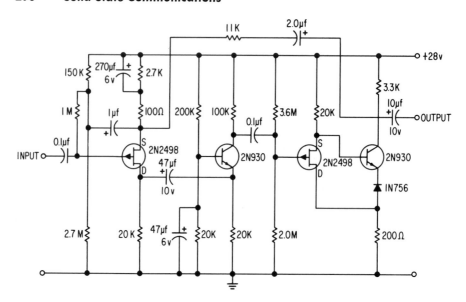

Fig. 1. High-impedance low-noise wideband amplifier.

Two-stage Low-level D-C Amplifier Using Complementary Pair. Both PNP and NPN dual transistors in six-lead TO-5 cases (from the 2N2802-07 and 2N2639-44 series) are used in this circuit (Fig. 2). They provide extremely high gain for greater stability and fewer stages. The circuit shown provides both low drift and high common-mode rejection for either differential or single-ended outputs.

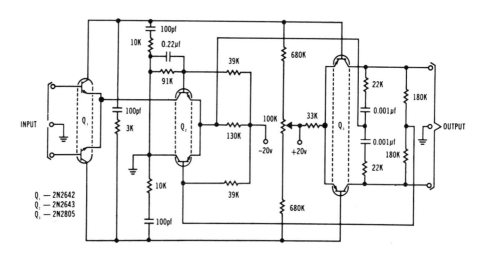

Fig. 2. Two-stage low-level d-c amplifier using complementary pair.

Characteristics:

Common mode rejection ratio = 120 db

Equivalent input current drift = 0.1 na/°C

Equivalent input voltage drift = 3 μv/°C

Differential input impedance = 500 kilohms min

Low-frequency voltage gain = 68 db

Gain-bandwidth product = 5 mc

Low-level Low-noise Amplifier. This low-level high-gain amplifier (Fig. 3) has a typical noise figure as low as 1 db. Advanced low-level planar technology of Texas Instruments 2N929 and 2N2586 transistors makes possible high gain at low current levels, plus the extremely low leakage currents necessary for true low-noise performance.

For high-impedance transducer applications, TI 2N930 and 2N2586 devices permit typical 1-db noise figure at emitter currents below 1 microampere and generator resistance over 1 megohm. These special characteristics allow direct coupling of low-level high-impedance sources . . . advantages previously available only with vacuum tubes and field-effect transistors. High gain at low levels plus very thin regions in these units combine to offer low power consumption and high radiation resistance, making the 2N930 and 2N2586 ideal for space applications.

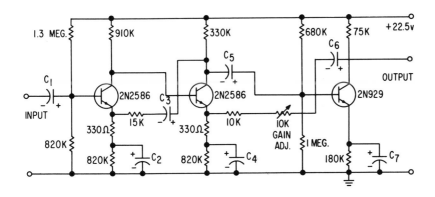

RESISTORS—ALL 1/2 watt, TI type CD1/2 MR

CAPACITORS
C_1, C_3, C_5, C_6 — 2µf, TI type SCM 225FP020C4
C_2, C_4 ————— 20µf, TI type SCM 226BP015C4
C_7 ————————— 20µf, TI type SCM226GP035C4

Fig. 3. Typical low-level high-gain amplifier.

Characteristics:

Amplifier gain $= 1000 = 60$ db

Feedback $= 4$ db at $R_g = 1$ kilohm

NF $= 0.4$ db at $R_g = 10$ kilohms

BW $(R_g = 50$ kilohm$) = 1.7$ db at $R_g = 100$ kilohms

Input impedance $= 340$ kilohms at 1 kc

Output impedance $= 12$ kilohms at 1 kc

First stage biased at 10 μa

The 2N2586 is ideal for critical low-level low-noise applications such as the input stage of amplifiers taking signals from high-impedance low-level transducers. Previously, such applications required either complex transistor circuitry or vacuum tubes.

Guaranteed minimum h_{FE} at 1 μa is 80. The guaranteed minimum low-temperature h_{FE} is 40 at 10 μa and $-55°$C. Because of this high available gain, simple amplifiers employing a minimum number of stages may be used.

The constant-noise contour curves for 2N2586 transistors (Fig. 4) enable you to select bias currents (I_C) for different source resistances. Noise figures of less than 2 db are easy to obtain for high-impedance transducers such as piezoelectric strain gauges.

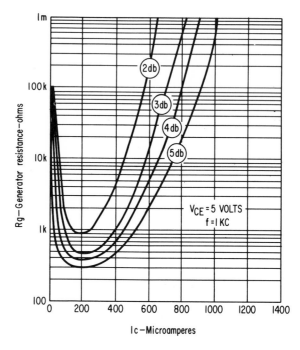

Fig. 4. Constant noise contour curves, 2N2586.

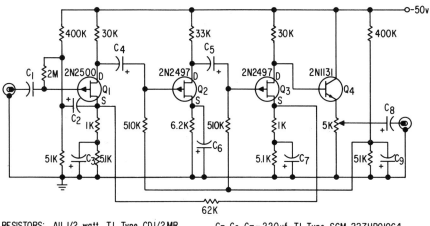

Fig. 5. 60-db low-noise amplifier.

RESISTORS: All 1/2 watt, TI Type CD1/2MR
CAPACITORS:
$C_1 - 0.1\mu f$
$C_2 - 5.6\mu f$ –TI Type SCM 565BP035C4

$C_3, C_6, C_7 - 220\mu f$ –TI Type SCM 227HP010C4
$C_4, C_5 - 1.0\mu f$ –TI Type SCM 105FP035C4
$C_8 - 10\mu f$ –TI Type SCM 106BP020C4
$C_9 - 68\mu f$ –TI Type SCM 686GP015C4

60-db Low-noise Amplifier. The circuit of Fig. 5 illustrates how Texas Instruments 2N2500 silicon field-effect transistors are used to achieve low-noise low-frequency operation. The 2N2497-2500 series field-effect transistors give you extremely low noise characteristics — as low as 5 db at 10 cycles. They are ideal for such low-frequency equipment as null-detection apparatus, medical research equipment, oscillographic and magnetic tape recorders, oscilloscopes, and all types of low-level transducers.

This circuit gives you a maximum voltage gain of 60 db ± 0.5 db from −55 to 125°C with built-in gain adjustment. You also get good low-frequency response and stable circuit operation.

Characteristics:

$NF = 1.5$ db at $R_g = 10$ kilohms

1.2 db at $R_g = 50$ kilohms

1 db at $R_g = 100$ kilohms

1 db at $R_g = 1$ megohm

High Input Impedance Amplifier. You can get input impedances greater than 1 megohm for your high-impedance transducer applications (Fig. 6) by using the TI 2N930 and 2N2411. Complementary TI 2N930 (NPN) and 2N2411 (PNP) transistors, both in the TO-18 case, also allow you single power supply design for direct coupling of low-level high-impedance sources. You get greater stability, reliability, and economy because you need fewer power supplies and fewer circuit elements.

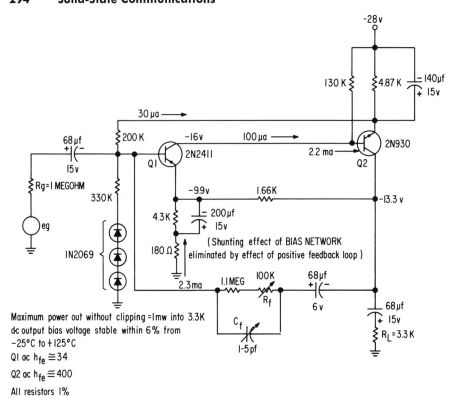

Fig. 6. High input impedance amplifier.

Characteristics:

Input impedance > 1 megohm

Wide frequency response $= A_V$ 1 db Bandwidth 100 cps to 230 kc at $R_g = 1$ megohm

Low noise voltage $= 1.2\ \mu v$ (rms), $R_g = 0$

Stable voltage gain $= 20$ db ± 0.05 db from -25 to $+125\,°C$

Low power consumption $= 65.5$ mw

Small loads possible $=$ down to 3.3 kilohms

Power gain $= 46$ db

(Also see Figs. 7 and 8)

Wideband Unity-gain Amplifier. This circuit employs a 2N2386 silicon field-effect transistor in a broadband unity-gain amplifier having an input impedance of about 100 megohms (Fig. 9). Frequency responses for various values of generator resistance are shown in Fig. 10.

Other designs may be used to extend response to d-c and give an input impedance in the order of 1000 megohms.

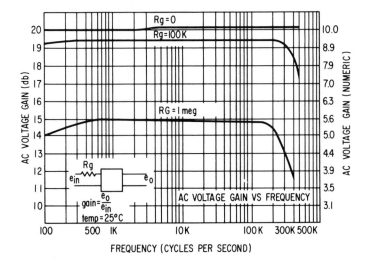

Fig. 7. A-C voltage gain vs. frequency.

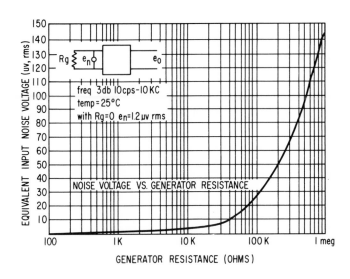

Fig. 8. Noise voltage vs. generator resistance.

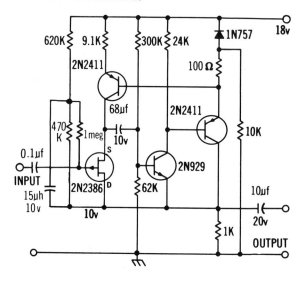

Fig. 9. High input impedance unity-gain amplifier employing 2N2386 FET.

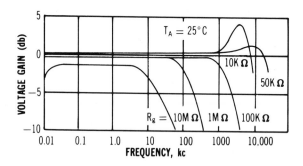

Fig. 10. Amplifier voltage gain vs. frequency for circuit of Fig. 9.

RF AMPLIFIERS

60- to 90-mc Voltage-tuned Amplifier. The close tolerance of TI's silicon XA585 voltage-variable capacitance diodes, together with a uniform slope and high Q, make the circuit shown in Fig. 11 extremely stable and give excellent tracking.

The ten new diodes from TI, typed XA580 through XA589, give capacitance ranges from 22 pf through 47 pf (at -4v), ±15% capacitance range, Q of 100 for five of the ten types, and guaranteed minimum capacitance ratios of 3.5 and 4.5 to 1.

Used in this two-stage voltage-tuned amplifier, the circuit gives more than 40-db gain from 60 to 90 mc with a 50-ohm source and 50-ohm load. The untuned input allows constant source impedance over the tunable frequency range.

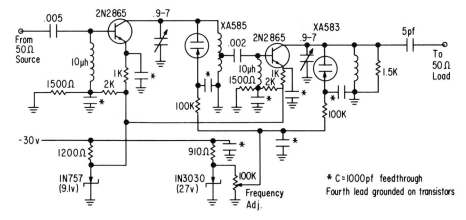

Fig. 11. 60- to 90-mc amplifier.

250-mc RF Amplifier. If you design for the military VHF band (216 to 260 mc), TI's silicon epitaxial planar 2N2865 offers an answer to your cost problems. The simple RF amplifier shown in Fig. 12 is built around the 2N2865 and demonstrates its capabilities; the amplifier gives a 12.5-db gain and a noise figure of only 5 db at 250 mc.

Since the TI 2N2865 is unconditionally stable in the common-emitter connection at 250 mc, it makes a highly stable amplifier. Input parameters of the 2N2865 are so consistent that a variable element is not needed in the input network; the 35-pf and 2.5-pf capacitors are ribbon types. The 300-pf capacitor C_1 is an undipped ceramic type whose sides are soldered directly to the BNC connector and to L_1; this effectively eliminates lead length and allows larger capacitance values without self-resonance. Insertion loss of only 0.4 db was obtained by using copper-strip inductors to give high values of unloaded-Q.

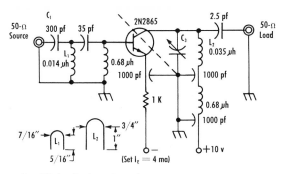

$C_1 = 300$-pf undipped ceramic capacitor
Bypass capacitors $=$ Aerovox Hi-Q EF4, 1000 pf, 1000 v
$C_3 = 1.8$-13 pf, set at 7 pf
$L_1 = 0.014$ μh: copper strip, 1/32" x 5/16", bent to 7/16" diam. $Q_u = 200$
$L_2 = 0.035$ μh: copper strip, 1/32" x 3/8", bent to 3/4" diam. $Q_u \approx 300$

Fig. 12. 250-mc RF amplifier.

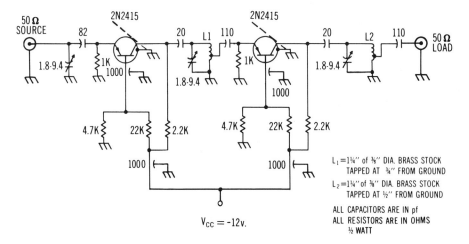

Fig. 13. 450-mc RF amplifier.

450-mc RF Amplifier. Figure 13 is a two-stage synchronously-tuned 450-mc RF amplifier using 2N2415 high-frequency low-noise transistors. This frequency is in the band allocated to aeronautical-navigational equipment (420-450 mc), and is also used for some telemetry systems. Tank circuits are contained in sections 1″ deep by 1″ wide by 2″ long. Inductors are brass rods ⅜″ in diameter tapped as indicated. All brass parts are silver-plated to a thickness greater than 0.5 mils to minimize losses.

The common-base configuration is used because it allows slightly more power gain than a common-emitter orientation at this frequency. The 2N2415, a diffused-base mesa transistor, is unconditionally stable at 450 mc, so that no source or load termination can be found that will cause oscillation.

Characteristics:

Two-stage performance: PG $= 20$ db

NF $= 4.5$ db

BW $= 10$ mc

UHF TV Tuner. Figure 14 shows a low-noise highly efficient UHF tuner using 2N2415 transistors. Full design data is available to interested manufacturers.

The circuit was designed for use as a UHF television tuner, but is adaptable to other uses. Input is tunable from 470 to 890 mc. Output is 45 mc. Power requirement is only 18 ma at 12 volts. Mixer-emitter current is 0.1 ma.

On test, the tuner indicated a typical noise figure of 7 to 9 db, compared with 10 or 12 db for comparable vacuum-tube circuits. Gain was 3 to 9 db—a substantial increase over the 6-db loss usually obtained from tube circuits in the 470- to 890-mc band.

Stability was excellent. At 935 mc, temperature fluctuations from 25 to 50°C caused the local oscillator frequency to vary only 600 kc, and supply-voltage changes of 10% caused frequency variances of only 400 kc.

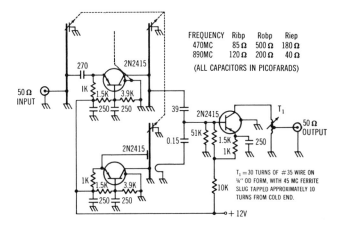

Fig. 14. UHF TV tuner.

The TI 2N2415 transistors in this circuit have an f_{max} of 3 Gc, the highest in the industry. Transistor noise figures through the UHF range are the lowest available today. A typical noise figure at 200 mc is 2.4 db. Collector-base time constant is unusually low — three picoseconds. Ruggedness of construction is confirmed by 100-percent centrifuge testing.

500-mc Amplifier. The TI 2N3570 provides high gain at 500 mc. Figure 15 shows how it may be used in a common-emitter single-stage amplifier. The small-signal circuit provides 17-db gain at a low 3-db noise figure (with $R_g = 50$ ohms). It has an input impedance of 51 ohms and an output impedance of 1300 ohms in parallel with 1.8 pf. Neutralizing voltage is obtained from the coupling loop L_3 which is a silver-plated strip of beryllium copper running parallel to L_2.

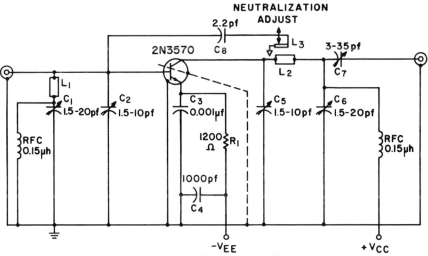

L_1=SILVER-PLATED BRASS ROD — 1 9/16" LENGTH, 1/4" DIA.
L_2=SILVER-PLATED BRASS ROD — 2 1/8" LENGTH, 1/4" DIA.

Fig. 15. 500-mc amplifier.

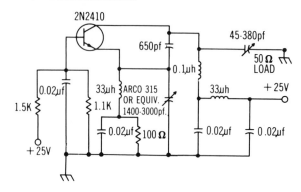

Fig. 16. 20-mc power oscillator using 2N2410.

OSCILLATORS, MIXERS, AND CONVERTERS

20-mc Power Oscillator. Figure 16 shows a 2N2410 in a Colpitts-type common-base oscillator circuit. Power output is about 500 mw to a 50-ohm load. The transistor dissipates about 750 mw at this output.

30- to 5.5-mc Mixer. This circuit mixes a 30-mc input and a 35.5-mc oscillator output to give a 5.5-mc IF signal (Fig. 17). The following shows the IF voltage output vs. the 30-mc input voltage, with an oscillator signal of 630 mv:

V_1	V_{OUT}
100 μv	3.5 mv
1 mv	11.5 mv
10 mv	100 mv
100 mw	880 mv

$(V_2 = 630 \text{ mv})$

$T_A = 25\,°C$

The 1000-pf capacitor eliminates most of the 30- and 35.5-mc signals from the output.

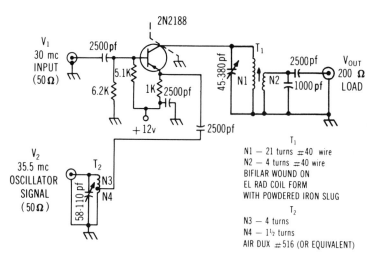

Fig. 17. 30- to 5.5-mc mixer.

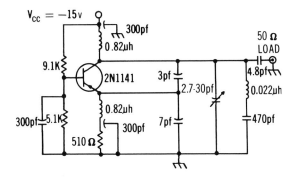

Fig. 18. 200-mc oscillator employing 2N1141.

200-mc Oscillator. This exceptionally stable oscillator (Fig. 18) varies less than 2 mc in frequency and 1.5 mw in power output over a temperature range of +25 to +80°C. Nominal power output is 22.5 mw at 25°C.

500-mc Oscillator. The Colpitts-type oscillator of Fig. 19 employs the high-frequency low-noise 2N2415 transistor. T_1 is a $1\frac{1}{2}''$ length of $\frac{3}{8}''$ brass rod with the ouput tap $\frac{1}{4}''$ from the bottom. Frequency variation is less than 1.5 mc as bias is varied from 6 to 9 volts. Frequency varies less than 3.0 mc with temperature variations from +25 to +75°C. Typical output to the 50-ohm load is 10 mw.

450- to 30-mc Mixer. This straightforward design (Fig. 20) employs the low-noise high-frequency 2N2415 transistor. Figure 21 shows power gain and noise figure of the 2N2415 at various levels of emitter current.

With a local oscillator feeding one milliwatt, conversion gain was about 15 db and noise figure was about 10 db. When an RF amplifier using a 2N2415 preceded the mixer, combined power gain was 25 db and noise figure was about 6 db.

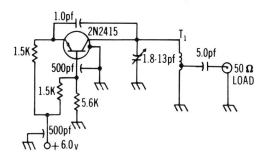

Fig. 19. 500-mc oscillator using 2N2415.

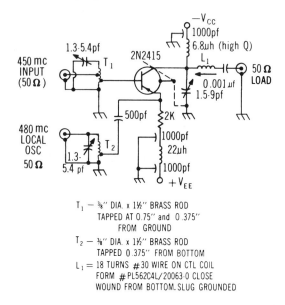

Fig. 20. 450- to 30-mc mixer using 2N2415.

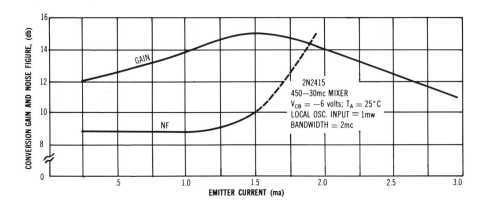

Fig. 21. Power gain and noise figure vs. emitter current, 2N2415.

250- to 60-mc Converter. The circuit of Fig. 22 consists of an RF amplifier, a mixer, a separate buffered local oscillator, and a two-stage IF amplifier — all using the 2N2865 transistor. Separate chassis were used to provide flexibility and utility. There is no tendency to oscillate with the RF amplifier disconnected.

The RF amplifier uses single-tuned input and output networks and provides a power gain of approximately 12 db, NF of 4.5 db ($R_g = 50$ ohms), and a bandwidth of 13 mc.

The mixer employs separate injection with the local oscillator injected into the emitter. A single-tuned network matches the 50-ohm cable to the base. A double-tuned network is used at the output to transform down to the 50-ohm cable

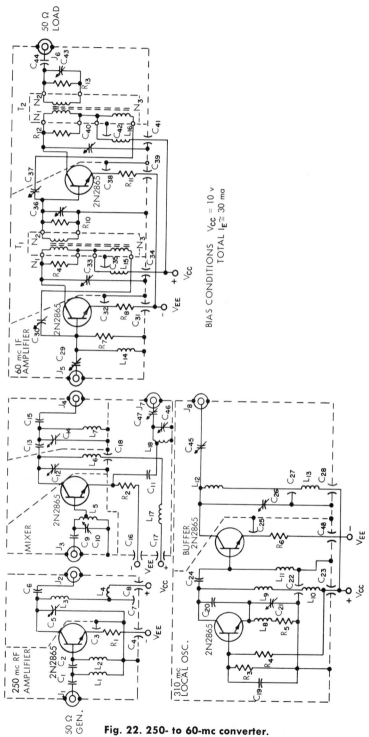

Fig. 22. 250- to 60-mc converter.

connecting the mixer and the IF amplifier. Local oscillator injection was set at approximately 60 mv. Conversion power gain was approximately 11 db.

The 310-mc local oscillator is a Colpitts-type which feeds a common-emitter buffer. Output is connected through a matching network to the emitter of the mixer stage.

The 60-mc IF amplifier consists of two neutralized double-tuned stages with approximately 45-db power gain and an effective bandwidth of 10 mc.

Typical Performance:

Power gain $= 69$ db

Bandwidth $= 5$ mc $(-3$ db$)$

Noise figure $= 7$ db $(R_g = 50$ ohms$)$

Sensitivity $= 3.5$ μv

Image rejection > 40 db

450- to 105-mc Converter Using 2N2996. The RF amplifier in the converter circuit of Fig. 23 is designed for low-noise operation at 450 mc. The 2N2996 in the common-base configuration has a typical power gain at 450 mc of 13 db, with a 5.9-db noise figure. Input is matched to the 50-ohm source and the output is coupled from a tap on T_1 to the mixer input. R_3 is used to obtain the desired stability factors for Q_1 and Q_2 for interchangeability considerations.

Q_1, Q_2, Q_3, Q_4, Q_5, Q_6 - 2N2996

C_1	-	10 pf	R_1	-	1.5 k
C_2	-	1.8 - 13 pf	R_2	-	3.0 k
C_3	-	1.8 - 13 pf	R_3	-	3.0 k
C_4	-	1000 pf (See C' below)	R_4	-	51 Ω
C_5	-	9 - 35 pf	R_5	-	1.5 k
C_6	-	3 pf	R_6	-	3.0 k
C_7	-	9 - 35 pf	R_7	-	3.0 k
C_8	-	10 pf	R_8	-	3.0 k
C_9	-	9 - 35 pf	R_9	-	3.0 k
C_{10}	-	3.0 pf	R_{10}	-	1.5 k
C_{11}	-	9 - 35 pf	R_{11}	-	3.0 k
C_{12}	-	10 pf	R_{12}	-	3.0 k
C_{13}	-	9 - 35 pf	R_{13}	-	1.5 k
C_{14}	-	3 pf	R_{14}	-	1.5 k
C_{15}	-	9 - 35 pf	R_{15}	-	3.0 k
C_{16}	-	10 pf	R_{16}	-	3.0 k
C_{17}	-	2.5 pf	R_{17}	-	1.5 k
C_{18}	-	0.9 - 7 pf	R_{18}	-	3.0 k
C_{19}	-	0.9 - 7 pf	R_{19}	-	3.0 k
C_{20}	-	220 pf	R_{20}	-	510 Ω
C_{21}	-	110 pf			
C_{22}	-	1.8 - 13 pf			
C'	-	1000 pf (Aerovox Hi-Q EF4 by-pass cap.)			

T_1 - 1/2 turn of 1/4" x 1/32" copper strip, tapped approx. 1/3 up from ground
L_1 - 2 turns # 20 Buss wire on 1/2 watt-1 megohm resistor
L_2 - 0.15 μh RFC
L_3 - 0.33 μh RFC
$L_{4,5,7,8,10,11}$ - 2 1/2 turns #30 wire on Cambion LS 9 coil form (adjusted to resonate with
    31 pf at 105 mc)
L_6 - 3.3 μh RFC
L_9 - 3.3 μh RFC
L_{12} - 0.15 μh RFC
L_{13} - 2 turns #20 Buss wire on 1/2-watt - 1 megohm resistor
L_{14} - 0.33 μh RFC

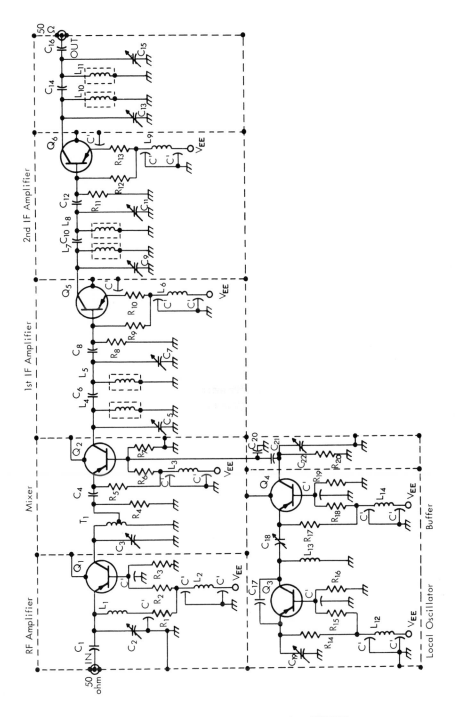

Fig. 23. 450- to 105-mc converter using 2N2996.

The 450-mc RF signal is mixed with a 345-mc oscillator signal to produce the 105-mc IF signal. Impedance at the base of the mixer is made as low as possible for maximum performance. A double-tuned network in the output attenuates all undesired signals. The 2N2996 is an excellent low-noise VHF/UHF mixer.

The stable 345-mc Colpitts oscillator is capable of 5-mw output power; however, less than 1 mw is required by the buffer stage for good mixing action. The buffer helps stabilize the oscillator by providing a relatively constant load, plus isolation from the RF signals. Buffer output is divided down for injection to the mixer with the proper signal level at a low impedance.

The 105-mc IF signal produced by the mixer is coupled to the first IF amplifier. This is a common-emitter amplifier with a stable power gain of 20 db and a noise figure of 2.5 db at 105 mc. The output circuit is another double-tuned network to further attenuate undesired signals. The second IF amplifier is identical to the first with the output coupled to a 50-ohm load.

Typical Performance:

Power gain = 63 db

Noise figure = 7 db

3-db bandwidth = 6.5 mc

30-db bandwidth = 20 mc

Power = +12 v at 42 ma

There are no signals above the noise level at the output with the absence of an input signal.

The 2N2998 transistor can replace the 2N2996 in the RF amplifier to provide a 3-db increase in power gain with an overall noise figure of only 3 db.

450- to 105-mc Converter Using 2N2415. This converter (Fig. 24) consists of a two-stage amplifier, a 450- to 105-mc mixer stage, and a 345-mc local oscillator. The two-stage RF amplifier uses the TI 2N2415, and has a typical power gain of 20 db, NF of 4.5 db, and a bandwidth of 10 mc. The mixer uses a TI 2N2415 and has a conversion gain of approximately 12 db. The local oscillator in this circuit uses a TI 2N1407.

The overall noise figure of this frequency converter is 5.0 db, and the circuit delivers a conversion gain from antenna terminals to IF strip terminals of 32 db.

IF AMPLIFIERS

5.5-mc IF Amplifier. Three 2N2189 germanium Dalmesa transistors are used in this high-gain low-noise 5.5-mc IF strip (Fig. 25).

Typical Performance:

Power gain = 62 db

Noise figure = 4 db

Bandwidth = 0.18 mc

Response curve is shown in Fig. 26.

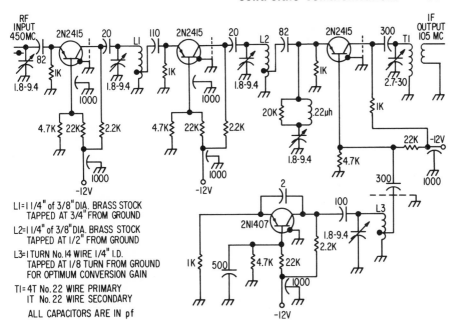

L1 = 1 1/4" of 3/8" DIA. BRASS STOCK
    TAPPED AT 3/4" FROM GROUND

L2 = 1 1/4" of 3/8" DIA. BRASS STOCK
    TAPPED AT 1/2" FROM GROUND

L3 = 1 TURN No. 14 WIRE 1/4" I.D.
    TAPPED AT 1/8 TURN FROM GROUND
    FOR OPTIMUM CONVERSION GAIN

T1 = 4T No. 22 WIRE PRIMARY
    1T No. 22 WIRE SECONDARY

ALL CAPACITORS ARE IN pf

Fig. 24. 450- to 105-mc converter using 2N2415.

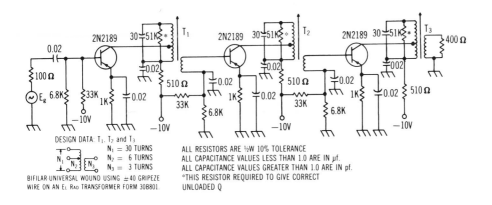

DESIGN DATA: T_1, T_2 and T_3

N_1 = 30 TURNS
N_2 = 6 TURNS
N_3 = 3 TURNS

BIFILAR-UNIVERSAL WOUND USING #40 GRIPEZE
WIRE ON AN EL RAD TRANSFORMER FORM 30B801.

ALL RESISTORS ARE ½W 10% TOLERANCE
ALL CAPACITANCE VALUES LESS THAN 1.0 ARE IN μf.
ALL CAPACITANCE VALUES GREATER THAN 1.0 ARE IN pf.
*THIS RESISTOR REQUIRED TO GIVE CORRECT
UNLOADED Q

Fig. 25. 5.5-mc IF amplifier.

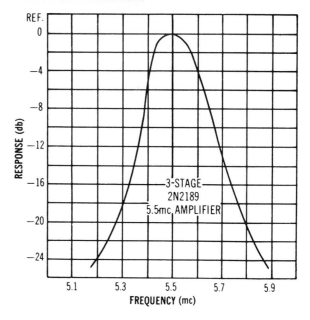

Fig. 26. Response curve for 5.5-mc IF strip.

30-mc IF Amplifier Using 2N2410. This circuit (Fig. 27) employs a 2N2410 epitaxial planar silicon transistor. Because of its large signal handling capability it may be used as the final stage of IF strips. Typical power gain at the indicated bias point is 16 db.

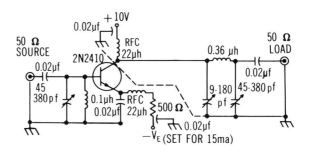

Fig. 27. 30-mc amplifier using 2N2410.

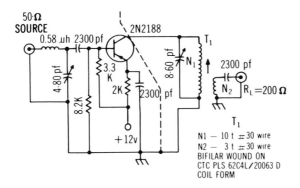

Fig. 28. 30-mc IF amplifier using 2N2188.

30-mc IF Amplifier Using 2N2188. The 2N2188 Dalmesa transistor is used in this circuit (Fig. 28), which includes an L-section to give an R_g of 350 ohms from a 50-ohm source. Typical performance is 13-db power gain, 4-db noise figure, and 5-mc bandwidth. Noise characteristics of the 2N2188 are shown in Fig. 29.

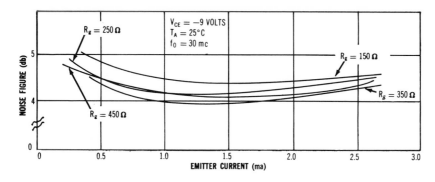

Fig. 29. Noise figure vs. emitter current, 2N2188 series.

30-mc Double-tuned Amplifier. The amplifier of Fig. 30 demonstrates the gain and noise capabilities of the 2N2996 at 30 mc. Good stability is achieved through proper loading, even though the 2N2996 is potentially unstable at this

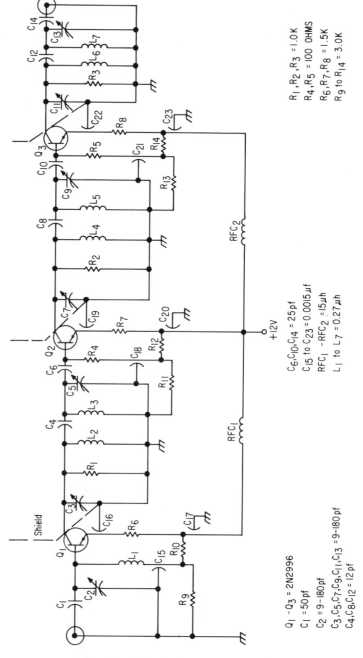

Fig. 30. 30-mc double-tuned amplifier.

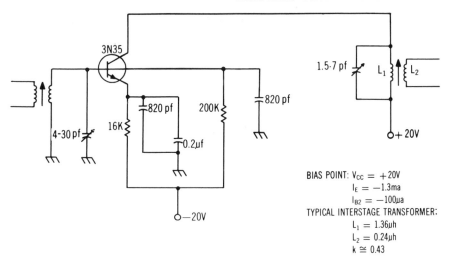

BIAS POINT: $V_{CC} = +20V$
$I_E = -1.3ma$
$I_{B2} = -100\mu a$
TYPICAL INTERSTAGE TRANSFORMER:
$L_1 = 1.36\mu h$
$L_2 = 0.24\mu h$
$k \cong 0.43$

Fig. 31. 60-mc tetrode IF amplifier.

frequency. Even with the necessary loading, the amplifier has a good gain figure of 21-db gain per stage.

Typical Performance:

Power gain $\cong 63$ db

Bandwidth $= 3$ mc

Noise figure $= 2.3$ db

60-mc Tetrode IF Amplifier. The 3N35 grown-junction tetrode transistor offers several advantages for 60-mc use (see Fig. 31). AGC characteristics are excellent and power requirements are much lower than for other silicon transistors at this frequency. Typical stage gains of 12 db are obtainable.

60-mc IF Amplifier Using 2N743. This circuit (Fig. 32) takes advantage of the excellent gain and noise figure capabilities of 2N743 silicon epitaxial transistors. Alignment is simplified because of the unconditional stability of the 2N743 at this frequency, and the heavy mismatch. Higher gains — up to 16 db per stage — are possible with a conjugate match at the output.

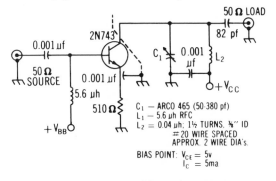

C_1 — ARCO 465 (50-380 pf)
L_1 — 5.6 µh RFC
$L_2 = 0.04$ µh; 1½ TURNS, ⅜″ ID
#20 WIRE SPACED
APPROX. 2 WIRE DIA's.
BIAS POINT: $V_{CE} = 5v$
$I_C = 5ma$

Fig. 32. 60-mc IF amplifier using 2N743.

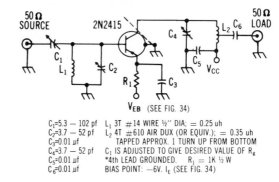

C₁=5.3 — 102 pf   L₁ 3T #14 WIRE ½″ DIA; = 0.25 uh
C₂=3.7 — 52 pf   L₂ 4T #610 AIR DUX (OR EQUIV.); = 0.35 uh
C₃=0.01 µf   TAPPED APPROX. 1 TURN UP FROM BOTTOM
C₄=3.7 — 52 pf   C₁ IS ADJUSTED TO GIVE DESIRED VALUE OF R_g
C₅=0.01 µf   *4th LEAD GROUNDED.   R₁ = 1K ½ W
C₆=0.01 µf   BIAS POINT: —6V. I_E (SEE FIG. 34)

Fig. 33. 70-mc low-noise amplifier.

Typical Performance:

Power gain = 13 db

Bandwidth = 20 mc

Noise figure = 5.5 db

70-mc Low-noise IF Amplifier. Dalcom 2N2415 transistors make possible extremely low noise IF strip circuitry in the 70-mc region. A typical amplifier stage design is shown in Fig. 33; Fig. 34 displays the noise figures available at various emitter currents and generator resistances.

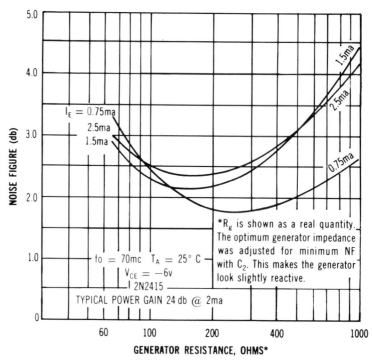

Fig. 34. Noise figure vs. generator resistance, 2N2415 at 70 mc.

70-mc Neutralized Amplifier. Chief design objective for the circuit in Fig. 35 was to achieve as much power gain as possible using only a single stage and maintaining good circuit stability.

Typical Performance:

(Conditions: $V_{CB} = -6v$, $I_C = -2$ ma)

Power gain = 27 db

Noise figure < 3 db

105-mc IF Amplifier. The circuit in Fig. 36 demonstrates that the 2N2996 still has excellent gain and noise capabilities at 105 mc. Although the 2N2996 is potentially unstable at 105 mc, proper loading yields good stability and still permits the circuit to achieve 19 db of gain per stage.

Typical Performance:

Power gain = 38 db

Bandwidth = 8 mc

Noise figure = 2.5 db

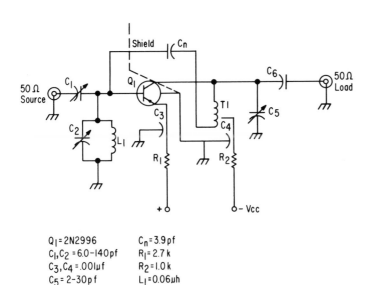

$Q_1 = 2N2996$ $C_n = 3.9$ pf
$C_1, C_2 = 6.0-140$ pf $R_1 = 2.7$ k
$C_3, C_4 = .001 \mu f$ $R_2 = 1.0$ k
$C_5 = 2-30$ pf $L_1 = 0.06 \mu h$
$C_6 = 10$ pf   T1 5 Turns No. 516 air dux tapped 4T from collector

Fig. 35. 70-mc neutralized amplifier.

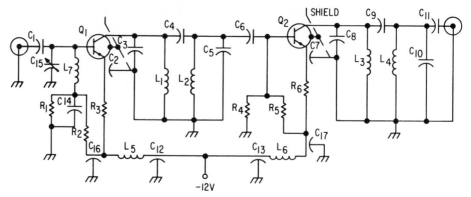

Q$_{1,2}$ = 2N2996
L$_1$,L$_2$,L$_3$,L$_4$ = 2 1/2 TURNS # 30 WIRE ON CAMBION
LS9 COIL FORM (ADJUSTED TO RESONATE WITH 3lpf AT 105mc)
L$_5$,L$_6$ = 3.3µh
L$_7$ = 0.07µh
R$_1$,R$_2$,R$_4$,R$_5$ = 3K
R$_3$,R$_6$ = 1.5K

C$_1$ = 250pf
C$_2$,C$_7$,C$_{12}$,C$_{13}$,C$_{14}$ = 1000pf
C$_3$,C$_5$,C$_8$,C$_{10}$ = 9–35 pf
C$_4$,C$_9$ = 1.3–5.4pf
C$_6$ = 1.5–20pf
C$_{11}$ = 10pf
C$_{15}$ = 9–180pf
C$_{16}$,C$_{17}$ = 1000pf

Fig. 36. 105-mc IF amplifier.

500-mc Staggered-tuned Amplifier. The amplifier of Fig. 37 is a two-stage slightly staggered type that offers excellent stability. This circuit will not oscillate with either an open circuit load or source. Midband gain is 21 db, and power requirement is 7 ma at 15 v.

POWER AMPLIFIERS

70-watt Audio Amplifier. Figure 38 shows a 70-watt audio amplifier output stage using the advanced TI3031 germanium alloy power transistor, which gives you the industry's highest power-to-cost ratio in a JEDEC TO-3 package. The output is capacitor coupled and does not require transformer coupling to the speaker coil. Thus, there is a significant cost reduction in output coupling to complement the low cost of the TI3031 transistors.

Characteristics: 90 watts at 55°C case temperature, 7-amp collector current, 45-120 volts BV$_{CBO}$, minimum h$_{FE}$ of 40 at 3 amps.

Other consumer and industrial applications include electronic organs, d-c converters, series regulators for power supplies, light flashers, and tape recorder bias oscillators.

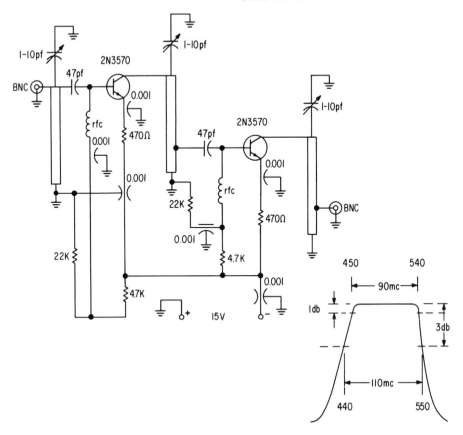

Fig. 37. 500-mc staggered-tuned amplifier.

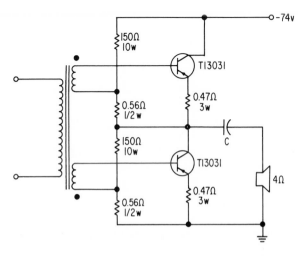

Fig. 38. 70-watt audio amplifier stage using TI3031.

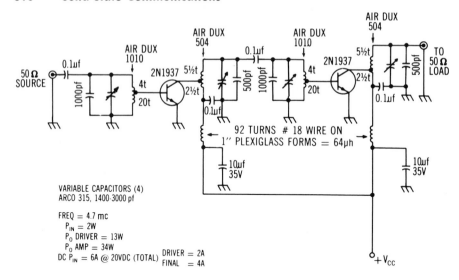

Fig. 39. 4.7-mc two-stage drive and amplifier.

4.7-mc Driver and Amplifier. This two-stage driver and amplifier (Fig. 39) employs two 2N1937's in a common-emitter circuit. Figure 40 shows characteristics of the 2N1937 with V_{CE} of 20 volts.

50-mc Power Amplifier. Figure 41 is the schematic of an amplifier stage used to test the characteristics of the 2N2410 for power amplifier service. Values shown are for 50-mc common-base operation.

Operating characteristics of the 2N2410 transistor are shown in Figs. 42 through 45.

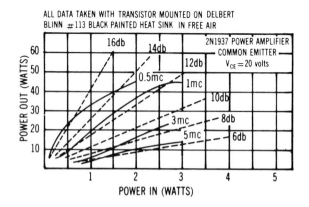

Fig. 40. Common-emitter amplifier characteristics, 2N1937.

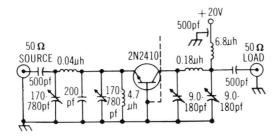

Fig. 41. 50-mc power amplifier using 2N2410.

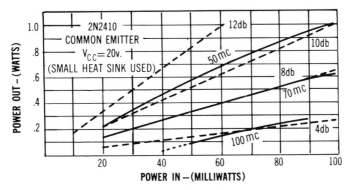

Fig. 42. Common-emitter amplifier characteristics, 2N2410.

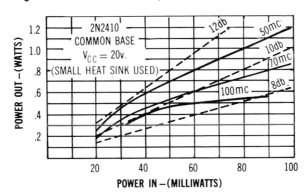

Fig. 43. Common-base amplifier characteristics, 2N2410.

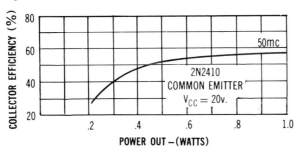

Fig. 44. Collector efficiency, 2N2410 as common-emitter amplifier at 50 mc.

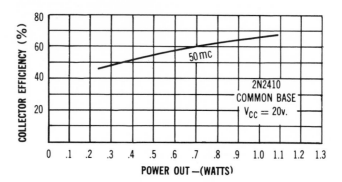

Fig. 45. Collector efficiency, 2N2410 as common-base amplifier at 50 mc.

160-mc Power Amplifier. This circuit (Fig. 46) is designed to operate as a Class C power amplifier at 160 mc with a power output of approximately 750 mw.

Since the minimum BV_{CBO} rating is 60 v, the collector supply is limited to 30 v. The BV_{CEO} rating is only 40 v; however, the common-emitter circuit is essentially in a BV_{CES} condition and the breakdown characteristic is the same as BV_{CBO}.

Pi matching networks are used at the input and output to reflect the proper impedance to the transistor for maximum performance. The transistor was measured with a 2″ x 2″ x ½″ aluminum plate attached.

The circuit was constructed on a 0.032″ brass chassis with a metal shield passing between the collector and emitter pins of the transistor socket. The output coil has an unloaded Q of 220 and the loaded Q is designed for a value of 10.

Power output was measured with a 50-ohm Hewlett-Packard Bolometer Mount, Model 476A. Power gain is the ratio of this power to the power measured out of the signal source into the same bolometer mount. See Figs. 47 and 48.

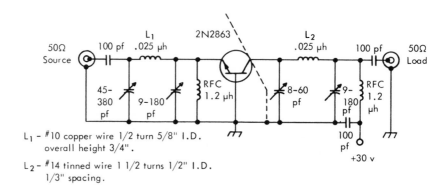

Fig. 46. 160-mc power amplifier.

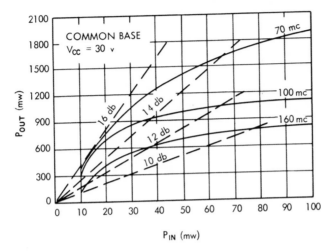

Fig. 47. Power out vs. power in, 2N2863 in common-base configuration.

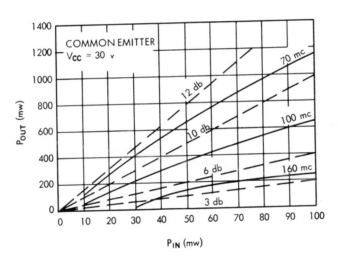

Fig. 48. Power out vs. power in, 2N2863 in common-emitter configuration.

Typical Performance:

Supply voltage = 30 v

Power output = 750 mw

Efficiency = 25%

3-db bandwidth = 15 mc

173-mc Power Amplifier. The 2N1141 transistor is useful to 500 mc and delivers excellent large-signal performance at 173 mc in the power amplifier cir-

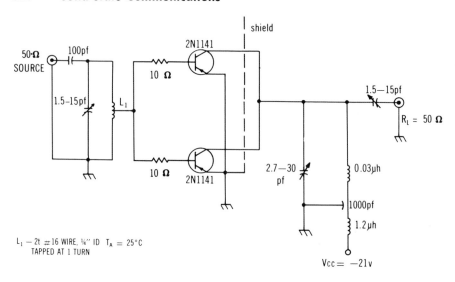

Fig. 49. 173-mc amplifier.

cuit of Fig. 49. Two 2N1141's are connected in parallel to deliver an average of 400 mw to a 50-ohm load. Base resistors equalize input signal power to the transistors. Small heat sinks (JADERO #1101 or equivalent) are used.

Typical Performance:

Power output = 400 mw

Power gain = 11.5 db

Collector efficiency = 41.8%

250-mc Power Amplifier. The 2N743 gives good large-signal performance as well as good small-signal performance. Figure 50 shows a common-base power amplifier test circuit with component values selected for 250-mc operation.

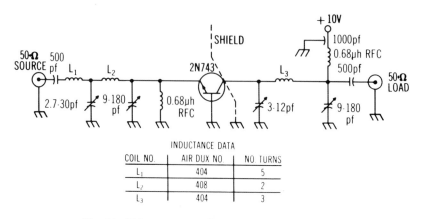

COIL NO.	AIR DUX NO.	NO. TURNS
L_1	404	5
L_2	408	2
L_3	404	3

INDUCTANCE DATA

Fig. 50. 250-mc common-base power amplifier.

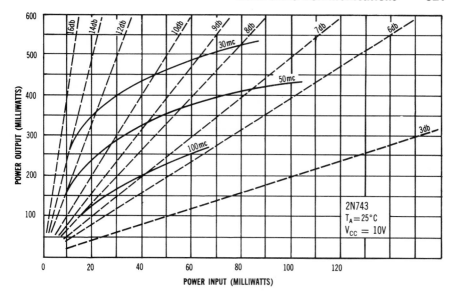

Fig. 51. Common-emitter amplifier characteristics, 2N743.

Figure 51 gives common-emitter amplifier performance, Fig. 52 gives common-base performance, and Fig. 53 indicates the desirable frequency at which to switch from common-emitter to common-base for two fixed drive levels.

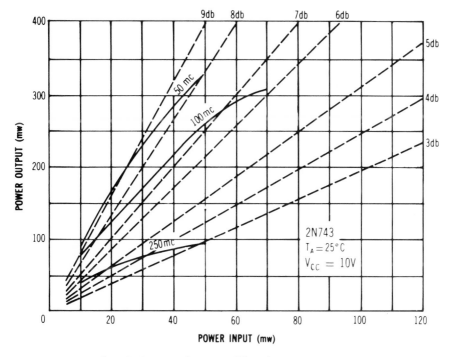

Fig. 52. Common-base amplifier characteristics, 2N743.

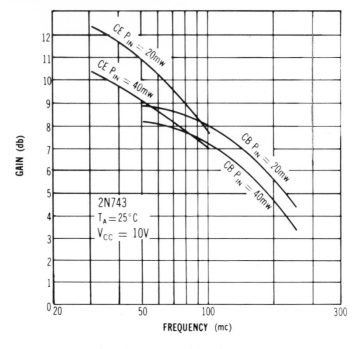

Fig. 53. Combined power amplifier characteristics, 2N743.

TRANSMITTERS

1-watt 50-mc Transmitter. TI's new L-52 makes 1 watt at 50 mc easily obtainable. The circuit of Fig. 54 is a common-emitter Class C amplifier with a π-L output circuit matching to a 50-ohm antenna. The input impedance matching network is designed to make the input impedance 50 ohms.

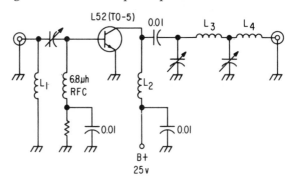

L_1= 3T NO. 16 Buss, 0.4 diam, 0.3" long, L=0.085μh
L_2= 4T NO. 16 Buss, 0.4 diam, 0.4" long, L=0.12μh
L_3= 8T NO. 16 Soldereze, 0.5 diam, 0.5" long, L=0.5μh
L_4= 10T NO. 16 Soldereze, 0.4 diam, 0.6" long, L=0.34μh

Power out = 1w
Power gain = 10 db

Fig. 54. 1-watt 50-mc transmitter.

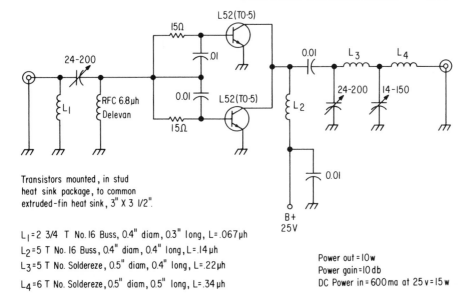

Fig. 55. 10-watt 50-mc transmitter.

The relatively high breakdown voltage of this device allows the amplifier to be amplitude modulated. The overall efficiency of the amplifier is approximately 65%.

10-watt 50-mc Transmitter. Two TI L-52's in parallel will produce 10 watts of output power with 10-db gain. Figure 55 is basically a common-emitter circuit with a π-L output matching network to match a 50-ohm antenna. Separate biasing resistors are used in the base circuits to balance the operating currents of the two transistors. The input circuit is designed to produce a 50-ohm input impedance. Overall efficiency of this circuit is approximately 65%.

1-watt 170-mc Transmitter. This circuit (Fig. 56) is a single common-emitter Class C amplifier utilizing TI's new L-52 to produce 1-watt output power

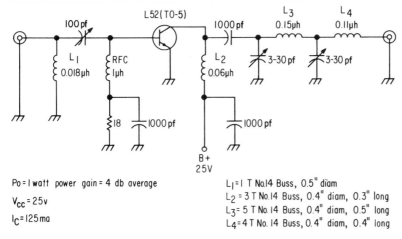

Fig. 56. 1-watt 170-mc transmitter.

at 170 mc. The output circuit is a π-L network designed to match the output of the transistor to a 50-ohm input impedance. The overall efficiency of this circuit is approximately 30%, with 1-watt output and 4-db power gain.

162- to 180-mc Transmitter. Figure 57 shows a narrowband transmitter capable of being tuned over a frequency range of 162 to 180 mc. The first stage acts as a buffer for an oscillator. Second and third stages provide frequency multiplication. The fourth stage isolates changes that might appear in the load, to prevent their being reflected across the tripler stage, which would cause frequency instability. The final stage is a Class C power amplifier; the two devices in parallel can deliver 300 mw to a 50-ohm load.

223-mc Transmitter. The 223-mc transmitter shown in Fig. 58 is satisfactory for many telemetry applications.

The crystal-controlled Colpitts-type oscillator employs a 2N743 transistor working in the common-base configuration. The oscillator delivers about 10 mw into a 50-ohm load.

The first doubler is a common-emitter amplifier with a pi-type circuit in the output tuned to the second harmonic and employing a trap network at the collector to eliminate the fundamental in the output. Power gain of this circuit is about 6 db and the power output to the second doubler is about 40 mw at 111.5 mc.

The second doubler is a common-base amplifier with a pi-filter in the output tuned to the second harmonic. The trap eliminates the 11.5-mc fundamental. Power output to the final is about 45 mw at 223 mc.

The final stage is a common-case Class C amplifier employing another pi-network in the 223-mc output. The final will deliver 80 to 100 mw to a 50-ohm load.

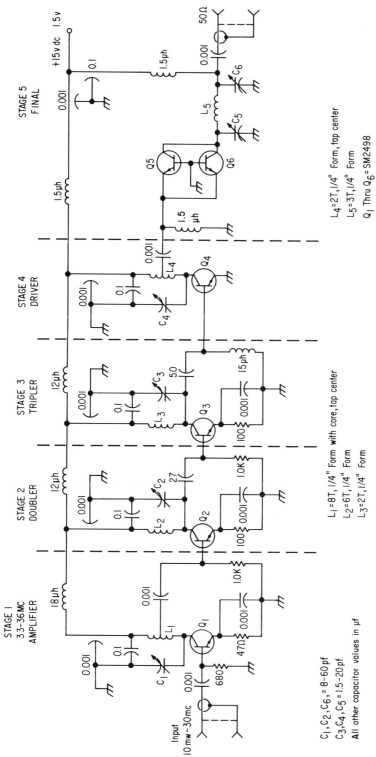

Fig. 57. 162- to 180-mc transmitter.

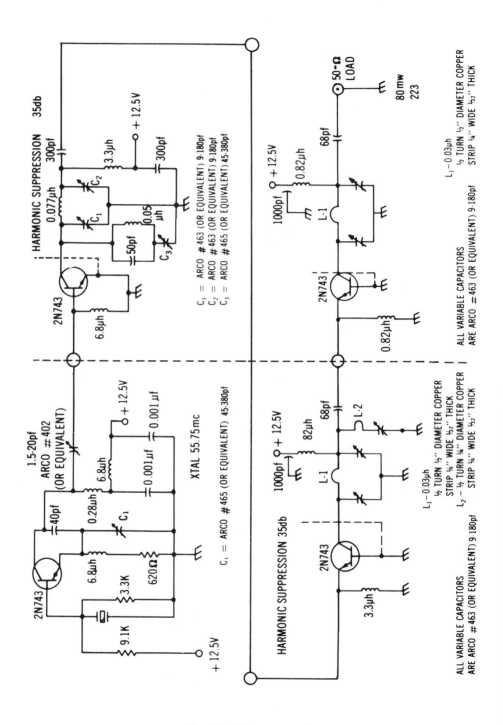

Fig. 58. 223-mc transmitter.

20

Device Nomenclature and Standard Test Circuits

GENERAL PRINCIPLES OF LETTER SYMBOL STANDARDIZATION

Electrical Quantities and Electrical Parameters. Electrical quantities deal primarily with voltage, current, and time quantities. Electrical parameters deal with the relationship between specific electrical quantities.

In studying the operation of a transistor, we assume it to be a black box with two input leads and two output leads. See Fig. 1.

In describing this black box, we write equations relating the input current, input voltage, output current, and output voltage. An example of this is the equation:

$$v_i = h_i i_i + h_r v_o$$

This equation states that the input voltage v_i equals the input current multiplied by a certain number h_i plus the output voltage v_o multiplied by a certain number h_r. The numbers h_i and h_r are parameters.

Although many electrical quantities (I_{co}, Zener voltage, etc.) are called parameters, they are not parameters in the true sense of the word.

Electrical Quantities and Associated Subscripts. The following is a list of accepted symbols for electrical quantities:

$$V = \text{voltage (d-c volts)}$$
$$v = \text{voltage (a-c volts)}$$

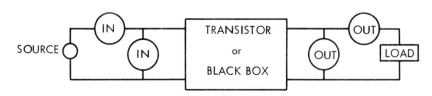

Figure 1

$$I = \text{current (d-c amperes)}$$
$$i = \text{current (a-c amperes)}$$
$$R = \text{resistance (ohms)}$$
$$Z = \text{impedance (ohms)}$$
$$Y = \text{admittance (mhos)}$$
$$P = \text{power (watts)}$$
$$f = \text{frequency (cycles per second)}$$
$$B = \text{breakdown}$$

The following subscripts are associated with these symbols for electrical quantities:

$$E \text{ or } e = \text{emitter electrode}$$
$$B \text{ or } b = \text{base electrode}$$
$$C \text{ or } c = \text{collector electrode}$$
$$O \text{ or } o = \text{open electrode}$$
$$X \text{ or } x = \text{other electrode not opened}$$

An upper-case subscript designates a d-c quantity while a lower-case subscript designates an a-c quantity.

Examples:

$$I_B = \text{d-c current in circuit B}$$
$$i_b = \text{a-c current in circuit B}$$

First subscript: designates the electrode at which current or voltage is measured with respect to the reference electrode.

Second subscript: designates the reference electrode. (If understood, this subscript may be omitted.)

Third subscript: designates circuit conditions at the instant the current or voltage is measured. (If the second subscript is omitted, this becomes the second subscript.)

Examples:

$$I_{CBO} = \text{collector-to-base d-c current with emitter circuit open.}$$
$$I_{CO} = \text{collector-to-base d-c current with emitter circuit open.}$$
$$V_{BE} = \text{d-c voltage between base and emitter.}$$
$$i_c = \text{a-c collector current in the collector circuit.}$$

Electrical Parameters and Associated Subscripts. The following is a list of the most commonly used subscripts. Formerly, double numbers were used instead of letter subscripts but these have fallen into disuse because they are not sufficiently informative. In all cases, the double number is considered as one subscript.

$$22 \text{ or } O \text{ or } o = \text{output}$$
$$11 \text{ or } I \text{ or } i = \text{input}$$
$$21 \text{ or } F \text{ or } f = \text{forward transfer ratio}$$
$$12 \text{ or } R \text{ or } r = \text{reverse transfer ratio}$$
$$E \text{ or } e = \text{emitter electrode}$$
$$B \text{ or } b = \text{base electrode}$$
$$C \text{ or } c = \text{collector electrode}$$
$$O \text{ or } o = \text{open (depending on relative position)}$$
$$S \text{ or } s = \text{short}$$

In most cases parameters have one, two, or three subscripts.

First subscript: designates input, output, or ratio function
Second subscript: designates circuit configuration
Third subscript: gives additional information

Examples:

h_{22} or h_{ob} = output admittance with the input open (this is assumed) and using a common-base circuit.

H_{OB} = output conductance (1/resistance) with the input open (this is assumed) and using a common-base circuit.

h_{11} or h_{ib} = input impedance with the output shorted (this is assumed) and using a common-base circuit.

Bias Voltage Symbols. Bias voltages are supplied from a d-c source and are designated by repeating the electrode subscript. The reference electrode may be designated by the third subscript.

Examples:

V_{EE} = d-c bias voltage applied to emitter circuit
V_{CC} = d-c bias voltage applied to collector circuit

DEFINITIONS AND TEST CIRCUITS

Schematic Nomenclature.

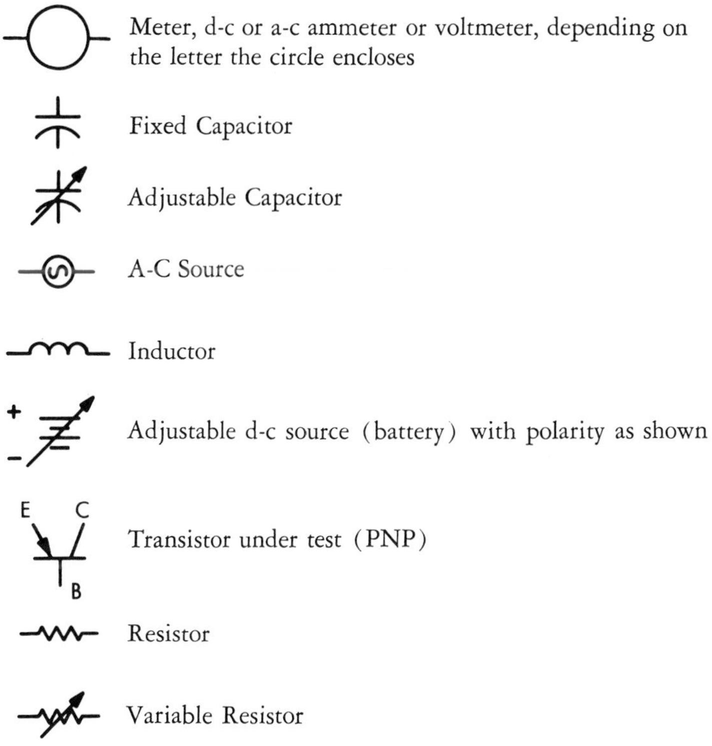

Meter, d-c or a-c ammeter or voltmeter, depending on the letter the circle encloses

Fixed Capacitor

Adjustable Capacitor

A-C Source

Inductor

Adjustable d-c source (battery) with polarity as shown

Transistor under test (PNP)

Resistor

Variable Resistor

Figure 2

D-C Measurements and Test Circuits.

See Fig. 3:

I_{CBO} = the current that flows when the collector-base junction is reverse biased to a specified d-c voltage with the emitter open-circuited.

BV_{CBO} = breakdown voltage. A d-c voltage, applied in the reverse direction of the collector-base junction with the emitter open-circuited, which gives a specified reverse current.

See Fig. 4:

I_{EBO} = the current that flows when the emitter-base junction is reverse biased to a specified d-c voltage with the collector open-circuited.

BV_{EBO} = breakdown voltage. A d-c voltage, applied in the reverse direction of the emitter-base junction with the collector open-circuited, which gives a specified reverse current.

See Fig. 5:

I_{CEO} = the current that flows when the collector-emitter junction is reverse biased to a specified d-c voltage with the base open-circuited.

BV_{CEO} = breakdown voltage. A d-c voltage, applied in the reverse direction of the collector-emitter junction with the base open-circuited, which gives a specified reverse current.

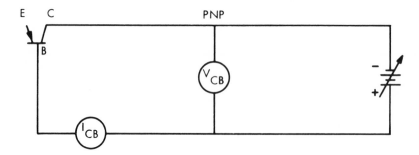

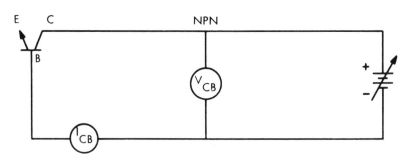

Figure 3

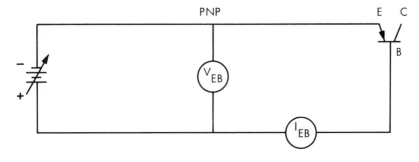

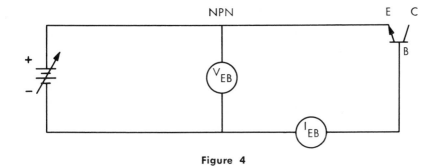

Figure 4

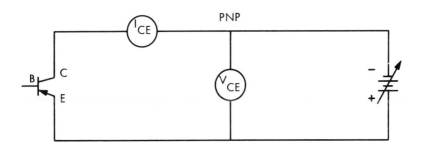

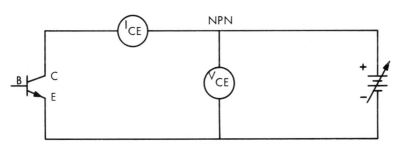

Figure 5

See Fig. 6:

I_{CER} = the current that flows in the collector with a specified voltage applied to the collector, and a resistor connected from the base to emitter.

BV_{CER} = the voltage measured between the collector and emitter with a specified current flowing in the collector, with a resistor connected from the base to emitter.

See Fig. 7:

I_L = Leakage current between the can of a transistor and all electrodes (emitter, base, and collector) at a specified voltage. This is a measure of insulation resistance. This test is omitted if one of the transistor leads is connected to the can.

See Fig. 8:

h_{FE} = d-c beta (β). Current transfer ratio of a common-emitter transistor circuit.

$$h_{FE} = \frac{I_C}{I_B}$$

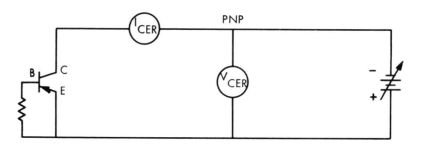

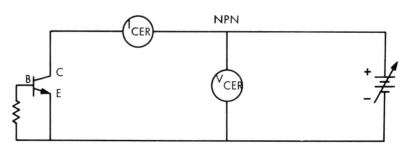

Figure 6

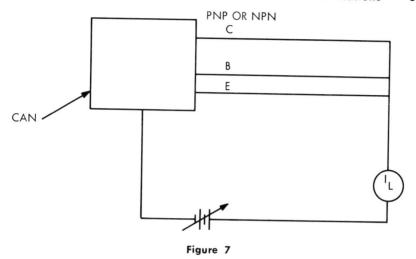

Figure 7

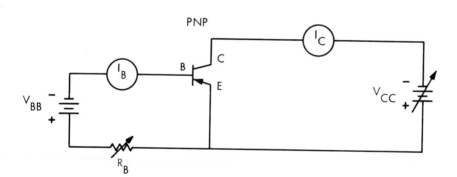

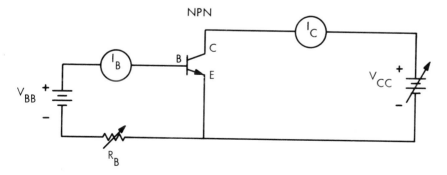

Figure 8

Operation:
1. With V_{CC} set at a specified value, adjust R_B until I_B *or* I_C reads a specified value, then read I_B and I_C.

See Fig. 9:

R_{CS} = saturation resistance. Ratio of collector-to-emitter voltage V_{CE}, which at times is referred to as the saturation voltage V_{CS}, to the collector current I_C at a specified base current I_B in a common-emitter transistor circuit.

$$R_{CS} = \frac{V_{CE}}{I_C} = \frac{V_{CS}}{I_C}$$

Operation:
1. Set I_B at a specified value by varying R_B.
2. Vary V_{CC} until I_C reads a specified value and read V_{CE} which equals V_{CS}.
3. Or, vary V_{CC} until V_{CE} reads a specified value and read I_C.

Pulse testing. Any of the d-c parameters may be measured under pulse conditions. This method is particularly useful for power transistors, for it allows testing of the units without the necessity of heat sinking. TI uses a 2% or less duty cycle, which means that the power pulse to the transistor is applied for 2% (or less) of the time during a 16.7-millisecond period.

A-C Measurements and Test Circuits.

See Fig. 10:

h_{fe} = a-c beta. Small-signal a-c current transfer ratio of a common-emitter transistor circuit with the collector and emitter short-circuited to a-c current.

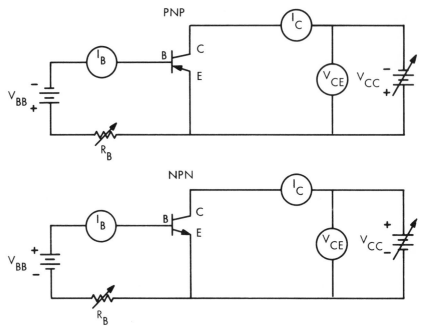

Figure 9

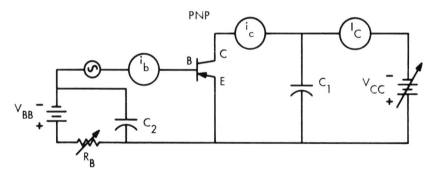

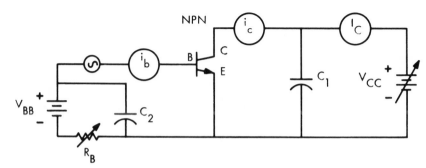

Figure 10

Operation:
1. C_1 shorts a-c current between emitter and collector.
2. C_2 allows a-c current to bypass bias battery V_{BB} and R_B.
3. With V_{CC} set a certain value, R_B is varied until I_C reaches a specified value.
4. Small a-c signal is applied and i_c and i_b are read.

5. $h_{fe} = \dfrac{i_c}{i_b}$

See Fig. 11:

   h_{oe} = small-signal a-c output admittance of a common-emitter transistor circuit with the base open-circuited to the a-c current.

Operation:
1. Capacitor C_1 allows a-c current to bypass V_{CC}.
2. Resonant circuit R constitutes infinite resistance (open) to a-c current, but zero resistance to d-c current.
3. With V_{CC} set at a specified value, R_B is varied until either I_C or I_E, as required, reaches a specified value. This is called the bias condition.
4. Small a-c signal is applied and v_{ce} and i_c are read.

5. $h_{oe} = \dfrac{i_c}{v_{ce}}$

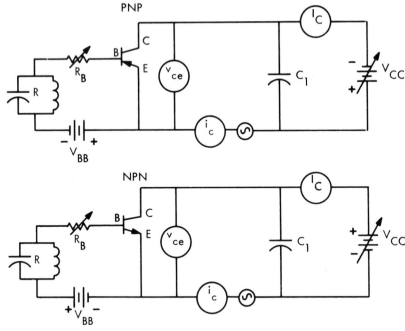

Figure 11

See Fig. 12:

h_{re} = small-signal a-c reverse voltage ratio of common-emitter transistor circuit with the base open-circuited to the a-c current.

Operation:

1. Capacitor C_1 allows a-c current to bypass V_{CC}.
2. Resonant circuit R constitutes infinite resistance (open) to a-c current, but zero resistance to d-c current.
3. With V_{CC} set at a specified value, R_B is varied until either I_C or I_E, as required, reaches a specified value. This is called the bias condition.
4. Small a-c signal is applied and v_{ce} and v_{be} are read.

5. $h_{re} = \dfrac{v_{be}}{v_{ce}}$

See Fig. 13:

h_{ie} = small-signal a-c input impedance of a common-emitter transistor circuit with the collector short-circuited to the a-c current.

Operation:

1. Capacitor C_1 shorts the a-c current in the collector circuit.
2. Capacitor C_2 allows the a-c signal to bypass the base d-c bias.
3. With V_{CC} set at a specified value, R_B is varied until either I_C or I_E, as required, reaches a specified value. This is called the bias condition.
4. Small a-c signal is applied and i_e and v_{be} are read.

5. $h_{ie} = \dfrac{v_{be}}{i_b}$

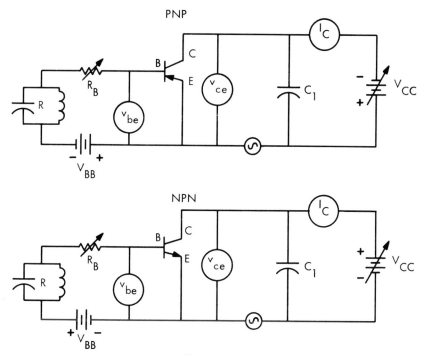

Figure 12

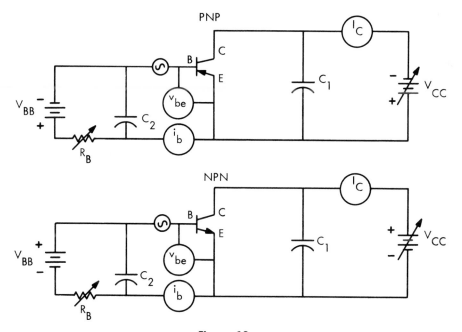

Figure 13

See Fig. 14:

$h_{ob}(h_{22})$ = small-signal a-c output admittance of a common-base transistor circuit with the emitter circuit open-circuited to the a-c current.

Operation:

1. Capacitor C_1 allows a-c current to bypass bias battery V_{CC}.
2. Resonant circuit R constitutes infinite resistance, but zero resistance to d-c current.
3. With V_{CC} set at a specified value, R_E is varied until I_E reaches a specified value. This is called the bias condition.
4. Small a-c signal is applied and v_{cb} and i_c are read.

5. $h_{ob} = \dfrac{i_c}{v_{cb}}$

See Fig. 15:

$h_{ib}(h_{11})$ = small-signal a-c input impedance of a common-base transistor circuit with the collector circuit short-circuited to the a-c current.

Operation:

1. Capacitor C_1 shorts the a-c current in the collector circuit.
2. Capacitor C_2 allows a-c current to bypass bias battery V_{EE}.
3. With V_{CC} set at a specified value, R_E is varied until I_E reaches a specified value. This is called the bias condition.
4. Small a-c signal is applied and i_e and v_{eb} are read.

5. $h_{ib} = \dfrac{v_{eb}}{i_e}$

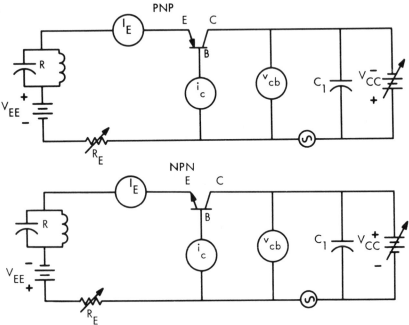

Figure 14

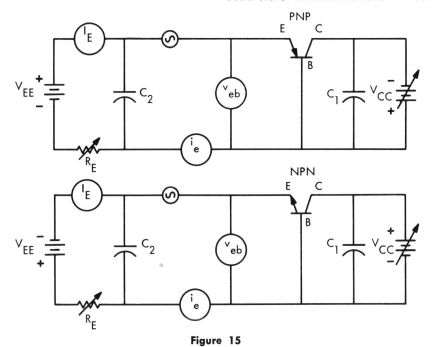

Figure 15

See Fig. 16:

$h_{fb}(h_{21})$ = small-signal a-c current transfer ratio of a common-base transistor circuit with the collector short-circuited to the a-c current.

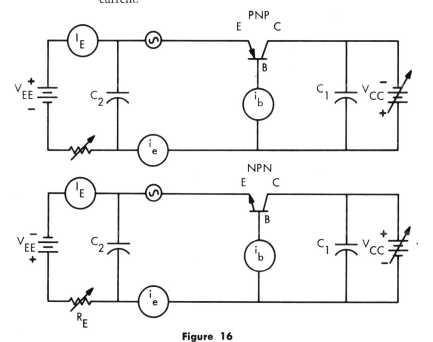

Figure 16

$$h_{fb} = \frac{i_c}{i_e} = -\alpha \ (\text{Sometimes referred to as a-c alpha})$$

For greater readability accuracy, $1 + h_{fb}$ is measured at TI:

$$1 + h_{fb} = \frac{i_b}{i_e}$$

Operation:

1. Capacitor C_1 shorts a-c current in the collector circuit.
2. Capacitor C_2 allows a-c current to bypass bias battery V_{EE} and R_E.
3. With V_{CC} set at a certain value, R_E is varied until I_E reaches a specified value.
4. Small a-c signal is applied and i_e and i_b are read.

See Fig. 17:

> h_{rb} = small-signal a-c reverse voltage ratio of a common-base transistor circuit with the emitter open-circuited to the a-c current.

Operation:

1. C_1 allows a-c current to bypass V_{CC}.
2. Resonant circuit R constitutes infinite resistance (open) to a-c current, but zero resistance to d-c current.
3. With V_{CC} set to a specified value, R_E is adjusted until I_E reaches a specified value.
4. Small a-c signal is applied and v_{cb} and v_{be} are read.
5. $h_{rb} = \frac{v_{be}}{v_{cb}}$

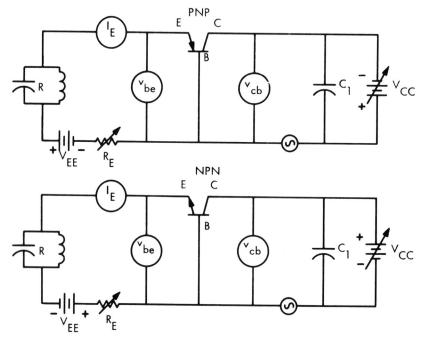

Figure 17

See Fig. 18:

$C_{ob}(C_o)$ = capacitance measured from the collector-to-base in a common-base transistor circuit with the emitter open-circuited to a-c current.

Operation:

1. C_1 allows a-c current to bypass bias battery V_{CC}.
2. Resonant circuit R presents open circuit to a-c current.
3. With V_{CC} set at certain value adjust R_E until I_E reads a specified value.
4. C_x is a calibrated adjustable capacitor. With the transistor removed, adjust C_x until a null on V is reached, then place transistor in test and again null V. The difference between the two C_x readings is C_{ob}.

P_g = a-c power gain. Ratio of output voltage multiplied by output current to input voltage multiplied by input current. Sometimes referred to as Ap.

$$P_g = Ap = \frac{i_o v_o}{i_i v_i}$$

PNP

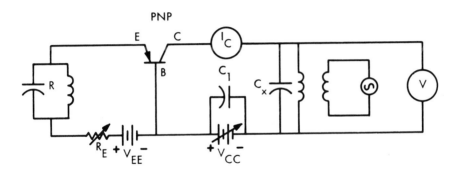

NPN

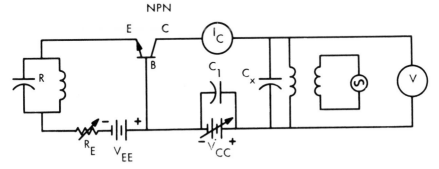

Figure 18

21

Noise Figure Measurement

by Harry F. Cooke

200-MC NF MEASUREMENT

Texas Instruments now includes 100% testing of 200-mc noise figure on several of its high-frequency transistors. The method of testing is semi-automatic and is based on the Hewlett-Packard 342A Noise Figure Meter. A block diagram of the test layout is shown in Fig. 1.

Description of Test Set-up. The noise source is a Hewlett-Packard type 343A temperature-limited diode which has a useful range of 10 to 600 mc. It is powered by the Hewlett-Packard 342A Noise Figure Meter and run at a constant current of 3.31 ma.

The test jig is a common-base amplifier with input and output tunable. Common-base operation is used since it avoids the problem of neutralization, which is sometimes necessary in the common-emitter connection operation to achieve sufficient

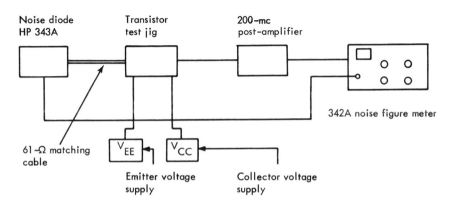

Fig. 1. Noise figure test set-up.

gain. The noise figure of common-emitter and common-base transistor amplifiers is essentially the same. The test jig circuit is shown in Fig. 2.

The post-amplifier is a three-stage transistor amplifier with a power gain of 40 db and a noise figure of 3.0 db. It uses three type 2N2415 germanium mesa transistors in a cascaded common-base connection. The circuit is shown in Fig. 3.

The Hewlett-Packard 342A Noise Figure Meter is the heart of the automatic noise figure measurement. It operates by pulsing the noise diode on and off while comparing the noise outputs of the amplifier with the diode on and off. It is self-contained and self-calibrating.

A majority of TI's customers are most interested in a noise test using a 75-ohm source resistance. The 343A noise diode has a 50-ohm output and thus it is necessary to transform the 50-ohm diode to 75 ohms with minimum losses. This is done by using a 200-mc quarter-wavelength 61-ohm cable. This cable is made by removing the #20 center conductor from a 7.5″ length of RG-58/U and substituting a #21 center conductor. The ends of the cable are fitted with standard UG-88/U BNC connectors.

Test Procedure.   After making the set-up shown in Fig. 1:

1. Turn on supply voltages and the post-amplifier
2. Adjust the 342A according to the manufacturer's instructions
3. Insert transistor into the test jig and set the emitter current to the correct value
4. Adjust input and output jig tuning for best noise figure. The input adjustment is usually adjusted only once for a given transistor type

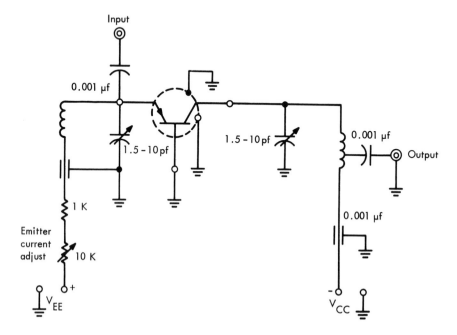

Fig. 2. 200-mc test jig.

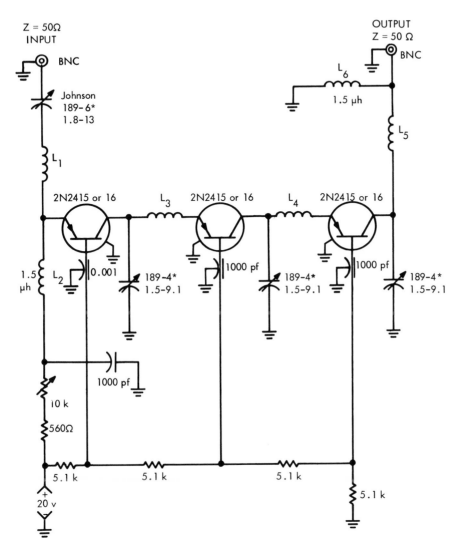

Fig. 3. 200-mc amplifier.

* or equivalent

L_1 = 3T #18 bus 1/2 diam

L_2, L_6 = Delavan 1537-16 or Equiv.

$L_{3,4}$ = 3T #18 bus, 3/8 diam

L_5 = 2T #18 bus, 3/8 diam

Gain = 40 db
Bandwidth = 25 Mc
Noise figure = 3 db

Note: Transistors on
3/4-inch centers

1-GC NF MEASUREMENT

Description of Test Set-up. In Fig. 4, the test layout is given in block form. The Hewlett-Packard 349A coaxial gas-tube noise source can be used to approximately 4 Gc. It has an excess noise of 15.7 ± 0.5 db, according to the manufacturer's specification. The HP 342A is an automatic noise figure indicator and provides the necessary power for the 349A. Noise figure is read directly in db with this system.

A 10-db attenuator is used between the noise source and the test jig to reduce the excess noise to 5.7 db. This gives a more accurate measurement of noise figures below 10 db.

The test jig is designed for TO-5 or TO-18 devices. It is essentially a four-port coaxially tuned common-base amplifier. By crossing the emitter and base leads, it can be used as a common-emitter amplifier, provided the biasing network is suitably modified. The common-base and common-emitter noise figures are the same if the transistor is operated at the same gain level. Figure 5 shows the construction details of the test jig.

Figure 6 shows in detail the elements of the tuning network which are part of the test jig. The tunable shorted lines L_1, L_2, and L_3 are used as follows:

L_1 tunes the source *susceptance only*. The source resistance is 50 ohms fixed, unless otherwise specified. L_2 tunes the collector circuit. L_3, in conjunction with L_2, comprises a double-stub tuner to tune and match the transistor output circuit to the converter.

A 200-mc post-amplifier with 40-db gain and a 3.0-db noise figure is used. The post-amplifier shown earlier in Fig. 3 is suitable.

The 1-Gc signal is converted down to 200 mc in the converter as shown in Fig. 4. The converter oscillator is operated at 1.2 Gc. Image response, which is thus at 1.4 Gc, is 30 db below the 1-Gc response. The converter has a 5.0-db noise figure and 10-db gain. A schematic of the converter is given in Fig. 7.

Test Procedure. To make a noise-figure measurement:
1. Insert transistor into the jig
2. Adjust bias according to manufacturer's specification
3. Adjust L_1, L_2, and L_3 for minimum noise figure. Once an appropriate setting has been made, L_2 usually will not require further adjustment for other transistors of a given type

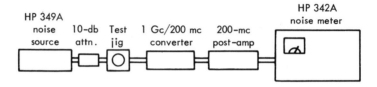

Figure 4

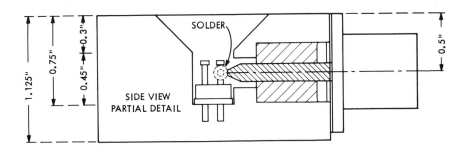

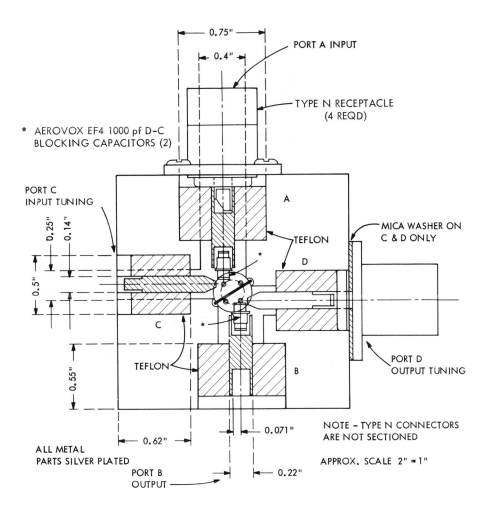

Fig. 5. TO-18, TO-5 common-base UHF amplifier module.

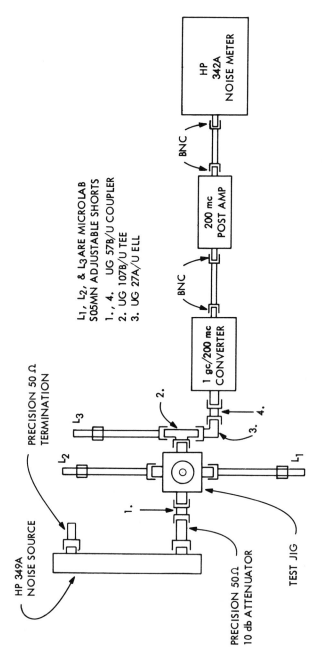

Fig. 6. 1-Gc noise figure test layout.

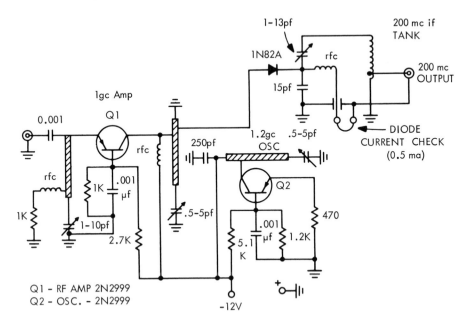

Fig. 7. 1-Gc 200-mc converter.

22

Power Oscillator Test Procedure

by Harry F. Cooke

1-GC POWER OSCILLATOR TEST

Fixture Description. Some devices are functionally tested for output power as self-excited oscillators at 1 Gc. The test fixture is a common-base tuned-collector tuned-emitter oscillator. Feedback is provided by the internal capacitance of the transistor itself and the incidental capacitance of the transistor socket. Figure 1 shows the test fixture. Since the length of the collector cavity is fixed, frequency is adjusted with the capacitive probe as shown. Collector loading is varied by the coaxial capacitive probe. Bias for the collector is brought in through the center conductor of the collector cavity by way of a 1000-pf feedthrough capacitor. Emit-

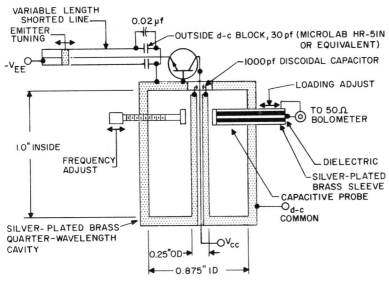

Fig. 1. 1-Gc oscillator power output test circuit.

ter bias is connected to the transistor via the emitter line through an outside d-c block (See Fig. 1).

Test Procedure. Figure 2 is the test layout. An outside d-c block and adjustable short are connected to the emitter via the type-N receptacle. Emitter bias is applied between the lead coming out through the bottom of the cavity, and ground. The output line is connected to the 10-db attenuator as shown. When the set-up is completed as in Fig. 2, the transistor is plugged into the socket from the *open* end (refer to Fig. 2) and the biases are set according to specifications. To tune the oscillator, use the following procedure:

1. Maximize output by adjusting the emitter line
2. Maximize output by adjusting the output probe
3. Maximize output by retuning the emitter line
4. Check frequency for 1.0 Gc
5. (a) Turn frequency adjust probe *in* (clockwise) to lower frequency, or
   (b) Turn frequency adjust probe *out* (counter clockwise) to raise frequency
6. Repeat steps 1 through 4

It may be necessary during the tuning procedure to reset the emitter bias since this is affected by strong oscillations. The correct power output is that obtained at 1 Gc with rated collector voltage and current.

1- TO 4-GC POWER OSCILLATOR TEST

Fixture Description. Figure 3 is a detailed drawing of the test fixture itself. It is basically a two-cavity oscillator with the internal capacitance of the transistor itself providing the necessary feedback. The tunable cavity between the base and emitter presents the proper susceptance to the emitter to give oscillation. In the collector-base circuit a double-stub tuner is used both as the collector tuning element and as an output matching device. To bias the transistor, the outside conductors of the emitter and collector lines are isolated from the V-shaped center piece by 0.001″ Mylar* film.

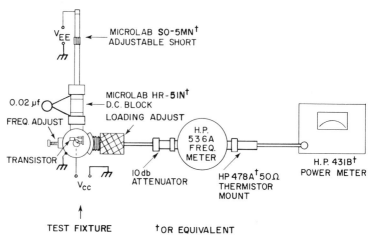

Fig. 2. 1-Gc oscillator power output test layout.

*Trademark of DuPont Corporation.

Test Procedure.   After the test layout has been completed as shown in Fig. 4, the transistor is inserted into the test fixture so that the collector connects to the double-stub tuner. The biases are then adjusted to the specified values.

Next, adjust the tuning stub nearest the transistor to about midway in its travel. The remaining stub and the emitter line are both adjusted for maximum power output as indicated on the power meter. It may be necessary to repeat the adjustment of these two elements several times to get the maximum power. At this point, the frequency should be checked with the frequency meter. If the frequency is low, shorten the stub nearer the transistor and then readjust the other stub and emitter line. If the frequency is high, lengthen the stub nearer the transistor. Once the correct frequency has been obtained, only minor adjustments will be necessary for other transistors of the same type. The correct power output is that which is obtained at the desired test frequency.

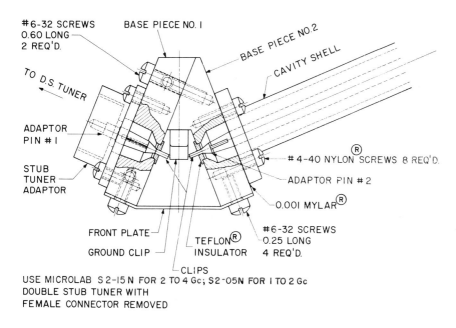

Fig. 3. Top view, 2-Gc cavity.

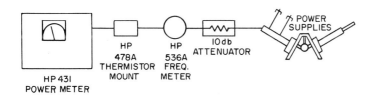

Figure 4

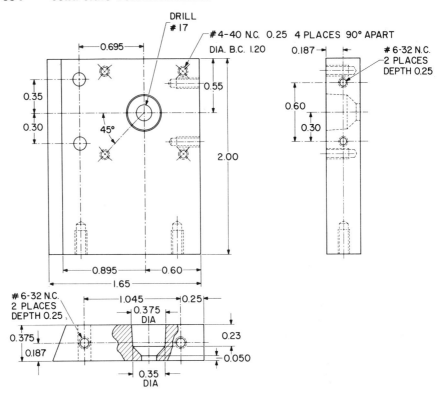

Fig. 5. Base piece No. 1, 2-Gc cavity.

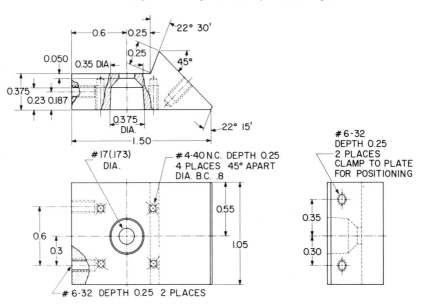

Fig. 6. Base piece No. 2, 2-Gc cavity.

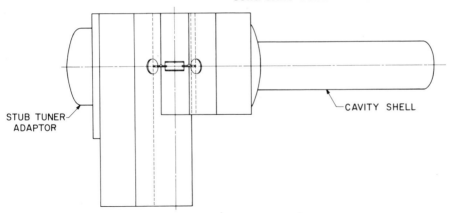

Fig. 7. Front view (without front plate), 2-Gc cavity.

STUB TUNER ADAPTOR

CAVITY SHELL

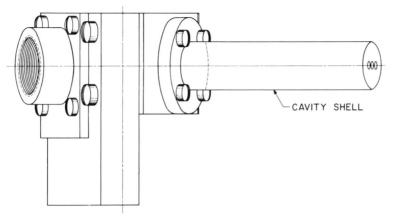

Fig. 8. Back view, 2-Gc cavity.

CAVITY SHELL

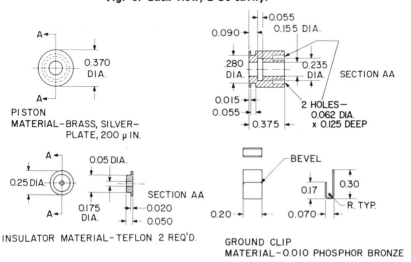

PISTON
MATERIAL–BRASS, SILVER–
PLATE, 200 μ IN.

0.370 DIA.

SECTION AA

2 HOLES–
0.062 DIA.
x 0.125 DEEP

INSULATOR MATERIAL–TEFLON 2 REQ'D.

SECTION AA

GROUND CLIP
MATERIAL–0.010 PHOSPHOR BRONZE

BEVEL

R. TYP.

Fig. 9. Piston, ground clip, and Teflon insulator, 2-Gc cavity.

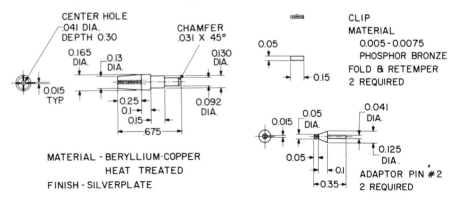

Fig. 10. Adaptor pin No. 1, 2-Gc cavity.

Fig. 11. Clip and adaptor pin No. 2, 2-Gc cavity.

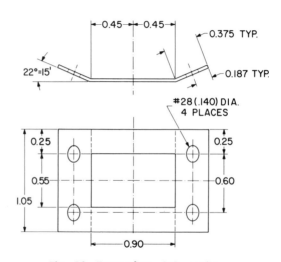

Fig. 12. Front plate, 2-Gc cavity.

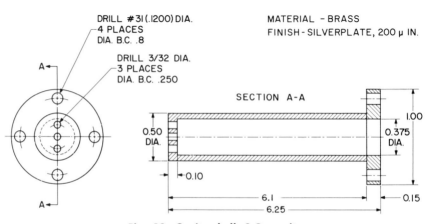

Fig. 13. Cavity shell, 2-Gc cavity.

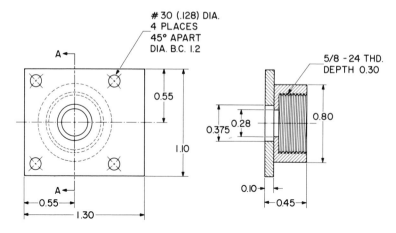

MATERIAL - BRASS
FINISH - SILVERPLATE, 200 µ IN.

Fig. 14. Stub tuner adaptor piece No. 1, 2-Gc cavity.

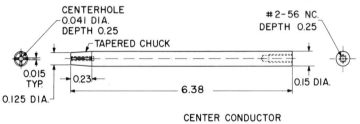

CENTER CONDUCTOR
MATERIAL - BRASS, SILVERPLATE 200 µ IN.

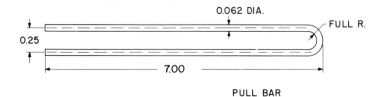

PULL BAR
MATERIAL - BRASS, SILVERPLATE

Fig. 15. Inner conductor and pull bar, 2-Gc cavity.

Index